Van Nostrand's

PRACTICAL FORMULARY

by

WILLIAM R. MINRATH, Ch.E.

Editor

D. VAN NOSTRAND COMPANY, INC.

PRINCETON, NEW JERSEY

TORONTO   LONDON

NEW YORK

D. VAN NOSTRAND COMPANY, INC.

120 Alexander St., Princeton, New Jersey (*Principal office*)
24 West 40 Street, New York 18, New York

D. VAN NOSTRAND COMPANY, LTD.
358, Kensington High Street, London, W.14, England

D. VAN NOSTRAND COMPANY (Canada), LTD.
25 Hollinger Road, Toronto 16, Canada

65847

First Published October 1957
Reprinted April 1958,
December 1961,
April 1965

PREFACE

This book comprises formulas for a very wide variety of products in common use. The basis of their selection has been ease of preparation, requiring a minimum of equipment and technical skill. These formulas are, therefore, well adapted for use in limited-quantity manufacture for starting a new small business; for supplying or expanding an existing enterprise; or for making a particular product for direct consumption in quantity.

Highly representative and up-to-date formulas have been chosen to yield products of competitive quality. Such products, moreover, can readily be "individualized" to distinguish them from those already established on the market.

In order to facilitate use of these formulas, certain special features of presentation have been adopted. All quantities of materials have been expressed in two units, one of weight and one of volume. Practically all formulas yield the same quantity of product, which can readily be increased or decreased in any desired proportion. All information needed for the safe and successful use of these formulas is given right where it is needed. Finally, all names and addresses of manufacturers of trade-mark materials (so essential to modern production) are given directly beneath the formulas in which they are used, and general lists of chemical and equipment suppliers are given in the Appendix.

The wide scope of this book has been made possible by the work, extending over so many years, of the patient experimenters and manufacturers whose efforts have been responsible for the high quality of the products available today. The organization and simplification of the formulas in these pages have been undertaken in the hope that others will be enabled thereby to advance still further the quality of formulated products.

WRM

TABLE OF CONTENTS

(For complete list of formulas, *see* Index, beginning on page 329)

CHAPTER		PAGE
1	How to Use This Book	1
2	Surface Treatment—Wood	8
3	Lacquers, Paints, Enamels and Related Products	49
4	Formulas for Metal Surfaces	94
5	Cements, Plaster, Glass and Related Substances	127
6	Household Cleaning, Polishing and Related Products	140
7	Photographic Formulas	179
8	Cosmetics, Hand Cleaners and Related Products	199
9	Food Products	251
10	Farm and Garden Products	289
	Appendix A Chemical Manufacturers	313
	Appendix B Laboratory Equipment and Chemical Supply Houses	321
	Appendix C Weights and Measures	322
	Appendix D Trade Journals	324
	Appendix E Certified Dyes	326
	Index	329

Chapter 1

HOW TO USE THIS BOOK

Selection of Formulas

The object of this book is, first of all, to provide suitable formulas for many purposes. These may vary from time to time—an organic coating composition may be used to finish living room furniture, or merely to coat a work bench—or a product may be prepared for on-the-premises consumption or for sale to others. Therefore, the formulas in these pages are sufficiently diversified to give this necessary selection. In further keeping with this policy, the explanations, while not lengthy, are detailed enough to enable you to find the product best suited to the job in hand. Obviously an expensive selective herbicide should not be used to kill the weeds behind a shed, yet all herbicides, and other garden sprays, should be formulated with reference to the plant *and animal* toxicity of the final product. That is in part what is meant by the use of the word practical in the title of this book.

Procurement of Ingredients

Another aspect of this matter of the practical outlook applies to the procurement of ingredients. In preparing a product for the first time, you will naturally prefer to buy the materials from a supplier whom you can visit in person. Therefore, the first step should be to consult the Classified Telephone Directories of nearby towns or cities to check them for (1) suppliers of materials for use in the particular type of product, and (2) general chemical and equipment supply houses. If you do not have convenient access to such suppliers, or if the local houses cannot furnish the necessary materials, then turn to the list in the Appendix of this book. The names in that list are also arranged in two groups—(A) Manufacturers of Chemicals; and (B) Laboratory Equipment and Chemical Supply Houses. When working with products of one kind only, remember that you can usually do best by dealing with houses specializing in serving that industry. An excellent way to obtain this information is from trade journals. For them, refer to the list in Appendix D, which gives representative journals in a number of product industries.

In addition to providing these lists of suppliers and journals, this book also furnishes the name and address of the manufacturer of every trade-

1

mark material directly below the formula in which it is used. This information is useful in two ways: (1) On an order given to a local or general supplier, for purposes of identification; (2) For ordering directly from the manufacturer. While many manufacturers do not sell smaller quantities of their products, they can furnish the name of a jobber or other supplier.

To simplify this supply situation, the formulas in this book have been chosen from two points of view. Formulas for products that are primarily of interest for on-the-premises consumption have been restricted as far as possible to commonly-available ingredients which are not trade-mark materials. On the other hand, formulas for products which are primarily made for sale, have been selected with present-day competition in mind, and therefore, they necessarily use more of the newly-developed and trade-mark ingredients. However, every formula in this book will give a good product that will do its job well, provided that you follow the clear and explicit directions.

Follow Directions

These directions have been written for the needs of the user who has had no experience whatever in the industry to which the product belongs. Therefore, they are quite detailed. However, they are not repetitive. Where a series of formulas are given for closely-related products, reference is made in each case to the directions given for the §1 formula of the series so that repetition of directions is avoided. This is done not only to provide in these pages as much useful information as possible, but also to avoid encouraging the natural tendency to skip directions. Simple as many of these steps are, every one of them is important. They have been written so that you can be sure of obtaining high-quality products by following every direction closely, and by measuring every quantity accurately.

Weights and Measures

This matter of quantity is so important that it has been standardized throughout this book. This has been accomplished in two ways:

(1) Every formula, with a few exceptions in Chapters 9-10, uses the metric system; and is expressed in only two units of that system, the gram (abbreviated as g.), and the milliliter (abbreviated as ml.). The gram is a unit of weight, and is generally used for measuring solids; the milliliter is a unit of volume, and is used for measuring liquids. One thousand grams are equivalent to about 2.2 pounds in the English system; and one thousand milliliters are equivalent to about one quart. This is essentially all the information necessary to follow the directions in this book; however, if you wish further data about weights and measures, consult the tables of the Metric and English systems, and their equivalents, in Appendix C.

For weighing, you need an inexpensive balance, which can be purchased from any of the equipment dealers listed in Appendix B, or in fact from many other sources. It should have a capacity of 1000 grams, and be sensitive to one gram, so that an open, pan-type beam balance will do. You should also have a set of weights in values from 1 gram to 500 grams. For measuring, you need a number of graduated cylinders, also obtainable from an equipment dealer. A useful set would consist of one 10-ml. (milliliter) size, one 50-ml. size, one or two 100-ml. sizes and one 250-ml. size. This measuring equipment will be sufficient to prepare the great majority of the products in this book. In the cases where very small quantities or very large quantities are required, specific recommendations are given for the necessary methods and equipment. In those cases where liquids are specified by weight (in g.), as in some of the cosmetic formulas, you need beakers for weighing the liquids.

(2) Each formula (with some exceptions in Chapters 8-9) yields about the same quantity of product—which is about 1000 grams (equivalent to about 2.2 pounds in the English system) of products that are solids—or about 1000 milliliters (which is equivalent to about 1 quart in the English system) of products that are liquids. This uniformity of quantity of product has been adopted to facilitate the use of this book. If you should need much less or much more of a product than 1000 grams or 1000 milliliters (2.2 pounds or 1 quart), merely divide or multiply each quantity in the formula accordingly. To make 500 grams or 500 ml. (1.1 pound or 1 pint) divide each quantity by 2; to make 10,000 grams or 10,000 ml. (22 pounds or 10 quarts) multiply each quantity in the formula by 10. However, be sure to try the recommended amount before you undertake production in larger quantities. This suggestion follows from two practical considerations.

The first and most important consideration is that preparation of most products is an art as well as a science. Therefore, you should regard any formula as a starting point for your own experimentation. This is especially true in the case of commercial products that must compete with the best the market has to offer. Many such products in use today are the result of many years of experience, as well as the newer findings of modern research. To offer one of your own you naturally wish to provide either an improvement, a new function, or an enhanced appeal—which may be in appearance, taste, aroma, consistency or range of use. Such appeals, to be valuable, must be distinctive—therefore, the formulas given in this book, or any other publication, should be "individualized" in some respect if they are to serve as the basis for a commercial enterprise.

Equipment

The second reason for trying the small-batch quantities before undertaking larger-quantity production is because of the different equipment required. The measuring equipment that is necessary for producing in 1000 g. or ml. (2.2 pounds or 1 quart) quantities has already been listed. In addition, preparation of many products also requires mixing, heating or cooling equipment, and containers. To work on the scale indicated, very little of such equipment is required. However, to process many times as much material, you will need larger, or even additional equipment, which can best be obtained on the basis of experience with smaller quantities, although such recommendations are also given in this book wherever they are obviously pertinent.

It must be recognized that there are various types of products which cannot be prepared on a 1000 gram (2.2 pound) scale, or in many cases, even on a considerably larger one. They include products made in tonnage quantities at low unit costs, products requiring high temperatures, high pressures, reduced pressures and other special and costly processes, and products containing an excessively large number of ingredients. In general, products in these categories are not included in this book, except where a modified formula has been developed to obviate the difficulties, and to yield a practical and useful result. Fortunately, the range of choice is so great that there has been no difficulty in providing in this book a representative coverage of formulas for most types of products in current use that can be prepared successfully on a small scale or a limited-commercial one.

General Plan

The overall plan of this book is to begin each chapter with general information about the application of the formulas in that chapter; and to precede each group of formulas with specific information about that particular class of product. By this arrangement much duplication has been avoided, and more formulas given than would otherwise be possible. For example, if you wish to prepare a product to bleach wood prior to finishing it, a good course of action would be to read the general information about wood surface treatment, given at the beginning of Chapter 2—Surface Treatment—Wood —and then to turn to the section on wood bleaches. By becoming familiar with this information, and with the formulas given for wood bleaches, you can readily choose the one best suited to your needs, and determine how to obtain the ingredients and assemble the equipment for applying it.

Most formulated products, particularly those suitable for small scale or limited-commercial scale production, are intended for application to surfaces. Consequently the nature of the surface—whether it is wood, metal, glass, etc.—determines the composition of the product. So by grouping the formulas in this book as far as possible according to the kind of surface to which they are to be applied, a considerable degree of coherence has been gained. Chapter 2, for example, deals entirely with products formulated for application to wooden surfaces; Chapter 4 with products for metallic surfaces; Chapter 5, with products for masonry, glass and related surfaces; and Chapter 8, with products for the most exacting surface of all, the human skin—that is, it comprises the cosmetics. However, this arrangement has been followed only insofar as it simplifies the arrangement of the formulas. Thus, all the organic film coatings—whether paints, lacquers, or others—are grouped together in Chapter 3. The household preparations, except those formulated for the four specific surfaces mentioned, are grouped in Chapter 6; while Chapters 9 and 10 deal, respectively, with formulas for food products, and formulas for garden and farm use. This overall arrangement, it is to be hoped, will help you find most readily the formula you need, and the information you require to prepare a high-quality product.

Package Design

In marketing a product, be sure to pay attention to the matter of packaging. In designing a package, the first consideration is ease of recognition, which has become increasingly important in light of the growing number of self-service stores. Packages must be distinctive and very plainly lettered. In selecting their color-combinations, remember that goods are often placed on shelves that are illuminated only by poor light or by colored light. This same principle applies to any selling message which may appear on the package—fewer words in larger type are preferable. Directions for the use of the product, recipes and similar information should be separated from the sales message by being placed on the sides or bottom of the package. They can be printed in small type because they will be read at home.

Of course, the outstanding packaging development of recent years has been the great increase in the use of metal foil and transparent plastic materials. The former owes its impetus to the expansion of aluminum production facilities during World War II, although metallic wrappings are not limited to aluminum, nor are aluminum wrappings limited to white-metal color. Plastic wrappings have the great advantage of enabling the purchaser to see the product without exposing it to handling. These wrappings protect their contents in great measure from atmospheric oxidation, and from loss of moisture by evaporation. Both types are readily available to any business regardless of its scale of operations.

When the product is a liquid, be sure to obtain from the bottle supplier full information on the ornamental bottle shapes that he can offer. Frequently one of these is so attractive that no carton is necessary, and a distinctive glass container can thus be obtained at a lower cost than the combined cost of a plain bottle and a carton. Another container for liquids which should be investigated is the plastic bottle, which is now available in several stock sizes. It has the further advantage that some types of plastic are sufficiently flexible to permit "squeeze bottle" construction, which offers the sales appeal of easy application.

The importance of this appeal is shown by the rapid growth in the use of fluid-spray packaging, in which a very volatile inert liquid or a gas is used in a valve-top container as a "propellant" for liquids and emulsions, comprising a host of products as diversified as cosmetics, foods, and insecticides. The containers and propellants for this type of packaging are now available to the small business, and enable it to maintain an advantageous competitive position. While the machinery for this packaging is too expensive for the individual small business, there are a number of companies who do this work on contract. Since, however, formulas prepared specifically for this type of packaging and its fine spray method of application are often not suitable for other methods of use, the number of such formulations in this book has been limited to a few examples.

Labeling

As implied above, the label is a very important part of the package, that also merits care in preparation. In designing a label, remember that in one sense it is an advertisement. Many prospective customers will be buying in supermarkets and other self-service stores where their only contact with the product is the outside of its package. Under such circumstances, the first requirement of a label, or the outside of a package, is its power to gain attention. It must catch the passing customer's eye, however poor the lighting or the angle of viewing, and then it must hold his interest until he reaches for it on the shelf. To accomplish these purposes, it must be printed in contrasting colors, with plain, easy-to-read lettering, especially of the name of the product.

There is another consideration which must always be remembered in preparing a label, and which is of critical importance. *Many governments have highly definite requirements on this subject, as they do on the contents of the products themselves.* In the United States, such regulations may be local, state, municipal, county and federal, and all should be checked in formulating a product. In general, these regulations are most exacting for food products, becoming somewhat less so for cosmetics, and still less rigid for products not designed for use directly in, or on, the human body. These considerations are discussed more in detail in later chapters. However, two rules are of paramount importance:

All actually or potentially dangerous products, regardless of their use, must carry warning labels. For example, all products that are poisonous, corrosive, or inflammable, or that are injurious in any other way to man or warm-blooded animals must be so labeled, and carry explicit warnings. Moreover, poisonous and corrosive products should carry directions for emergency action if accidentally consumed or brought into contact with animal tissues.

The second rule is that formulas and labels alike must avoid misrepresentation. In the United States, all products for internal consumption must specify their ingredients upon their labels, noting specifically the presence of preservatives or artificial coloring. In formulating such products, colors which simulate those of natural products may not be added where they might deceive (e.g. red to meat products or yellow to baked goods).

Lest these restrictions seem discouraging to the small producer, it may be added that the various government agencies are ready to supply this information. Moreover, the companies that prepare the food additives that are uneconomical for the small-scale or medium-scale manufacturer to make himself—such as colors, perfumes, flavors, antioxidants, antistaling compounds and the like—are always ready to give practical, up-to-the-minute advice.

Chapter 2

SURFACE TREATMENT—WOOD

There are several reasons for placing the formulas for the products used primarily on wooden surfaces in the first position in this book. They require a minimum of equipment beyond the simple measuring scales and vessels described in Chapter 1. They are widely used, because wood is, after all, the most common of the worked materials, especially for indoor use. Most important of all, they illustrate so clearly the relation between the formulation and use of a product, and the nature of that use, which in this case is application to a wooden surface.

Wood differs from metals, plastics, and concrete in that it is a vegetable substance, the result of the growth of a living organism. Therefore, it is not uniform in composition and gross structure, consisting of different chemical substances, which may act differently with products used on it. It is also not uniform in fine structure, having pores through which applied materials may penetrate, to a greater or less extent, depending upon their nature. For example, penetrating oil stains carry their pigment further into the wood than water stains do. Furthermore, the cells of wood readily absorb water from such products, which therefore "raise the grain," and must be followed by a surface-smoothing operation.

Wood Bleaches

Bleaches are used upon wooden surfaces when the later finishing coatings are to be transparent, that is, those that show the grain of the wood, and when the appearance of the wood is unsatisfactory. This condition may be due to the presence of stains from rust, glue, weathering, etc., which would be visible through the finish. In some cases, the bleaching operation is necessary to lighten the natural shade of the wood. For example, dark woods such as walnut, oak, mahogany and cherry require bleaching before transparent finishes can be applied.

The equipment necessary to prepare wood bleaches consists only of glass, porcelain, or enameled vessels in which to dissolve the ingredients. They react with metals. A wooden stick or paddle may be used for stirring.

The ingredients used in these formulas may be obtained readily from any chemical supply house, with the exception of hydrogen peroxide 30%, which must be ordered for you.

8

Wood Bleach §1 (Light Action)
Sodium Hypochlorite Bleach

Dilute Sodium Hypochlorite Solution (Household
    Laundry Bleach) . . . .   60 ml.
Water . . . . 1000 ml.

Directions: Mix the bleach with the water, and apply uniformly with a cloth. Allow to stand for 15 minutes, and wash off thoroughly with water. Allow surface to dry thoroughly. If it is not sufficiently bleached, the operation should be repeated; but if an exceptional degree of bleaching is desired, such as the lightening of the color of walnut to a pale gray, one of the powerful bleaches should be used.

Precautions: Bleaches skin, toxic internally.*

Wood Bleach §2 (Moderate Action)
Oxalic Acid Bleach

Oxalic Acid . . . .   100 g.
Water . . . . 1000 ml.

Directions: Heat the water nearly to boiling, 85°C (185°F) and dissolve the salt. Apply evenly to the surface with a cloth. After allowing to dry for about five minutes, apply another treatment, and continue this process until the desired degree of bleaching has been obtained. Like Wood Bleach §1, oxalic acid bleach is one of the milder-acting, general purpose bleaches.

Precautions: Bleaches skin, a specific poison if swallowed or absorbed through skin cuts or abrasions.

Wood Bleach §3 (Light Action)
Alcoholic Oxalic Acid Bleach

Oxalic Acid . . . .   100 g.
Alcohol (denatured) . . . .   800 ml.
Water . . . .   200 ml.

Directions: Dissolve the oxalic acid in the alcohol-water mixture. Apply as Wood Bleach §2, but without heating.

Precautions: Bleaches skin, a specific poison if swallowed or absorbed through skin cuts or abrasions.

Note: The words "toxic internally" as used in this book indicate the fact that the substance so designated is an acid, alkali or oxidizing agent which would cause death or serious internal injury if swallowed. Specifically poisonous substances are so designated.

Wood Bleach §4 (Moderate Action)
Two-Solution Oxalic Acid Bleach

Solution a

Oxalic Acid	100 g.
Water (hot)	1000 ml.

Solution b

Sodium Thiosulfate	180 g.
Water	1000 ml.

Directions: Prepare Solution *a* by dissolving the oxalic acid in the hot water (85°C or 185F). Prepare Solution *b* by dissolving the sodium sulfate water at room temperature. Apply hot solution *a* to the surface with a cloth. After it has dried for 15 minutes, apply solution *b* with another cloth. After 15 minutes, wash thoroughly with water. Allow to dry thoroughly; and repeat operation if further bleaching action is desired.

Precautions: Solution *a* bleaches skin, and is a specific poison if swallowed or absorbed through skin cuts or abrasions.

Wood Bleach §5 (Very Strong Action)
Two-Solution Hydrogen Peroxide Bleach

Solution a

Sodium Hydroxide	125 g.
Water	1000 ml.

Add the sodium hydroxide and allow to stand until solution is complete,

Solution b

Hydrogen Peroxide 30%

Directions: Hydrogen peroxide of 30% strength is a special chemical reagent, many times stronger than the antiseptic solution sold in drug stores. The 30% product is obtainable from chemical and industrial supply houses. Solution *a* will become hot as the sodium hydroxide dissolves in the water. Apply it while hot to the surface (using a cloth for the operation), and allow it to dry for ½ hour. Then apply Solution *b* with another cloth, and allow it to dry. Finally, rinse the surface with water.

Precautions: Destroys skin and internal tissues. Rubber gloves and goggles recommended. Also hydrogen peroxide 30% tends to evolve gas (oxygen) on standing, and should not be stored, or exposed to heat or light.

Wood Stains (A) Preservative Stains

Preservative stains are used to protect wood from rotting and other types of deterioration under the most severe service conditions, such as those to which shingles are exposed. For this reason, this type of stain was known as a "shingle stain," and was once used extensively for that purpose. While the declining use of wooden shingles has reduced the consumption of preservative stains for this purpose, they still have important applications. They are used to some extent instead of paint on exterior wooden surfaces of structures, to which they impart a dull finish. In fact, any wooden surface that is exposed to frequent wetting, such as that of a water trough, the lower parts of a boat house, the boards and timbers in stalls for livestock, etc. will last many times as long if treated with a preservative stain.

Preservative stains are formulated to contain (1) a substance toxic to microorganisms, such as cresol, and (2) sufficient oil to saturate the wood and keep it water-repellent.

The ingredients for making preservative stains can be obtained from any wholesale paint dealer, and from most retail paint dealers, provided that their stock is not restricted to packaged paint products. The one ingredient that may sometimes be difficult to obtain in this way is coal-tar creosote. It is produced by coal tar distillation companies, such as the Barrett Company of 40 Rector Street, New York, N.Y. Coal-tar creosote contains creosol, a skin irritant and toxic agent and should be handled with moderate care.

Any metal pails or containers may be used for mixing preservative stains, but the mixing of the pigment, especially the asbestine, with the oils requires vigorous grinding or rubbing action. This may be accomplished by slow stirring by pressing the stick or paddle against the bottom of the container where the pigment settles. A mortar and pestle in which you grind the pigment in the oil will do the job much more quickly. If you plan to make much of these products, a power grinder of the edge-runner type will pay for itself.

Preservative stains are made by dissolving or suspending pigments in a vehicle. Since the vehicle is the same for all these stains, its formula is given once only, immediately following this section. Then the pigments for each color of stain are listed separately, and the same vehicle is used in all of them. This arrangement will be clear from a reading of the formula for Preservative Stain §1.

Note: A new development in shingle stains is the formulation of fire retardent stains by use of the Chlorowaxes, trade-mark products of the Diamond Alkali Co. Information about them may be obtained from that company, whose address is Union Commerce Bldg., Cleveland 14, Ohio.

Preservative Stain §1

Mahogany

Medium

Raw Linseed Oil	450 ml.
Coal-Tar Creosote	200 ml.
Turpentine	200 ml.
Japan Drier	100 ml.

Pigments

Raw Sienna	160 g.
Asbestine	40 g.

Directions: Grind the pigments (the burnt sienna and the asbestine) in 250 ml. of the linseed oil, reserving the other 200 ml. for later mixing. Add the oil slowly, with constant grinding until the 250 ml. of oil are thoroughly incorporated. Then the remaining 200 ml. of linseed oil, the creosote oil, the drier, and the turpentine can be added more quickly, but with constant stirring.

Preservative Stain §2

Golden Oak

Medium (as for Preservative Stain §1)

Pigments

Raw Sienna	160 g.
Asbestine	40 g.

Directions: The same as for Preservative Stain §1.

Preservative Stain §3

Dark Red

Medium (as for Preservative Stain §1)

Pigments

Indian Red	180 g.
Asbestine	20 g.

Directions: The same as for Preservative Stain §1.

Preservative Stain §4
Light Red

Medium (as for Preservative Stain §1)

Pigments

Venetian Red	180 g.
Asbestine	20 g.

Directions: The same as for Preservative Stain §1.

Preservative Stain §5
Dark Brown

Medium (as for Preservative Stain §1)

Pigments

Burnt Umber	180 g.
Asbestine	20 g.

Directions: The same as for Preservative Stain §1.

Preservative Stain §6
Brown

Medium (as for Preservative Stain §1)

Pigments

Raw Umber	180 g.
Asbestine	20 g.

Directions: The same as for Preservative Stain §1.

Preservative Stain §7
Green

Medium (as for Preservative Stain §1)

Pigments

Chrome Green	190 g.
Asbestine	10 g.

Directions: The same as for Preservative Stain §1.

Preservative Stain §8

Yellow Green

Medium (as for Preservative Stain §1)

Pigments

Chrome Green	140 g.
Yellow Ochre	50 g.

Directions: The same as for Preservative Stain §1.

Preservative Stain §9

Olive Green

Medium (as for Preservative Stain §1)

Pigments

Chrome Green	190 g.
Lampblack	2 g.
Asbestine	8 g.

Directions: The same as for Preservative Stain §1.

Preservative Stain §10

Gray

Medium (as for Preservative Stain §1)

Pigments

Lithopone	120 g.
Whiting	50 g.
Asbestine	28 g.
Lampblack	2 g.

Directions: The same as for Preservative Stain §1.

Wood Stains (B) Pigment Oil Stains

The pigment oil stains consist essentially of four ingredients (1) a mineral or lake pigment; (2) a drying oil; (3) a drier; (4) a vehicle or thinner.

The essential difference between the properties of this formulation, and that of other stains such as penetrating oil stains and spirit stains (given later in this chapter), is in the depth of penetration of the color into the wood. The pigment oil stains do not penetrate far into the wood, but deposit their pigment particles close to the surface. They color only the top layer of the wood, and are subject to fading on exposure for years to the action of light. Interior woodwork stained in this way may fade uniformly, and not be too noticeable, but this statement is true only if the exposure of the woodwork to light (especially sunlight) is uniform. Pictures and other semipermanent objects should not be placed on such surfaces.

Another disadvantage of this type of stain resulting from its rapid deposition of particles is its tendency to form cloudy finishes. This effect can be minimized by wiping it off after it has been partially absorbed, following if necessary with another application. This need for more than one application illustrates the importance of the general rule which applies to all methods of wood staining: Work on the light side of the desired color.

Another reason why this rule applies particularly to the pigment oil stains is because they produce too dark colors on soft woods like pine. To overcome this difficulty, and still work with stain of a color not too far removed from the final shade desired, a "slowing-up coating" may be applied to soft woods and to "end grain" surfaces before staining. Such a coating should be a light application of linseed oil or thin shellac, which will retard the absorption of the stain to the degree desired.

Finally, fillers (discussed later in this chapter) cannot be applied directly over oil pigment stains, because they will react, regardless of how dry the stain may be. Therefore, a thin coat of shellac should be applied over the stain before the filler is used.

In view of all these precautions to be observed with pigment oil stains, the natural question that arises is why they are used at all. The fact is that they are the easiest of all stains to apply. A stiff bristle brush, filled with stain, produces a uniform color, which will dry clear and transparent if wiped promptly with a soft cloth. Simply brush and wipe over successive sections of the job, always working with the grain, and allowing sufficient time for penetration before wiping. Any area that becomes too dark may be lightened with turpentine.

As you may have noticed with the preservative stains, the names of the colors of the stains are those of the kinds of wood to which they are frequently applied, as is the trade practice. This method of naming colors does not imply, of course, that the use of that color of stain is limited to that particular wood, because good working procedure will assure good staining results on most woods. However, care should be taken to avoid too great a discrepancy between grain-pattern and color of stain.

The ingredients for making pigment oil stains can be obtained from wholesale paint dealers, and some retailers. Any metal pails or containers may be used for mixing. This operation is important, and while not so laborious with ground-in-oil pigments as with dry ones, where grinding action is necessary, still mixing should be thorough, to avoid streaking of color.

Pigment Oil Stain §1

Light Oak

Medium

Boiled Linseed Oil	250 ml.
Japan Drier	25 ml.
Turpentine	675 ml.

Pigments

Raw Sienna Pigment in Oil	240 ml.
Ultramarine Blue Pigment in Oil	80 ml.

Directions: The pigments should be purchased in the ground-in-oil form that is supplied by many manufacturers and dealers. Stir them slowly into the turpentine until thoroughly mixed, then add the linseed oil and Japan drier. Check for shade on a slat or piece of the wood to be stained.

Pigment Oil Stain §2

Dark Oak

Medium (as for Pigment Oil Stain §1)

Pigments

Raw Sienna Pigment in Oil	160 ml.
Burnt Sienna Pigment in Oil	80 ml.
Burnt Umber Pigment in Oil	80 ml.

Directions: The same as for Pigment Oil Stain §1.

Pigment Oil Stain §3

Mission Oak

Medium (as for Pigment Oil Stain §1)

Pigments

Ivory Black Pigment in Oil	210 ml.
Rose Pink Pigment in Oil	110 ml.

Directions: The same as for Pigment Oil Stain §1.

Pigment Oil Stain §4
Antique Oak

Medium (as for Pigment Oil Stain §1)

Pigments

Raw Sienna Pigment in Oil	230 ml.
Burnt Umber Pigment in Oil	60 ml.
Lampblack	30 ml.

Directions: The same as for Pigment Oil Stain §1.

Pigment Oil Stain §5
Golden Oak

Medium (as for Pigment Oil Stain §1)

Pigments

Raw Sienna Pigment in Oil	210 ml.
Burnt Umber Pigment in Oil	110 ml.

Directions: The same as for Pigment Oil Stain §1.

Pigment Oil Stain §6
Yellow Maple

Medium (as for Pigment Oil Stain §1)

Pigments

Yellow Ochre Pigment in Oil	240 ml.
Ultramarine Blue Pigment in Oil	40 ml.
Burnt Sienna Pigment in Oil	40 ml.

Directions: The same as for Pigment Oil Stain §1.

Pigment Oil Stain §7
Honey-Brown Maple

Medium (as for Pigment Oil Stain §1)

Pigments

Burnt Sienna Pigment in Oil	240 ml.
Ultramarine Blue Pigment in Oil	80 ml.

Directions: The same as for Pigment Oil Stain §1.

Pigment Oil Stain §8
Pumpkin-Brown Maple

Medium (as for Pigment Oil Stain §1)

Pigments

Burnt Sienna Pigment in Oil	320 ml.
Ultramarine Blue Pigment in Oil	5 ml.

Directions: The same as for Pigment Oil Stain §1.

Pigment Oil Stain §9
Red Mahogany

Medium (as for Pigment Oil Stain §1)

Pigments

Burnt Sienna Pigment in Oil	240 ml.
Rose Pink Pigment in Oil	80 ml.

Directions: The same as for Pigment Oil Stain §1.

Pigment Oil Stain §10
Dark Mahogany

Medium (as for Pigment Oil Stain §1)

Pigments

Vandyke Brown Pigment in Oil	240 ml.
Rose Pink Pigment in Oil	80 ml.

Directions: The same as for Pigment Oil Stain §1.

Pigment Oil Stain §11
Light Cherry

Medium (as for Pigment Oil Stain §1)

Pigments

Burnt Sienna Pigment in Oil	160 ml.
Raw Sienna Pigment in Oil	160 ml.

Directions: The same as for Pigment Oil Stain §1.

Pigment Oil Stain §12
Cherry

Medium (as for Pigment Oil Stain §1)

Pigment

Burnt Sienna Pigment in Oil . . . .   320 ml.

Directions: The same as for Pigment Oil Stain §1.

Pigment Oil Stain §13
Walnut

Medium (as for Pigment Oil Stain §1)

Pigments

Burnt Umber Pigment in Oil . . . .   160 ml.
Vandyke Brown Pigment in Oil . . . . . .   160 ml.

Directions: The same as for Pigment Oil Stain §1.

Pigment Oil Stain §14
Dark Walnut

Medium (as for Pigment Oil Stain §1)

Pigment

Vandyke Brown Pigment in Oil . . . . . .   320 ml.

Directions: The same as for Pigment Oil Stain §1.

Pigment Oil Stain §15
Ebony

Medium (as for Pigment Oil Stain §1)

Pigments

Coach Black Pigment in Oil . . . .   305 ml.
Prussian Blue Pigment in Oil . . . .   15 ml.

Directions: The same as for Pigment Oil Stain §1.

Pigment Oil Stain §16

Gray

Medium (as for Pigment Oil Stain §1)

Pigments

Zinc Oxide Pigment in Oil	285 ml.
Lamp Black Pigment in Oil	35 ml.

Directions: The same as for Pigment Oil Stain §1.

Wood Stains. (C) Penetrating Stains

There are many types of stains which penetrate into the wood. The original type was that of the penetrating oil stains, prepared from the pigment oil stains (Class B preceding) by using the same formulas, and replacing ⅓ to ½ of the boiled linseed oil with benzene or toluene, which are called benzol or toluol in the trade. (Benzene is a coal tar distillate, and must be distinguished from benzine, which is closely related to gasoline.) You can make a good penetrating stain of the oil type by using the formulas just given for Pigment Oil Stains, and replacing part of the linseed oil with benzene or toluene, as stated above.

However, modern penetrating stains have a medium consisting substantially of toluene (or benzene) and use dyes dissolved in the medium instead of suspended pigments. These dyes are very widely sold in packaged form. Because these stains penetrate into the wood, and become more uniformly distributed throughout it, the color produced depends upon the kind of wood stained. That is, light oak stain will stain oak the shade that we call "light oak," but if this stain is used on some other kind of wood, it may produce a quite different color. Therefore, in using these stains, it is customary to test them on a slat or piece of wood, or a hidden surface, before proceeding with the staining.

Because of the specific nature of the penetrating stains, the colors used in formulating them must be closely specified. Since dye manufacturers distinguish so many hundreds of dyes, varying in shade, solubility, and other properties, it is necessary to specify them by manufacturers' designations. The colors used in the following group of formulas are all products of the General Dyestuff Corporation, 435 Rector Street, New York 14, N.Y. If, however, you desire to use the products of another manufacturer, you can, by citing the information given here, inquire whether or not equivalents are obtainable. Of course, the other ingredients, toluene, Japan drier and naphtha, are obtainable from a wholesale or larger retail paint supply house. Naphtha, by the way, is a refined petroleum fraction close to gasoline in its properties, and should be handled accordingly. Any metal pail or container may be used for mixing, which must be thorough to be complete.

Penetrating Stain §1

Light Oak

Medium

Toluene	540 ml.
Japan Drier	330 ml.
Naphtha	120 ml.

Pigments

*Sudan Yellow GGA	20 g.
*Sudan Brown 5BA	5 g.

*These Sudan dyes are trade-mark products of the General Dyestuff Co., 435 Hudson St., New York 14, N.Y.

Directions: Dissolve the dyes in the toluene at ordinary temperature, with gentle stirring, then stir in the drier and naphtha.

Precautions: Toluene is somewhat toxic; even its vapor should not be inhaled to any extent. Naphtha is inflammable. Therefore, these stains should be prepared and used with good ventilation and skin protection, and in absence of flames or other combustion (No Smoking! !).

Penetrating Stain §2

Dark Oak

Medium (as for Penetrating Stain §1)

Pigments

*Sudan Yellow GGA	15 g.
*Sudan Brown 5BA	10 g.

For directions, trade-mark products (*) and precautions, see Penetrating Stain §1.

Penetrating Stain §3

Mission Oak

Medium (as for Penetrating Stain §1)

Pigments

*Sudan Yellow GGA	10 g.
*Sudan Red GGA	10 g.
*Sudan Black BR	5 g.

For directions, trade-mark products (*) and precautions, see Penetrating Stain §1.

Penetrating Stain §4
Antique Oak

Medium (as for Penetrating Stain §1)

Pigments

*Sudan Brown 5BA	10 g.
*Sudan Dark Brown BG	10 g.
*Sudan Black BR	5 g.

For directions, trade-mark products (*) and precautions, see Penetrating Stain §1.

Penetrating Stain §5
Golden Oak

Medium (as for Penetrating Stain §1)

Pigments

*Sudan Yellow GGA	10 g.
*Sudan Brown 5BA	15 g.

For directions, trade-mark products (*) and precautions, see Penetrating Stain §1.

Penetrating Stain §6
Yellow Maple

Medium (as for Penetrating Stain §1)

Pigments

*Sudan Yellow GGA	21 g.
*Sudan Brown 5BA	2 g.
*Sudan Blue GA	2 g.

For directions, trade-mark products (*) and precautions, see Penetrating Stain §1.

Penetrating Stain §7
Honey Brown Maple

Medium (as for Penetrating Stain §1)

Pigments

*Sudan Yellow RA	20 g.
*Sudan Blue GA	5 g.

For directions, trade-mark products (*) and precautions, see Penetrating Stain §1.

Penetrating Stain §8
Pumpkin Brown Maple

Medium (as for Penetrating Stain §1)

Pigments

*Sudan Brown 5BA	22 g.
*Sudan Blue GA	3 g.

For directions, trade-mark products (*) and precautions, see Penetrating Stain §1.

Penetrating Stain §9
Red Mahogany

Medium (as for Penetrating Stain §1)

Pigments

*Sudan Brown 5BA	20 g.
*Sudan Red 4BA	5 g.

For directions, trade-mark products (*) and precautions, see Penetrating Stain §1.

Penetrating Stain §10
Dark Mahogany

Medium (as for Penetrating Stain §1)

Pigments

*Sudan Dark Brown BG	20 g.
*Sudan Red 4BA	5 g.

For directions, trade-mark products (*) and precautions, see Penetrating Stain §1.

Penetrating Stain §11
Light Cherry

Medium (as for Penetrating Stain §1)

Pigments

*Sudan Brown 5BA	10 g.
*Sudan Dark Brown BG	15 g.

For directions, trade-mark products (*) and precautions, see Penetrating Stain §1.

Penetrating Stain §12
Cherry

Medium (as for Penetrating Stain §1)

Pigments

*Sudan Brown 5BA . . . . 5 g.
*Sudan Dark Brown BG . . . . 20 g.

For directions, trade-mark products (*) and precautions, see Penetrating Stain §1.

Penetrating Stain §13
Walnut

Medium (as for Penetrating Stain §1)

Pigments

*Sudan Brown 5BA . . . . 12 g.
*Sudan Dark Brown BG . . . . 12 g.
*Sudan Black BR . . . . 1 g.

For directions, trade-mark products (*) and precautions, see Penetrating Stain §1.

Penetrating Stain §14
Dark Walnut

Medium (as for Penetrating Stain §1)

Pigments

*Sudan Dark Brown BG . . . . 22 g.
*Sudan Black BR . . . . 3 g.

For directions, trade-mark products (*) and precautions, see Penetrating Stain §1.

Penetrating Stain §15
Ebony

Medium (as for Penetrating Stain §1)

Pigment

*Sudan Deep Black BB . . . . 25 g.

For directions, trade-mark products (*) and precautions, see Penetrating Stain §1.

Wood Stains (D) Spirit Stains

Spirit stains are essentially solutions of dyes in ethyl, or less commonly, in methyl alcohol. The great advantage of this type of stain is speed of drying. Moreover, spirit stains have little tendency to raise the grain. For these reasons, spirit stains are widely used for touching-up purposes, as well as on new work. They can also penetrate certain finishes, and have been used over shellacked and lacquered coatings, although this operation is often uncertain in its results.

Of course, the speed of drying is also a disadvantage, because it requires fast and dexterous application to avoid streaking, lapping, and other differences in color. Moreover, because this is essentially a surface rather than a penetrating stain, it cannot be wholly fast to light. The best that can be expected is "good" fastness, and the dyes recommended here belong in that category.

Application should be made to a smooth clean wooden surface by stiff-bristle brushes, using a suitable width of brush, if possible, to cover the cross-grain dimension. Use a full, but not dripping brush, and work as quickly as possible, moving with the grain from the center to the ends of the surface.

As in the case of the penetrating stains, the colors used in formulating these spirit stains should be closely specified. Therefore, they are expressed by manufacturer's designations. The colors used in the following group of formulas are all products of the General Dyestuff Corporation, 435 Rector St., New York 14, N.Y. If you wish to use the products of another manufacturer, you can, by citing the information given here, inquire whether or not equivalents are obtainable.

The other ingredients, the methyl alcohol and the ethylene glycol can be obtained readily from a chemical supply house or manufacturer. (See Appendix A and B.) While spirit stains can be formulated somewhat better if ethyl alcohol is used, the legal technicalities to be met in purchasing it even for industrial use (nonbeverage) are too time-consuming unless you wish to make stains commercially.

In choosing equipment for mixing these spirit stains, use glass or porcelain vessels if possible. Some of the dyes are acid, and may react enough with metallic pails to affect their colors.

Spirit Stain §1

Light Oak

Medium

Ethylene Glycol	100 ml.
Methyl Alcohol	900 ml.

Pigments

*Fast Light Yellow D3GA	18 g.
*Fast Light Orange GA (conc.)	7 g.
*Pluto Black GA (conc.) CF	1 g.

* Trade-mark product of the General Dyestuff Co., 435 Hudson St., New York 14, N.Y.

Directions: Dissolve the dyes in 100 ml. of the methyl alcohol with gentle stirring, then add the remainder of the methyl alcohol and the ethylene glycol.

Precautions: Methyl alcohol is toxic and somewhat inflammable. Therefore, these stains should be prepared and used with good ventilation and skin protection.

Spirit Stain §2

Dark Oak

Medium (as for Spirit Stain §1)

Pigments

*Fast Light Yellow D3GA	15 g.
*Fast Light Orange GA (conc.)	8 g.
*Pluto Black GA (conc.) CF	2 g.

For directions, trade-mark products (*) and precautions, see Spirit Stain §1.

Spirit Stain §3

Golden Oak

Medium (as for Spirit Stain §1)

Pigments

*Fast Light Yellow D3GA	10 g.
*Fast Light Orange GA (conc.)	10 g.
*Pluto Black GA (conc.) CF	3 g.

For directions, trade-mark products (*) and precautions, see Spirit Stain §1.

Spirit Stain §4
Yellow Maple

Medium (as for Spirit Stain §1)

Pigments

*Fast Light Yellow D3GA . . . . 18 g.
*Fast Light Orange GA (conc.) . . . . . . 8 g.
*Azosol Fast Blue BLA extra . . . . . . 2 g.

For directions, trade-mark products (*) and precautions, see Spirit Stain §1.

Spirit Stain §5
Honey Brown Maple

Medium (as for Spirit Stain §1)

Pigments

*Fast Light Orange GA (conc.) . . . . . . 20 g.
*Azosol Fast Blue BLA extra . . . . . . 5 g.

For directions, trade-mark products (*) and precautions, see Spirit Stain §1.

Spirit Stain §6
Red Mahogany

Medium (as for Spirit Stain §1)

Pigments

*Azosol Brilliant Red B . . . . 14 g.
*Azosol Fast Orange RA (conc.) . . . . . 11 g.
*Spirit Nigrosine Jet . . . . 1 g.

For directions, trade-mark products (*) and precautions, see Spirit Stain §1.

Spirit Stain §7
Dark Mahogany

Medium (as for Spirit Stain §1)

Pigments

*Azosol Fast Red 3BA . . . . 8 g.
*Azosol Fast Orange RA (cone) . . . . . 18 g.
*Spirit Nigrosine Jet . . . . 4 g.

For directions, trade-mark products (*) and precautions, see Spirit Stain §1.

Spirit Stain §8
Light Cherry

Medium (as for Spirit Stain §1)

Pigments

*Azosol Fast Red BE	8 g.
*Azosol Fast Yellow RCA	18 g.
*Spirit Nigrosine Jet	2 g.

For directions, trade-mark products (*) and precautions, see Spirit Stain §1.

Spirit Stain §9
Cherry

Medium (as for Spirit Stain §1)

Pigments

*Azosol Fast Red BE	8 g.
*Azosol Fast Yellow RCA	16 g.
*Spirit Nigrosine Jet	4 g.

For directions, trade-mark products (*) and precautions, see Spirit Stain §1.

Spirit Stain §10
Walnut

Medium (as for Spirit Stain §1)

Pigments

*Azosol Brilliant Red B	4 g.
*Azosol Fast Yellow RCA	20 g.
*Spirit Nigrosine Jet	6 g.

For directions, trade-mark products (*) and precautions, see Spirit Stain §1.

Spirit Stain §11
Dark Walnut

Medium (as for Spirit Stain §1)

Pigments

*Azosol Brilliant Red B	4 g.
*Azosol Fast Yellow RCA	17 g.
*Spirit Nigrosine Jet	9 g.

For directions, trade-mark products (*) and precautions, see Spirit Stain §1.

Spirit Stain §12

Ebony

Medium (as for Spirit Stain §1)

Pigment

*Spirit Nigrosine Jet . . . .   18 g.

For directions, trade-mark products (*) and precautions, see Spirit Stain §1.

Wood Stains (E) Water Stains

Water stains are used by skilled wood finishers for work of the highest quality. They penetrate deeply, and are therefore highly resistant to fading. They do not precipitate their dyes under any normal conditions of application, and therefore, do not require wiping to avoid muddiness. Their disadvantage is the fact that since, as indicated at the beginning of this chapter, wood grows as a cellular structure containing watery sap, the action of water stains upon dried wood is to swell the grain and thus cause roughness. You can avoid this trouble by applying first plain water to the surface to be stained and sanding the surface lightly to remove the roughness. Then the stain may be applied without causing roughening. This preliminary treatment will also make it easier for you to obtain "even" staining.

Formulas for water stains are not given in this book because they are so widely available and so inexpensive. Any retail painter's supply store will have them in a great variety of wood colors and shades. They are sold as packaged powders, with directions to be followed in preparing the solution. Care should be taken to make sure that you obtain a water stain powder, because some stores also offer spirit and penetrating stain powders.

Wood Stains (F) Chemical Stains

Unlike all the other wood stains, chemical stains owe their action, not to a colored substance which they contain and add to the wood, but to their chemical reaction with components of the wood, which produces a colored substance. They are, therefore, limited both in the range of colors which they produce and the kinds of wood which they color. They are also definitely inferior in their results and are used largely on lower quality work. However, they are cheap and penetrating and reasonably dependable after the technique of using them has been mastered. Many of them are corrosive to hands, clothes, etc., and they should be handled with care.

Chemical Stain §1
Light Brown

Sodium Hydroxide (lye) . . . .   45 g.
Water . . . . 1000 ml.

Directions: Add sodium hyroxide to water in glass or porcelain container. After solution is complete, stir and allow to cool. Apply to surface lightly with brush (do not spatter).
Precautions: Strongly corrosive to skin. Wear rubber gloves and goggles.

Chemical Stain §2
Brown

Sodium Carbonate (washing soda) . . . .   75 g.
Water . . . . 1000 ml.

Directions: The same as Chemical Stain §1.
Precautions: Corrosive to skin, though somewhat less so than Chemical Stain §1.

Chemical Stain §3
Medium Brown

Potassium Permanganate . . . . . .   60 g.
Water . . . . 1000 ml.

Directions: The same as Chemical Stain §1.
Precautions: Oxidizing agent; do not store in wooden or paper container. Stains skin.

Chemical Stain §4
Dark Brown

Concentrated Ammonium Hydroxide . . .   700 ml
Water . . . . 300 ml.

Directions: Mix water and ammonia; apply mixture with brush in well ventilated place. Do not use this solution unless air current is strong enough to carry off fumes so rapidly that the worker does not inhale them.
Precautions: Corrosive liquid; avoid inhaling fumes.

Chemical Stain §5

Gray

Iron (ordinary nails) . . . .   10 g.
Vinegar . . . .   1000 ml.

Directions: Allow the vinegar and nails to stand for one day in a glass container. Filter off the sludge and apply the solution to the surface to be stained. If the shade of gray is not deep enough on drying, repeat the treatment.

Wood Fillers

It is customary in finishing wood for most purposes to add a "filler" to close up the pores of the wood. Unless the finish to be used is one for which no stain is used the filler is applied after the staining operation. This requires that it be colored to match the stain. This is done by use of the corresponding oil pigments, in the proportions that they were used in the oil pigment stains given earlier in this chapter. That is, to prepare a paste filler, use the following basic formula:

Paste Filler—Basic Formula

Silex Powder (fine) . . . .   400 g.
Japan Drier . . . .   300 ml.
Linseed Oil   . . . .   500 ml.
Oil Colors . . . .   As necessary

Directions: Refer to section on "Wood Stains (B) Pigment Oil Stains" to find the corresponding color which the wood has been stained. Suppose for example, it is Red Mahogany. Then you will find, from the formula for Pigment Oil Stain §9 that the pigments used there were Burnt Sienna Pigment in Oil—240 ml.—and Rose Pink Pigment in Oil—80 ml. These are the oil colors and proportions to use in coloring the paste filler basic formula above to obtain a Paste Filler for Red Mahogany. The amount of color to be used depends upon the depth of stain in the wood, so a good plan for you to use is to mix the basic ingredients (Silex Powder, Japan Drier and Linseed Oil) in the quantities in the basic formula. Then mix separately the colors from the correct Pigment Oil Stain Formula (for Red Mahogany §9, this would be 240 ml. of Burnt Sienna Pigment in Oil and 80 ml. Rose Pink Pigment in Oil). Now add the mixed colors to the basic paste filler mixture until you have produced the desired depth of color to match the stained wood.

Be sure to try the paste filler on the wood before discarding the unused portion of the mixed color, because often the stained wood "draws" the color out of the paste filler and leaves it too light. This effect is so pronounced if the wood has been stained with a water spirit or chemical stain (and sometimes even an oil stain) that a very light coating of shellac is necessary before the filler is used.

To apply a paste filler, first thin it with turpentine to a heavy brushing consistency. The correct consistency must be found by trial, so that the filler is thin enough to enter the pores, and thick enough to remain there. Then lay on the filler, *across the grain*, with a stiff brush, rubbing it well into the pores. It is now allowed to set. This action is usually complete in about fifteen minutes, but should be checked by rubbing a small spot and noting if the filler remains in the pores of the wood. As soon as the filler is set it is wiped with a piece of burlap or other coarse absorbent material. Wipe first across the grain, and finally with it. At least ten hours should be allowed for drying. Then, after light sanding, the wood is ready for the later finishing materials (shellac, varnish, etc.)

Paste fillers are commonly used on all the open-grain (large-pore) woods. These are chestnut, ash, elm, mahogany, rosewood, American walnut and oak (except for certain oak finishes). For close-grain woods, on the other hand, liquid fillers are used. Liquid fillers may be shellac or lacquer, provided that the shellac or varnish lacquer is never used over a varnish filler, and provided that filling with these liquids is conducted carefully. (For example, the shade of shellac, varnish or lacquer should be in keeping with the lightness or darkness of the stain.) Liquid fillers may also be compounded, usually in a formulation based upon varnish and turpentine. A basic liquid filler formula is:

Liquid Filler—Basic Formula

Silex Powder (fine)	400 g.
Rubbing Varnish	400 ml.
Japan Drier	300 ml.
Linseed Oil	100 ml.
Turpentine	100 ml.
Oil Colors	As necessary

Directions: Follow directions under Paste Filler—Basic Formula for preparing colors, then add estimated amount of them to the 100 ml. of linseed oil. Then stir in drier, silex and varnish (for rubbing varnish, see Varnish §4 below) and turpentine and add additional color to match wood, stirring thoroughly after each addition.

In applying liquid fillers be sure, of course, to do any necessary thinning with a solvent contained in, or compatible with that already in the product (i.e. turpentine for oil products, alcohol for shellac, etc.) Two light coats, with light sanding between, will often give better results than one coat, provided that ample time is allowed for the first coat to dry. (Remember that while shellac and lacquer dry in two or three hours, oil media take much longer.)

Shellac Solutions

Some mention of shellac obviously belongs in this book, even though it is commonly used in simple alcoholic solution (95% ethyl alcohol) and therefore does not require statement of formulas. Strength of shellac solutions is commonly expressed, by trade practice, in terms of "cuts." A 5-pound cut of shellac means that 5 pounds of shellac have been dissolved in 1 gallon of ethyl alcohol, a 3-pound cut means 3 pounds per gallon, etc. Therefore, from the prices quoted for the various "cuts," you can decide which is the best buy currently, and then thin it with alcohol to the working consistency you want, which depends upon the work and should be determined by trial. Since shellac itself is an imported product, the dried secretion of the tropical lac insect, it varies greatly in quality and should be purchased from a reputable dealer.

Natural shellac is orange in color, but its shade is not pronounced, and is generally preferable even for quite light woods to "white" shellac. The latter is produced by a bleaching process, and is neither as durable nor as water-resistant as the orange variety. Of course, neither of the varieties of shellac are suitable for direct exposure to water and shellacked articles should not be exposed to the weather. In spite of these limitations shellac finishes have long been used on fine furniture, and much of the old furniture was finished in this way and is still good.

Shellac may be applied in various ways. If you use a brush, work with the grain and remember that shellac does not spread. Therefore, try to avoid overlapping, which will cause unevenness of color. A good way to minimize this effect is by applying a larger number of coats, using a thinner shellac. Another means is to spray the shellac instead of brushing it. (Do not place your spray gun less than 8 inches from the work.) Still another means of application is by use of a soft, absorbent cloth pad, which is dipped in turpentine and shellac and pressed against the work while the latter is being turned in a lathe. Finally, remember that after the final coat all shellac finishes should be rubbed with fine steel wool (or pumice for a dull or semi-gloss finish).

Varnishes

There are probably more kinds of varnish, formulated for more fields of use, than of almost any product encountered in our daily life. This is partly attributable to the long period of manufacture of varnishes from the natural gums and partly to the recent development of the synthetic resins and their use to replace the natural resins, partly or entirely, with resulting improvement in properties of the product.

Most of the functional classes of varnish in use today were known before the time of synthetic resins. The exterior varnishes were usually formulated with more oil to withstand outdoor conditions. One of the most important subclasses was *spar varnish* used on ships. *Floor varnish* was, as the name indicates, expected to have considerable water-resistance, and yet to dry fairly rapidly. *Flowing varnish* was designed for application to furniture without leaving brush marks. *Rubbing varnish* was usually formulated with less drier, for greater surface hardness, and was also intended primarily for use on furniture.

In presenting formulas for varnishes, the policy followed in this book is to include representative products of the various types. The first eleven formulas are based entirely, with the exception of the one containing ester gum, upon natural resins. These have been chosen as far as possible from those most commonly available to minimize any difficulty you may encounter in obtaining them, as well as the other ingredients, from your supply house. Moreover, formulas 9, 10, and 11 are simple solutions of natural resins because, as you will see from the other formulas, the standard method of preparing varnishes involves high temperatures and other hazards. If you prepare the quantities indicated, keep the naphtha in a different room from that in which you perform the other operations. Then when the mixture has cooled, and all fires are out, you can bring in the naphtha to complete the formula. If you prepare such varnishes on a larger scale, visit a plant first to observe the additional precautions necessary.

Among the advantages of the varnishes formulated with synthetic resins are greater purity of the resin, which gives a better product, and incidentally, simplifies the process, although the melting operation is still necessary. This is exemplified in Varnish formulas §12, 13, 14, 15 and 16. Moreover, the short-oil types, such as §14, dry more quickly than the natural resin products. Even greater advantages can be obtained by the manufacturer who uses both types of resins in the same formula, but such multiplication of ingredients complicates the production operations to an extent that is not consistent with the policy of this book.

However, it is clearly consistent with that purpose to add a few words about varnishing methods. The greatest requirement is complete freedom from dirt and moisture. The surface to be varnished should be as smooth as fine steel wool, or fine sandpaper can make it, and then it should be entirely freed from dust (a cloth barely dampened with varnish does a good job). The need for dryness is so important that you should never varnish on a humid day.

Varnish should be flowed onto the surface. Always work with a full brush, covering a small area at a time and avoiding pressure on the brush. In varnishing properly smoothed surfaces of high-grade woods, the brush should pass over the surface only once. This "once-over" technique yields the best results, but requires some practice to acquire an even rhythm of stroking that joins perfectly the area covered by each stroke with that covered by the previous stroke. The method of varnishing more commonly used for average work is first to cover a small area by brushing cross-grain with a full brush, and then to blend with the grain. For some purposes and tastes, an eggshell gloss is preferred to the high gloss of shellac or varnish. After thorough drying, usually for 48 hours, an attractive dull finish is produced with pumice and water rub. Place some finely powdered pumice stone in an open dish. Wet the surface to be rubbed with water. Soak a felt pad in the water. Dip the wet felt pad in the powdered pumice stone and rub in the direction of the grain, using long, even strokes. A satin finish is obtained by working the same as in the case of pumice and water, except that a neutral mineral or a paraffin oil is used.

Varnish §1

Marine Spar Varnish

Water-White Rosin	100 g.
Calcium Hydroxide (dry)	5 g.
Lead Tungate	25 g.
Litharge	7 g.
Manganese Borate	1 g.
China Wood Oil	200 ml.
Raw Linseed Oil	175 ml.
Naphtha	600 ml.

Directions: Heat the rosin in a kettle to 500°F. Withdraw from fire and sprinkle the calcium hydroxide on the surface. When reaction has subsided, return to fire and heat to 550°F. Then add the lead tungate in small pieces, with stirring. When addition is complete, allow to cool, and divide into two portions, one of which is about 3 times as great as the other. To the larger portion, add the china wood oil, and heat to 580°F. Pull from fire, and add the smaller portion. When foaming has subsided, and temperature has fallen to about 550°F., sprinkle the litharge and manganese borate on the surface of the varnish slowly, with stirring, allowing foam to subside before adding more of the metal salts. When addition is complete, stir in the cold linseed oil. Allow to cool to 150°F., *extinguish all flames*, and stir in the naphtha slowly.

Precautions: High temperature, naphtha highly inflammable.

Varnish §2

Tool Varnish

Water-White Rosin	100 g.
Calcium Hydroxide (dry)	5 g
Litharge	7 g.
Red Lead	2 g.
China Wood Oil	300 ml.
Raw Linseed Oil	50 ml.
Naphtha	600 ml.
*Japan Drier	10 ml.

* In this formula, and succeeding varnish formulas, the Japan drier can be replaced to advantage by the Nuodex products of the Nuodex Products Co., Inc., 630 Magnolia Ave., Elizabeth, N.J.

Directions: Place the rosin in a kettle, sprinkle the calcium hydroxide on top, and pour in the china wood oil. Heat to 550°F. and withdraw from fire. The temperature will continue to rise, due to the chemical reaction. When it reaches 580°F., add the linseed oil with stirring. When the temperature falls to 550°F., add the litharge and red lead slowly and with stirring. When the temperature falls to 150°F. *extinguish all flames*, and stir in the naphtha and the Japan drier.

Precautions: High temperature, naphtha highly inflammable.

Varnish §3

Floor Varnish

Water-White Rosin	100 g.
Calcium Hydroxide	5 g.
Litharge	7 g.
Red Lead	2 g.
China Wood Oil	200 ml.
Raw Linseed Oil	100 ml.
Naphtha	600 ml.
Japan Drier	30 ml.

Directions: The same as Varnish §1 omitting the lead tungate, and using red lead instead of manganese borate.

Precautions: High temperature, naphtha highly inflammable.

Varnish §4
Rubbing Furniture and Trim Varnish

Congo Gum	250 g.
Ester Gum	50 g.
Lead Resinate	20 g.
Manganese Resinate	2 g.
China Wood Oil	200 ml.
Turpentine	400 ml.
Naphtha	240 ml.

Directions: Heat the Congo Gum to 550°F. in a kettle. Remove from fire, allow to cook for 15 minutes. Return to fire; heat to 650°F. and add the cold china wood oil slowly with stirring (beware of spattering). Let cool to 450°F. and add the ester gum. Reheat to 540°F., remove from fire, let cool to 525°F., and add the resinates with stirring. Allow to cool to 400°F., and add the turpentine. Allow to cool to 150°F., *extinguish all flames,* and add the naphtha.

Precautions: High temperature, naphtha highly inflammable.

Varnish §5
Mixing Varnish for Paint

Manila Gum	160 g.
Water-White Rosin	40 g.
Sodium Hydroxide	4 g.
Boiled Linseed Oil	140 ml.
Turpentine	280 ml.
Naphtha	420 ml.

Directions: Heat the Manila Gum and the rosin in a kettle to 550°F., remove from fire, allow to cool to 450°F., and add the sodium hydroxide slowly with stirring. Reheat to 520°F., and hold there for 10 minutes. Withdraw from fire; heat the linseed oil to 350°F., and add it to the kettle, with stirring. Return kettle to fire, heat to 500°F. and hold for 20 minutes. Remove from fire, allow to cool to 400°F., add the turpentine. When further cooling has reached 150°F., *extinguish all flames,* and add the naphtha.

Precautions: High temperature, naphtha highly inflammable.

Varnish §6
Pale Polishing Varnish

Pale Manila Gum	250 g.
Water-White Rosin	60 g.
Calcium Hydroxide (dry)	3 g.
Litharge	5 g.
Manganese Borate	2 g.
China Wood Oil	100 ml.
Bleached Linseed Oil	100 ml.
Turpentine	720 ml.

Directions: Heat the rosin and manila to 550°F., remove kettle from fire and allow to cool to 500°F., then reheat to 525°F., and hold there for ten minutes, or as much longer as necessary to melt gums. Remove kettle from fire, and add the china wood oil and the linseed oil, which had first been mixed and heated to 350°F. Then reheat the kettle to 500°F., stir in the calcium hydroxide slowly, and hold at 500°F. for 30 minutes. Remove from fire, and while cooling to 425°F., stir in the litharge and the manganese borate. Finally, stir in the turpentine.

Precautions: High temperature.

Varnish §7
6-Hour Quick-Polishing Floor Varnish

Kauri Gum	200 g.
Manganese Borate	4 g.
Litharge	4 g.
Raw Linseed Oil	350 ml.
Turpentine	650 ml.

Directions: First prepare the linseed oil by heating it to 450°F., adding the manganese borate and litharge and then heating at 500°F., for 5 hours. Set this oil aside, and heat the kauri gum to 600°F., holding it there until it becomes thin (usually 2-3 hours). Remove it from fire, and add the prepared oil (heated to 450°F.). Reheat mixture to 525°F., hold it there for 20 minutes, allow to cool to 425°F., and add the turpentine.

Precautions: High temperature.

Varnish §8

Elastic Varnish

Manila Gum	130 g.
Water-White Rosin	25 g.
Calcium Hydroxide (dry)	5 g.
Litharge	5 g.
Raw Linseed Oil	400 ml.
Turpentine	450 ml.
Naphtha	100 ml.

Directions: Heat the manila gum to 550°F., and hold there until melted. Remove from fire, add the rosin. Reheat to 525°F., remove from fire, sprinkle in the calcium hydroxide and heat to 500°F., for 10 minutes. Remove from fire, add the linseed oil (heated to 450°F. for 4 hours). Cool to 425°F., add the turpentine, cool to 150°F. *extinguish all flames* and add the naphtha.

Precautions: High temperature; naphtha highly inflammable.

Varnish §9

Dammar Varnish

High-Quality Dammar Gum	500 g.
Turpentine	250 ml.
Naphtha	250 ml.

Directions: Stir gum with turpentine and naphtha at room temperature in closed vessel until dissolved. This takes several hours.

Precautions: Naphtha highly inflammable.

Varnish §10

Orange Shellac (Varnish)*

Orange Shellac	350 g.
Alcohol	600 ml.

* Note that this product differs from a shellac in its very high concentration.

Directions: Stir the shellac and alcohol at room temperature in a closed container until dissolved. This takes several hours.

Varnish §11

Hard Manila Spirit Varnish

Manila Gum	500 g.
Alcohol	400 ml.
Benzene	150 ml.

Directions: Same as Varnish §9.

Precautions: Benzene is poisonous to skin and tissues, and its vapor is poisonous on inhalation.

Varnish §12

Floor Varnish

Bakelite Resin (BR 253)*	250 g.
Linseed Oil	350 ml.
Toluene	65 ml.
Cobalt Resinate	4 g.
Naphtha	400 ml.

*Trade-mark product Union Carbide Corp., 30 East 42 St., New York 17, N.Y.

Directions: Heat the oil and resin until the latter has melted to form a uniform liquid with the oil. Heat slowly for 15 minutes more. Cool to 150°F., *extinguish all flames,* and add the naphtha. When cooling to room temperature has occurred, add the cobalt resinate and the toluene.

Precautions: High temperature, naphtha is highly combustible.

Varnish §13

Water Resistant Varnish

Bakelite Resin (BR 253)*	175 g.
Linseed Oil	425 ml.
Toluene	65 ml.
Cobalt Resinate	4 g.
Naphtha	400 ml.

*Trade-mark product Union Carbide Corp., 30 East 42 St., New York 17, N.Y.

Directions: The same as for Varnish §12.

Varnish §14
Rubbing Varnish

Modified Alkyd Resin*	420 g.
Tung Oil	125 ml.
Zinc and Cobalt Resinates	6 g.
Mineral Spirits**	600 ml.

* Alkyd resins are obtainable from various sources. One is the American Resinous Chemical Corp., 103 Foster St., Peabody, Mass.
** Mineral spirits are a petroleum fraction between gasoline and kerosene.

Directions: Heat the oil and resin to 420°F. until the latter melts, then raise temperature slowly to 500°F. Cool to 250°F. and add the resinates. *Extinguish all flames* and add the mineral spirits.

Precautions: High temperatures, mineral spirits are highly inflammable.

Varnish §15
Floor Varnish

Modified Alkyd Resin*	375 g.
Tung Oil	200 ml.
Zinc Resinate	4 g.
Mineral Spirits**	600 ml.

* Alkyd resins are obtainable from various sources. One is the American Resinous Chemical Corp., 103 Foster St., Peabody, Mass.
** Mineral spirits are a petroleum fraction between gasoline and kerosene.

Directions: The same as Varnish §14.

Varnish §16
Water Resistant Varnish

Modified Alkyd Resin*	325 g.
Tung Oil	250 ml.
Zinc Resinate	2 g.
Mineral Spirits**	600 ml.

* Alkyd resins are obtainable from various sources. One is the American Resinous Chemical Corp., 103 Foster St., Peabody, Mass.
** Mineral spirits are a petroleum fraction between gasoline and kerosene.

Directions: The same as Varnish §14.

Varnish §17

Modified Alkyd Resin	125 g.
China Wood Oil	110 g.
Boiled Linseed Oil	55 g.
Tung Oil Fatty Acids	15 g.
Ethyl Cellulose	30 g.
*Nuodex	10 g.
Isopropyl Alcohol	130 ml.
Naphtha	500 ml.

* Trade-mark product of Nuodex Products, Inc., 830 Magnolia Ave., Elizabeth, N.J.

Directions: Heat first two ingredients at 450°F (232°C) for 1 hour. Then add next two ingredients, and heat for ½ hour at that temperature. Then add ethyl cellulose and stir until dissolved. (Care!) Mix remaining ingredients and add them to other mixture after it has cooled to 203°F (95°C).

Precautions: High temperatures, naphtha is highly inflammable.

Polishes

While many wooden surfaces are finished with varnish, shellac or certain special processes so that they do not require a final polishing operation, there are others to which the craftsman wishes to apply that treatment. Moreover, polishes are widely used on already finished wooden surfaces, in some cases primarily as a cleaning operation, but in others to restore gloss by rubbing. Finally, there are manufactured a wide variety of "no-rubbing" polishes designed to deposit a smooth uniform film on the surface. The foregoing sequence has been followed in the arrangement of the formulas in this section, beginning with the older "rubbing" varieties, composed mostly of widely-available ingredients, and extending to the newer formulations, many of which contain trade-mark products of individual manufacturers.

Wood Polishes (A) Mixed Oil Polishes

The oil-containing polishes for wood are called "mixed-oil" polishes to distinguish them from the simple oil polishes, which usually consist only of a single substance. Thus paraffin oil, a water-white petroleum product and lemon oil, a yellowish oil of vegetable origin, are used widely as wood polishes. They are rapidly losing ground, however, because of the improved properties of the newer, formulated products, which include the mixed oil polishes.

Mixed Oil Polish §1

Vinegar (white)	350 ml.
Alcohol (denatured)	350 ml.
Paraffin Oil	350 ml.

Directions: Mix the vinegar with the alcohol, then add the oil and shake vigorously. This polish is excellent for many surfaces, although it has the disadvantage that it separates on standing and must be shaken before using. The surface to be polished should first be washed with soapy water and thoroughly dried. Then the polish is applied sparingly, and the excess rubbed off with a clean, soft cloth, followed by continued rubbing until sufficiently glossy.

Mixed Oil Polish §2

Water	600 ml.
Alcohol	200 ml.
Raw Linseed Oil	200 ml.

Directions: The same as for Mixed Oil Polish §1.

Mixed Oil Polish §3

Rottenstone (powdered)	100 g.
Vinegar	300 ml.
Alcohol (denatured)	300 ml.
Paraffin Oil	300 ml.

Directions: Mix the liquids, and stir in the powder until product is uniform in consistency. Apply to surface with a coarse cloth (cheesecloth) rubbing with the grain of the wood until desired gloss has been obtained.

Mixed Oil Polish §4

Beeswax	30 g.
Turpentine	500 ml.
Raw Linseed Oil	500 ml.

Directions: Heat the linseed oil to no more than 85°C (185°F); this can be done by use of a bath of heated water; then dissolve the wax in the oil. Discontinue heating and add the turpentine. Apply with a soft cloth, wiping off excess, and rub until the desired gloss has been obtained.

Mixed Oil Polish §5

Furniture Polish

Mineral Oil	400 ml.
*Span 85	35 g.
*Tween 81	35 g.
Water	530 g.

* Span and Tween are trade-mark products of the Atlas Powder Co., Wilmington 99, Delaware.

Directions: Mix oil and the emulsifiers at room temperature. Add the water slowly with constant agitation until inversion occurs (that is, change from a water-in-oil system to an oil-in-water one). Then the remainder of the water may be added rapidly.

Mixed Oil Polish §6

Furniture Polish

Mineral Seal Oil	250 ml.
*Span 40	21 g.
*Tween 40	49 g.
Paraffin Oil	250 ml.
Water	530 ml.

* Span and Tween are trade-mark products of the Atlas Powder Co., Wilmington 99, Delaware.

Directions: Mix the oils and emulsifiers and heat to 122°F (50°C). Add the water at room temperature, very slowly until inversion occurs (i.e. change from a water-in-oil system to an oil-in-water one). Then the remainder of the water may be added rapidly.

Wood Polishes (B) Wax Polishes

The wax polishes have passed through a long process of development to the point where some of them now are based on solid ingredients that are synthetics, rather than vegetable or animal waxes. However, all these wax polishes differ from the mixed oil polishes in that the action of a wax polish is to leave a wax film on the surface being polished. Therefore, their durability depends upon the hardness of the wax used, for example, carnauba wax is harder than beeswax.

Another characteristic of the wax polishes is their need for a coloring agent, when they are used on fine furniture. For the film they leave on the surface tends to be thicker in mouldings and other areas which cannot be rubbed so hard; thick enough, in fact, so that it would be noticeable if it were the color of the wax used in the polish. Therefore, wax polishes are often colored to match the wood on which they are used. The colors used for this purpose are the oil pigments mixed in accordance with the proportions in which they were used in the pigment oil stains given earlier in this chapter.

Wax Polish §1

Beeswax	1600 g.
Turpentine	900 ml.
Color as desired.	

Directions: Flake beeswax with a knife and heat in water bath (as described for Mixed Oil Polish §4) until wax has melted. Then remove it from the heat and add the turpentine slowly and with constant stirring. Then add the color, as desired. Allow to cool before using. Since this polish has such a high-wax content, it should be applied only to a limited area at a time, using a saturated cloth, allowed to set for a few minutes, and then polished to the desired gloss with a soft cloth. This product yields a high gloss.

Wax Polish §2

Carnauba Wax	800 g.
Paraffin Wax	800 g.
Turpentine	900 ml.
Color as desired.	

Directions: The same as for Wax Polish §1. The chief difference between the two polishes is that this §2 formula yields a harder wax surface which requires more rubbing to develop the desired gloss, but lasts much longer under ordinary service conditions.

Wax Polish §3

Furniture Polish

Liquid

Carnauba Wax	60 g.
Candelilla Wax	35 g.
Paraffin Wax	35 g.
Naphtha	750 ml.
Turpentine	125 ml.

Directions: Heat three waxes separately until molten. Withdraw from fire and add the carnauba wax to the candelilla wax, and then the paraffin wax to the mixture. Withdraw from fire, extinguish all flames and add turpentine slowly to the molten wax. Then allow to cool to room temperature and add the naphtha. This polish is relatively inexpensive and easy to apply.

Precautions: Naphtha is a fire hazard and must be handled accordingly, as must this furniture polish.

Wax Polish §4

Paste Furniture Polish

Carnauba Wax	150 g.
Beeswax	150 g.
Naphtha	250 ml.
*Span 60	30 g.
*Tween 65	70 g.
Water	350 ml.

*Span and Tween are trade-mark products of the Atlas Powder Co., Wilmington 99, Delaware.

Directions: Heat the waxes, emulsifiers and naphtha at 185°F (85°C) until the waxes dissolve. Heat water separately to 90°C, and add to solution with moderate stirring.

Precautions: Naphtha is a fire hazard and must be handled accordingly, as must this polish.

Wax Polish §5

Lotion Cleaner-Polish

Candelilla Wax	50 g.
Naphtha	100 ml.
*Tween 40	50 g.
**Cellosolve	110 g.
Water	690 ml.

*Tween is a trade-mark product of the Atlas Powder Co., Wilmington 99, Delaware.
**Cellosolve is a trade-mark product of the Union Carbide Corp., 30 East 42 St., New York 17, N.Y.

Directions: Heat the wax and naphtha at 140°F. (60°C) until the wax dissolves. Add the emulsifier. Heat Cellosolve and water to 140°F., and add to the mixture with stirring. Cool rapidly to room temperature with continued stirring.

Precautions: Naphtha is a fire hazard and must be handled accordingly, as must this polish.

Wax Polish §6

Lotion-Cleaner Polish (Silicone Type)

Turkey Red Oil	42 ml.
Mineral Oil	53 ml.
**Silicone Oil (L-41)	31 ml.
Water	402 ml.
Naphtha	422 ml.
*Brij 30	25 g.
*Brij 35	25 g.

* Brij is a trade-mark product of the Atlas Powder Co., Wilmington 99, Delaware.
** Silicone Oil (L-41) is a trade-mark designation of the Linde Air Products Co., 30 East 42 St., New York 17, N.Y.

Directions: Add the water slowly to the mixture of oils, naphtha and emulsifiers (the two Brij products) with vigorous stirring (mechanical is possible) until inversion occurs (change from water-in-oil to oil-in-water system). The remaining water may then be added rapidly.

Precautions: Naphtha is a fire hazard and must be handled accordingly, as must this polish.

Wax Polish §7

Dust Repellent Silicone Cream-Type Polish

*SF-96-300 Silicone Fluid	50 ml.
Carnauba Wax	10 g.
**Cardis 319 Wax	15 g.
Paraffin Wax	25 g.
Mineral Spirits	250 ml.
***Span 60	15 g.
***Tween 60	15 g.
****Sodium CMC	3 g.
Water	675 ml.

* SF-96-300 Silicone Fluid is a trade-mark designation of the General Electric Co., Schenectady, N.Y.
** Cardis 319 is a trade-mark product of the Sun Oil Co., 1608 Walnut St., Philadelphia 3, Pa.
*** Span and Tween are trade-mark products of the Atlas Powder Co., Wilmington 99, Delaware.
**** Sodium CMC is a trade-mark product of the Hercules Powder Co., 900 Market St., Wilmington, Delaware.

Directions: Heat the waxes in the mineral spirits at 140°F (60°C) until solution is complete. Add the Span, Tween and silicone fluid. Heat Sodium CMC and water to 140°F., and add to the mixture with stirring. Cool rapidly to room temperature with continued stirring.

Precautions: Mineral spirits is a petroleum fraction; handle as gasoline.

Wax Polish §8
"Self-Cleaning" Type

Carnauba Wax	40 g.
Candililla Wax	20 g.
Beeswax	20 g.
*Cerice Wax	20 g.
Turpentine	50 ml.
Stoddard Solvent	375 ml.
**Onyxol	50 ml.
Water	500 ml.

* Cerice wax is the trade-mark product of Socony Vacuum Oil Company, 26 Broadway, New York 4.
** Onyxol is the trade-mark product of the Onyx Oil and Chemical Co., Jersey City, N.J.

Directions: Melt wax at 176°F (80°C) with steam heat. Add turpentine and Stoddard solvent and stir. Then mix the Onyxol with water, heat to 176°F (80°C), and add this mixture to the wax solvent mixture stirring until product has cooled to room temperature.

Precautions: Stoddard solvent is a lower boiling petroleum fraction and should be handled as gasoline.

Lacquers, Paints, and Enamels

Since this class of products is used for all kinds of surfaces, they have been placed in the following chapter. However, the special formulations for use on wooden surfaces are clearly indicated.

Chapter 3

LACQUERS, PAINTS, ENAMELS AND RELATED PRODUCTS

Wood Lacquers

One reason for arranging the formulas in this chapter so that the lacquers occur at the start is to permit the wood lacquers to follow the preceding chapter on wood surfaces. A still more basic reason is to begin this chapter with a more modern type of product. For while paints as manufactured today represent every type of formulation from the oldest to the most modern, the term lacquers no longer denotes chiefly products made from natural "lac" (see shellac in previous chapter) but primarily synthetic products (although often compounded with some natural resins).

The wide range of formulas possible with these materials makes available many types of products, differing in their appearance, method of application, field of usefulness, and manner of finishing.

The uncolored clear wood lacquers have certain advantages over shellac, and certain limitations. Their drying time is much shorter, they do not deteriorate seriously with age or by oxidation, and they can readily be formulated for resistance to water, alcohol and heat. On the other hand, they cannot be applied to wood which has been varnished, painted or stained with penetrating oil stain. Moreover, because of their high drying speed they must be sprayed or brushed uniformly and somewhat rapidly. In spite of these limitations, they are among the most useful materials available to the woodworker. One of the popular finishes for which clear, water-white lacquers are used is the "blond" finish, which usually requires a preliminary bleaching of the wood (see Chapter 2).

The opaque wood lacquers represent one of the most important developments in modern technology. Their ready adaptability to high-speed, high-temperature drying methods, and the extremely durable coatings so produced, has led to vast improvement in the finishes on automobiles, appliances, tools and many other quantity products. While such processes do not fall within the scope of this book, many other lacquer formulations are of interest here. Therefore, the pages following give ten formulas for wood lacquers and seven formulas for metal lacquers, including clear and opaque, glossy and flat, and brushing and spraying types, with directions for preparing and coloring them.

Wood Lacquer §1

Clear Glossy Brushing Lacquer

*Nitrocellulose—Wet RS ¼ second	100 g.
Ester Gum	80 g.
Boiled Linseed Oil	200 g.
**Butyl Cellosolve	100 g.
**Cellosolve	90 ml.
Butyl Propionate	120 ml.
Ethyl Alcohol	180 ml.
Naphtha	130 ml.

* One manufacturer of nitrocellulose is Hercules Powder Co., of Wilmington, Delaware. The quality specified above is RS ¼ second (Regular Soluble of ¼ second viscosity). For small quantity production, some of the lacquer dealers listed in the Classified Telephone Directories will sell nitrocellulose base solutions.
** Trade-mark products of the Union Carbide Corp., 30 East 42 Street, New York 17, N.Y.

Directions: Add the linseed oil and butyl propionate to the nitrocellulose and ester gum, and stir until mixture is uniform. Then add with continued stirring and in order, the Cellosolve, Butyl Cellosolve, alcohol and naphtha. Preparation of this product requires long stirring, so a mechanical mixer is desirable.

Precautions: Never let nitrocellulose become dry or heated. This product is inflammable.

Wood Lacquer §2

Clear Semi-Gloss Brushing Lacquer

*Nitrocellulose—Wet RS ¼ second . . .	100 g.
Ester Gum	80 g.
Tricresyl Phosphate	35 g.
Butyl Propionate	300 ml.
Blown Linseed Oil	75 ml.
Ethyl Lactate	70 ml.
Ethyl Acetate	120 ml.
Butanol	80 ml.
Ethyl Alcohol	160 ml.

* See note on Wood Lacquer §1.

Directions: Add the linseed oil to the mixture of nitrocellulose, tricresyl phosphate and ester gum and stir until mixture is uniform. Then add other ingredients with continued stirring.

Precautions: Never let nitrocellulose become dry or heated.

Wood Lacquer §3

Clear, Water-Resistant Brushing Lacquer

Ester Gum	70 g.
Blown Linseed Oil	65 ml.
Tricresyl Phosphate	20 g.
*Nitrocellulose—Wet RS ¼ second	120 g.
Amyl Acetate	230 ml.
Butanol	190 ml.
Toluene	300 ml.
Xylene	30 ml.

* See note on Wood Lacquer §1.

Directions: Heat ester gum and linseed oil with stirring at 550°F (288°C) for 30 minutes. Then allow the mixture to stand until it has cooled to 200°F., add amyl acetate, and allow to cool to room temperature. Then add with stirring the tricresyl phosphate and nitrocellulose. When solution is complete, add other ingredients in order.

Precautions: Never let nitrocellulose become dry or heated.

Wood Lacquer §4

Clear Floor Brushing Lacquer

*Nitrocellulose—Wet RS ¼ Second	150 g.
Ester Gum	60 g.
Dibutyl Phthalate	60 ml.
Ethyl Acetate	200 ml.
Butyl Acetate	200 ml.
Naphtha	350 ml.

* See note on Wood Lacquer §1.

Directions: Stir dibutyl phthalate with nitrocellulose and ester gum until uniform, then stir in other ingredients in order.

Precautions: Never let nitrocellulose become dry or heated.

65842

Wood Lacquer §5

Clear Furniture Spraying Lacquer, High Gloss

*Nitrocellulose—Wet RS ¼ Second	160 g.
Ester Gum	40 g.
Tricresyl Phosphate	30 g.
Blown Linseed Oil	50 ml.
Ethyl Acetate	300 ml.
Ethyl Lactate	30 ml.
Butanol	60 ml.
Ethyl Alcohol	110 ml.
Toluene	220 ml.

* See note on Wood Lacquer §1.

Directions: The same as Wood Lacquer §4.

Precautions: Never let nitrocellulose become dry or heated.

Wood Lacquer §6

Clear Furniture Spraying Lacquer, Flat Finish

*Nitrocellulose—Wet RS ¼ Second	160 g.
Ester Gum	40 g.
Tricresyl Phosphate	20 g.
Blown Linseed Oil	40 ml.
Starch, Powdered	90 g.
Ethyl Acetate	300 ml.
Ethyl Lactate	30 ml.
Butanol	60 ml.
Ethyl Alcohol	125 ml.
Toluene	220 ml.

* See note on Wood Lacquer §1.

Directions: The same as Wood Lacquer §4.

Precautions: Never let nitrocellulose become dry or heated.

Coloring Clear Lacquers

If it is desired to color the clear lacquers, this can readily be done by the use of spirit colors, which are dissolved in the ethyl alcohol in the foregoing six formulas for wood lacquers. In the case of §3 and §4, which contain no ethyl alcohol, 20 ml. may be added for the purpose. If it is desired to use the conventional wood colors, then use the spirit color combinations provided for the Spirit Stains in Chapter 2. If ordinary colors are desired, then the corresponding single spirit colors, such as orange, yellow, red, blue, green, etc., may be used alone or in combination. If opaque wood lacquers are desired, see the following formulas and directions.

Wood Lacquer §7

White Opaque Brushing Lacquer
(Lacquer Enamel) Semi-Gloss

*Nitrocellulose—Wet RS ¼ Second . . .	150 g.
Ester Gum	30 g.
Tricresyl Phosphate	30 g.
Blown Linseed Oil	50 ml.
Amyl Acetate	100 ml.
Butyl Acetate	90 ml.
Butanol	150 ml.
Toluene	260 ml.
Boiled Linseed Oil	90 ml.
Titanium Oxide	100 g.
Zinc Oxide	100 g.

* See note on Wood Lacquer §1.

Directions: Stir tricresyl phosphate with nitrocellulose and ester gum until mixed, then stir in blown linseed oil, amyl acetate, butyl acetate, and butanol. Now stir the titanium oxide, zinc oxide, and boiled linseed oil in a separate vessel until thoroughly mixed, and add to first mixture with thorough stirring. Finally stir in toluene.

Precautions: Never let nitrocellulose become dry or heated.

Coloring Opaque Lacquers

If it is desired to produce colored opaque lacquers, there are two methods available. The first applies to cases in which only a fairly light tint is required. Refer to the table of Toning Pigment Color Formulas on Pages 63-65; choose a toning color of the hue desired; and add it to the formula above, or to any other opaque lacquer formula in this chapter, in quantity sufficient to produce the desired depth of color.

If a more deeply-colored opaque lacquer is desired, the quantities of the white pigments (such as titanium dioxide and zinc oxide in Wood Lacquer §7) must be reduced to a limited extent, and correspondingly larger quantities of the colored pigments used. In this case, the colored pigment should be chosen from the list of Nonfading Pigments on Page 58. While this list contains only eighteen pigments, their combinations provide a wide range of colors. In changing a formula to replace in part white pigments by colored ones, be sure to prepare a small trial batch of the paint, because pigments differ markedly in covering power.

Wood Lacquer §8

White Opaque Brushing Lacquer
(Lacquer Enamel) Glossy

*Nitrocellulose—Wet RS ¼ Second . . .	150 g.
Ester Gum	80 g.
Butyl Propionate	100 ml.
Boiled Linseed Oil	120 ml.
**Cellosolve	100 ml.
**Butyl Cellosolve	100 ml.
Titanium Oxide	100 g.
Ethyl Alcohol	150 ml.
Naphtha	300 ml.

* See note on Wood Lacquer §1.
** Trade-mark products of Union Carbide Corp., 30 E. 42 St., New York 17, N.Y.

Directions: After stirring the first three ingredients, then stir in the linseed oil, followed by the pigment (titanium oxide). Then the other four ingredients may be added in order listed above. This formula avoids separate mixing of oil and pigments.

Precautions: Never let nitrocellulose become dry or heated.

Wood Lacquer §9

White Opaque Brushing Lacquer (Lacquer
Enamel) Flat Finish—Water Resistant

Ester Gum	80 g.
Boiled Linseed Oil	120 ml.
Tricresyl Phosphate	40 g.
*Nitrocellulose—Wet RS ¼ Second . . .	160 g.
Butyl Acetate	100 ml.
Zinc Oxide	200 g.
Titanium Oxide	200 g.
Butanol	150 ml
Ethyl Alcohol	150 ml.
Toluene	300 ml.

* See note on Wood Lacquer §1.

Directions: Heat boiled linseed oil to 550°F. (288°C.) with ester gum for 30 minuttes. Cool to room temperature. Add with stirring tricresyl phosphate, butyl acetate and nitrocellulose. Stir until uniform. Then stir in pigments (which may be modified with colored pigments—see directions on Page 53), then the butanol, alcohol and toluene.

Precautions: Never let nitrocellulose become dry or heated.

Wood Lacquer §10

Yellow Opaque Spraying Lacquer
(Crackle Lacquer)

*Nitrocellulose—Wet RS ¼ Second	50 g.
Ester Gum	50 g.
Tricresyl Phosphate	30 g.
Butyl Acetate	90 ml.
Ethyl Acetate	60 ml.
Chrome Yellow	200 g.
Asbestine	70 g.
Zinc Oxide	50 g.
Ethyl Alcohol	200 ml.
Toluene	200 ml.

* See note on Wood Lacquer §1.

Directions: The usual method may be followed of stirring the first three ingredients, followed by the others in order. Of course, the chrome yellow may be replaced by other colored pigments (see directions on Page 53).

A crackle lacquer is applied over another lacquer coating (which must be dry) to give a two-tone effect. The former is formulated to have low film strength, so that it will crack all over its surface on drying, to produce an interesting novelty effect. The undercoat should be heavy.

Precautions: Never let nitrocellulose become dry or heated.

Metal Lacquers

Metal lacquers differ in their formulation from wood lacquers, due primarily to the greater elasticity needed by a plastic film to adhere to a metallic surface. Consequently great care must be taken to insure that metallic surfaces are free from dirt, grease, scale, etc., before lacquers are applied. The formulas and methods for cleaning metallic surfaces are covered in Chapter 4—Formulas for Metal Surfaces. It should also be noted that metallic surfaces to be finished with clear lacquers should be attractive enough so they will look well, because the surface sheen of even the glossiest transparent lacquer is lost against a dingy undersurface.

Note that metal lacquers, clear and opaque, are colored in the same manner as wood lacquers, which has been explained for the two types (i.e. clear and opaque.)

Metal Lacquer §1

Clear Brushing Lacquer, Semi-Gloss

*Nitrocellulose—Wet RS ¼ Second . . .	100 g.
Ester Gum	75 g.
Tricresyl Phosphate	30 g.
Blown Linseed Oil	75 ml.
Butyl Propionate	240 ml.
Ethyl Lactate	60 ml.
Ethyl Acetate	100 ml.
Butanol	60 ml.
Ethyl Alcohol	360 ml.

* One manufacturer of nitrocellulose is the Hercules Powder Co., 900 Market St., Wilmington, Del.; their many varieties include the RS ¼ second (Regular Soluble, of ¼ second viscosity) specified here. For small quantity production, some of the lacquer dealers listed in the Classified Telephone Directory will sell nitrocellulose base solutions.

Directions: Stir together the first three ingredients and then add the others in the above order with constant stirring.

Precautions: Never let nitrocellulose become dry or heated.

Metal Lacquer §2

Clear Brushing Lacquer, Gloss

*Nitrocellulose—Wet RS ¼ Second . . .	150 g.
Ester Gum	150 g.
Tricresyl Phosphate	20 g.
Butyl Acetate	120 ml.
Ethyl Acetate	180 ml.
Butyl Alcohol	60 ml.
Toluene	400 ml.

* See note Metal Lacquer §1.

Directions: The same as Metal Lacquer §1.

Precautions: Never let nitrocellulose become dry or heated.

Metal Lacquer §3

Clear Spraying Lacquer, Gloss

*Nitrocellulose—Wet RS ¼ Second . . .	150 g.
Ester Gum	150 g.
Tricresyl Phosphate	20 g.
Butyl Acetate	270 ml.
Ethyl Acetate	80 ml.
Butyl Alcohol	200 ml.
Ethyl Alcohol	200 ml.
Toluene	500 ml.

* See note Metal Lacquer §1.

Directions: The same as Metal Lacquer §1.
Precautions: Never let nitrocellulose become dry or heated.

Metal Lacquer §4

Clear Dipping Lacquer, Gloss

*Nitrocellulose—Wet RS ¼ Second . . .	150 g.
Ester Gum	150 g.
Tricresyl Phosphate	20 g.
Butyl Acetate	200 ml.
Ethyl Acetate	80 ml.
Butyl Alcohol	150 ml.
Ethyl Alcohol	100 ml.
Toluene	450 ml.

* See note Metal Lacquer §1.

Directions: The same as Metal Lacquer §1.
Precautions: Never let nitrocellulose become dry or heated.

Metal Lacquer §5

White Opaque Automobile Lacquer

*Nitrocellulose—Wet RS ¼ Second . . .	160 g.
Ester Gum	30 g.
Tricresyl Phosphate	10 g.
Polymerized Linseed Oil	120 ml.
Butyl Acetate	100 ml.
Ethyl Acetate	70 ml.
Butanol	100 ml.
Toluene	320 ml.
Titanium Oxide	100 g.
Zinc Oxide	200 g.

* See note Metal Lacquer §1.

Directions: The same as Metal Lacquer §1. To produce other colors, replace the titanium oxide and zinc oxide partly with the pigments in the table of Toning Colors listed later in this chapter (following Wood Paint Formula §7). However, be sure to choose those of greatest stability to light, which include the following:

NONFADING PIGMENTS

Venetian red	Vermilion
Indian red	Burnt umber
Toluidine red	Burnt sienna
Tuscan red	Raw umber
Vandyke brown	Cobalt blue
Chromium oxide green	Lamp black
Raw sienna	Carbon black
Yellow ochre	Ivory drop black
Ultramarine blue	Black oxide of iron

Precautions: Never let nitrocellulose become dry or heated.

Metal Lacquer §6

Metal Powder Lacquer
(See also Aluminum Paints)

Ester Gum	65 g.
Boiled Linseed Oil	110 ml.
*Nitrocellulose—Wet RS ¼ Second	160 g.
Tricresyl Phosphate	30 g.
Butyl Acetate	190 ml.
Butyl Alcohol	130 ml.
Toluene	350 ml.
**Aluminum Powder	160 g.

* See note Metal Lacquer §1.
** Aluminum Powder is preferably obtained in paste form from a manufacturer, such as Aluminum Co. of America, Alcoa Bldg., Pittsburgh, Pa.

Directions: Heat ester gum and linseed oil to 550°F. (288°C) for 30 minutes. Cool to room temperature. Stir in nitrocellulose and tricresyl phosphate until uniform, then the other ingredients. Other metallic powders, in equivalent volume, may be used instead of aluminum.

Precautions: Never let nitrocellulose become dry or heated.

Metal Lacquer §7
Enamel Type

Titanium Oxide	170 g.
*Acryloid 72 (40% Solution in Toluene)	530 g.
**Vinylite (20% solution in methyl isopropyl ketone)	120 g.
Methyl Isobutyl Ketone	90 g.
Toluene	90 g.

* Trade-mark product of Rohm and Haas Co., 222 West Washington Square, Philadelphia 5, Pa.
** Trade-mark product of Union Carbide Corp., 30 East 42 St., New York 17, N.Y.

Directions: Grind the titanium oxide with about 150 g. of the Acryloid 72 solution and 25 g. of the toluene. Transfer to mixer, and add the methyl isobutyl ketone, the remainder of the Acryloid 72 and toluene, and the Vinylite. Stir continually during addition, and thereafter until product is uniform.

Lacquer Thinner

Butyl Acetate	170 ml.
Ethyl Acetate	100 ml.
Butanol	200 ml.
Ethyl Alcohol	130 ml.
Toluene	400 ml.

Directions: Add in above order, with stirring. A good general purpose thinner for nitrocellulose lacquers.

Painting Wood

Before painting an unpainted (or new) wooden surface, it is desirable to seal any knots by application to them of a coat of shellac. It is also desirable to fill any cracks by use of a crack filler or plastic wood. Therefore, formulas for these crack fillers are given immediately after this section. (Information about shellac has already been covered in Chapter 2.)

Paints for wooden surfaces may be grouped in various ways. There are the older oil-pigment-drier types which are still in extensive use, especially by commercial painters and others who need or wish to "mix their own." Then there are the newer products, based upon synthetic resins, latex and other products which permit formulations that often give superior results, especially for certain specialized uses, and which are important as well, or even primarily, because of their ease of application. They are usually more complex products, containing more ingredients, and require specific knowledge of their composition if you wish to modify them to any further degree than is provided by the directions on the label. This section gives representative formulas for both these types, and will also, as far as consistent with the size of the book, show how these formulas are modified for different conditions—outdoors and indoors, first coat and later coats, new wood and work being repainted. Representative materials have been chosen from the great variety of those available to the present-day formulator of paints. Thus, the Japan drier used in the oil-pigment-drier type of paints, as well as in other paints, can be replaced to advantage by the Nuodex driers, produced by Nuodex Products Inc., 830 Magnolia Ave., Elizabeth, N.J.

Wood Crack Filler §1

Powdered Silica	700 g.
Plaster of Paris	175 g.
Powdered Gum Arabic	125 g.

Directions: Be sure to obtain finely-ground silica and gum arabic. Mix the three powders in a dry container and keep tightly closed until used. To apply, moisten until workable and press firmly into place.

Wood Crack Filler §2

Wood Flour	250 g.
Cellulose Acetate	100 g.
Ester Gum	60 g.
Acetone	400 ml.
Alcohol	150 ml.

Directions: Mix solids intimately and stir in acetone-alcohol mixture.

Wood Paint §1

Oil-Pigment-Drier Type

Exterior—Priming Coat—New Wood

White Lead, Ground in Oil	1250 g.
Raw Linseed Oil	450 ml.
Turpentine	225 ml.
Japan Drier	15 ml.

Directions: Place white lead in large container; add oil slowly, with vigorous stirring until uniform mixture is obtained. Then add drier and turpentine with continued stirring.

Wood Paint §2

Oil-Pigment-Drier Type

Exterior—Second Coat—New Wood

White Lead, Ground in Oil	1800 g.
Raw Linseed Oil	250 ml.
Turpentine	285 ml.
Japan Drier	15 ml.

Directions: The same as for Wood Paint §1.

Wood Paint §3

Oil-Pigment-Drier Type

Exterior—Third Coat—New Wood

White Lead, Ground in Oil	1650 g.
Raw Linseed Oil	520 ml.
Turpentine	100 ml.
Japan Drier	15 ml.

Directions: The same as for Wood Paint §1.

Wood Paint §4

Oil-Pigment-Drier Type

Exterior—First Coat—Old Woodwork

White Lead, Ground in Oil	1600 g.
Raw Linseed Oil	285 ml.
Turpentine	285 ml.
Japan Drier	15 ml.

Directions: The same as for Wood Paint §1.

Wood Paint §5

Oil-Pigment-Drier Type

Exterior—Second Coat—Old Woodwork

White Lead, Ground in Oil	1600 g.
Raw Linseed Oil	450 ml.
Turpentine	35 ml.
Japan Drier	15 ml.

Directions: The same as for Wood Paint §1.

Wood Paint §6

Oil-Pigment-Drier Type

Exterior—Third Coat (Semi-flat)*—Old Wood

White Lead, Ground in Oil	2000 g.
Raw Linseed Oil	180 ml.
Turpentine	360 ml.
Japan Drier	10 ml.

*If the usual more glossy effect is desired, use Wood Paint §3 as formulated for the third coat on new wood.

Directions: The same as for Wood Paint §1.

Wood Paint §7

Oil-Pigment-Drier Type

Exterior—Surfaces Not in Direct Contact with Weather (Such as Underside of Porch Floors)

White Lead, Ground in Oil	1650 g.
Raw Linseed Oil	520 ml.
Turpentine	37 ml.
Japan Drier	15 ml.

Directions: The same as for Wood Paint §1.

In using the foregoing seven formulas, you can readily adapt them to your needs. Today three coats are applied to new work only on exceptionally costly structures, or under conditions of severe exposure, such as on the weather side of houses, especially in locations directly facing large bodies of water. Similarly, three coats are used on repainting jobs on old wood only in cases where the previous paint film is so old, or has disintegrated so badly that, after the necessary scraping, it is practically non-existent. Therefore, it will tend to absorb the oil so avidly as to leave insufficient oil to produce a durable film with the pigment. This condition can best be met by a three-coat job, using high oil in the first. On the other hand, for fir, cypress, and other resinous woods that absorb oil poorly, a low-oil first coat is desirable. This principle of varying the formula to fit the conditions is further exemplified in Wood Paint §7, where the surface is not to withstand direct erosion by the elements, and so the amount of pigment can be reduced, with resulting saving in cost.

Before proceeding with additional formulas for the paints used for other purposes, the methods of adding color to the basic oil-pigment-drier type paints remains to be treated. Since many of the colors used in wood painting are relatively light, they may be prepared by adding the tinting pigments to the basic formulas, thus retaining the excellent covering power and film-forming ability of the white lead. Where deep colors are desired, separate formulations are necessary, as appears later in this chapter. First, however, a table of pigment combinations for various colors is given. To use them, simply add to the basic formula that quantity of the desired color which is necessary to produce the depth of color wanted. You should also reduce the white lead accordingly, especially where you add considerable amounts of other pigments.

Toning Pigment Color Formulas

(For Use with White Pigment-Oil-Drier Paints)

Color Desired	Pigments Required Percentages by Weight (To facilitate mixing, use these pigments in the ground-in-oil form)
Amber	Burnt Umber 18%; Medium Chrome Yellow 18%; Orrange Chrome Yellow 64%
Blue (Indigo)	Prussian Blue, 28%; Lampblack 72%
Blue (Azure or Royal)	Ultramarine Blue
Blue (Pale)	Cobalt Blue
Blue (Sky)	Ultramarine Blue, 50%; Cobalt Blue, 50%
Blue (Turquoise)	Ultramarine Blue, 75%; Chrome Green, Light, 25%
Brick	French Ochre, 65%; Indian Red, 35%
Brown (Snuff)	Burnt Umber, 65%; Chrome Yellow, Medium, 35%
Brown (Olive)	Burnt Umber, 72%; Prussian Blue, 24%; Chrome Yellow, Medium, 4%
Brown (Chestnut)	Chrome Yellow, Medium, 40%; Indian Red, 40%; Lampblack 20%
Brown (Amber)	Burnt Umber, 58%; Chrome Yellow, Medium, 21%; Burnt Sienna, 21%
Brown (Golden)	French Ochre
Brown (Orange)	Burnt Sienna, 50%; Chrome Yellow, Orange, 38%; Vermilion, 12%
Brown (Walnut)	Burnt Umber, 75%; Raw Sienna, 25%

Brown (Light) . . . Burnt Umber, 65%; Chrome Yellow, Medium, 35%

Brown (Stone) . . . Burnt Umber, 75%; Venetian Red, 16%; French Ochre, 9%

Bronze . . . . . . Lampblack, 75%; Chrome Yellow, Medium, 5%; Chrome Green, 15%; Venetian Red, 5%

Buff . . . . French Ochre, 95%; Chrome Yellow, Medium, 5%

Claret . . . . . . Venetian Red, 75%; Ultramarine Blue, 25%

Clay . . . . Raw Umber, 65%; Raw Sienna, 32%; Chrome Green, 3%

Cream . . . . . . Raw Sienna

Ecru . . . . . . Burnt Umber

Fawn . . . . . . Chrome Yellow, Medium, 50%; Indian Red, 25%; Burnt Umber, 25%

Flesh . . . . . . Indian Red, 50%; Chrome Yellow, Medium, 50%

Gray (Light) . . . . Ultramarine Blue, 50%; Lampblack, 50%

Gray (Silver) . . . . Lampblack, 95%; Chrome Yellow, Medium, 5%

Gray (French) . . . Lampblack, 50%; Ultramarine Blue, 25%; Indian Red, 25%

Gray (Pearl) . . . . Indian Red, 50%; Ultramarine Blue, 25%; Chrome Yellow, Medium, 25%

Gray (Opal) . . . . Cobalt Blue, 65%; Venetian Red, 35%

Green (Apple) . . . Chrome Green, Medium, 95%; Chrome Yellow, Lemon, 5%

Green (Bottle) . . . Chrome Green, Light, 85%; Lampblack, 15%

Green (Citron) . . . Chrome Green, Medium, 65%; Lampblack, 35%

Green (Blue) . . . . Chrome Green, Deep, 88%; Prussian Blue, 12%

Green (Emerald) . . . Chrome Green, Medium

Green (Nile) . . . . Chrome Green, Medium, 60%; Prussian Blue, 40%

Green (Olive) . . . . French Ochre, 70%; Raw Umber, 30%

Green (Pea)	Chrome Green, Light, 65%; Chrome Yellow, Lemon, 35%
Green (Peacock) . . .	Chrome Green Light, 50%; Prussian Blue, 50%
Green (Sea)	Chrome Green, Medium, 95%; Raw Sienna, 5%
Green (Slate)	Lampblack, 55%; Chrome Green, Dark, 45%; Raw Umber, 10%
Lavender	Ultramarine Blue, 65%; Mauve 35%
Lilac	Ultramarine Blue, 50%; Mauve, 50%
Maroon	Indian Red, 60%; Venetian Red, 30%; Lampblack, 10%
Old Rose	Crimson Madder
Orange	Chrome Yellow Orange, 90%; Chrome Yellow, Medium, 10%
Peach	Indian Red, 80%; Chrome Yellow, Medium, 20%
Primrose	Chrome Yellow Medium, 80%; Chrome Green Light, 20%
Purple	Ultramarine Blue, 65%; Indian Red, 35%
Purple (Royal) . . .	Prussian Blue, 70%; Indian Red, 24%; Lampblack, 6%
Salmon	French Ochre, 75%; Burnt Sienna, 25%
Tan	Burnt Umber, 65%; Burnt Sienna, 35%
Terra Cotta	Venetian Red
Violet	Ultramarine Blue, 75%; Mauve, 25%
Yellow (Colonial) . . .	Chrome Yellow, Medium, 65%; Raw Sienna, 35%
Yellow (Canary) . . .	Chrome Yellow, Medium
Yellow (Jonquil) . . .	Chrome Yellow, Medium, 50%; Chrome Yellow, Lemon, 25%; Indian Red, 25%
Yellow (Lemon) . . .	Chrome Yellow, Lemon
Yellow (Ivory) . . .	French Ochre, 65%; Burnt Sienna, 35%

As stated in the earlier directions for the use of these toning colors, they are not intended for use as primary pigments (that is, to produce deep colors by replacing all the white lead in the basic pigment-oil-drier formulas given earlier), although some have the necessary qualities of covering power, film formation and stability to fading to be used in that way. However, the chrome pigments are only fairly resistant to fading, and the rose madder, mauve, and other delicate shades even less so. Therefore, if you wish deep-colored exterior paints for exterior use, you need to consult other sources, since it is obviously impracticable to give all colors in this general book. However, to show how they are formulated, an excellent medium red is the following:

Wood Paint §8

Oil-Pigment-Drier Type

Venetian Red Ground in Oil	450 g.
Yellow Ochre Ground in Oil	450 g.
Raw Linseed Oil	650 ml.
Turpentine	150 ml.
Japan Drier	30 ml.

Directions: Place pigments in large container, and add oil slowly with vigorous stirring until uniform mixture is obtained. Then add drier and turpentine with continued stirring.

In addition to the older exterior wood paints, that were formulated with white lead as their major pigment, there have been developed other formulas which, while also essentially pigment-oil-drier compositions, include other white pigments such as titanium dioxide and zinc oxide. The following three formulas are representative of such newer products. Note that one of them, §10, is the chalking variety, that is, it is formulated so that as its surface ages, it disintegrates from the outer surface by chalking (flaking of small particles), which are then washed off by rain. This characteristic preserves a cleaner surface, as well as one that is easier to repaint when necessary.

Wood Paint §9

Oil-Pigment-Drier Type
(Titanium Dioxide and White Lead)

Exterior—Priming Coat

Titanium Dioxide	225 g.
White Lead	225 g.
Asbestine	160 g.
Litharge	7 g.
Raw Linseed Oil	200 ml.
Boiled Linseed Oil	100 ml.
Ester-Gum Varnish	50 ml.
Drier (5% Cobalt Naphthenate)	5 ml.
Turpentine	250 ml.

Directions: Mix raw linseed oil and boiled linseed oil. Add with constant stirring the titanium dioxide, the white lead, the asbestine, and the litharge. When uniform in texture, add with continued stirring the varnish, drier and turpentine. In quantity manufacture, the pigments should be ground in the oil, to insure thorough incorporation. For small scale work, they should be purchased in the ground-in-oil form, if available.

Wood Paint §10

Oil-Pigment-Drier Type
(Titanium Dioxide, White Lead, Zinc Oxide)

Exterior—Second or Later Coat—Chalking

Titanium Dioxide	75 g.
Zinc Oxide	270 g.
White Lead	75 g.
Asbestine	170 g.
Refined Linseed Oil	400 ml.
Boiled Linseed Oil	50 ml.
Drier (6% Cobalt Naphthenate)	10 ml.
Turpentine	50 ml.

Directions: Same as Wood Paint §9.

Wood Paint §11

Oil-Pigment-Drier Type
(Titanium Dioxide—Zinc Oxide)

Exterior—Second or Later Coat—Chalk-Resistant

Titanium Dioxide	120 g.
Zinc Oxide	300 g.
Asbestine	190 g.
Raw Linseed Oil	400 ml.
Boiled Linseed Oil	40 ml.
Drier (6% Cobalt Naphthenate)	10 ml.
Turpentine	50 ml.

Directions: Same as Wood Paint §9.

An important class of exterior paints are those formulated with synthetic resins, in an oil medium, and with the usual pigments and driers. Such paints dry to form a somewhat more elastic film than the conventional types where the resins are not used. They are especially useful for repainting purposes.

Wood Paint §12

Synthetic Resin—Oil Type

General Exterior Use

Titanium Oxide	225 g.
White Lead	225 g.
Litharge	10 g.
Raw Linseed Oil	300 ml.
*Beckosol Solution (#1319)	250 ml.
Turpentine	100 ml.
Cobalt Naphthenate Drier	20 g.

* Trade-mark alkyd resin product of Reichhold Chemicals, Inc., White Plains, New York.

Directions: Grind the pigments in the oil, or obtain them in ground-in-oil form. Stir in Beckosol solution, drier, and linseed oil. Finally add turpentine.

Wood Paint §13

Synthetic Resin—Varnish Type

General Exterior Use

Zinc Oxide	200 g.
White Lead	80 g.
Lithopone	360 g.
Asbestine	80 g.
Ground Silica	80 g.
China Wood Oil	180 ml.
Boiled Linseed Oil	30 ml.
*Durez Resin #500	60 g.
Raw Linseed Oil	250 ml.
Turpentine	100 ml.
Japan Drier	15 ml.

* Trade-mark of Durez Plastics Div., Hooker Electrochemical Co., North Tonawanda, N.Y.

Directions: Heat together the china wood oil, boiled linseed oil, and Durez Resin to 460°F., and hold there for 20 minutes. After cooling to about 200°F. grind into it the pigments (the first five ingredients above), or add them in ground-in-oil form. Then add the raw linseed oil, turpentine, and Japan drier, with thorough mixing.

An important development in recent years has been that of the latex paints. Latex is the name originally applied to the sap of the rubber tree, in which the particles of rubber are in suspension in a watery liquid. The term has been extended to other rubber suspensions, and to suspensions of other polymers than rubber (including various synthetic resins), particularly as they are used in the surface coating industry.

When their medium is water, they differ in many properties from the oil-medium paints. They have the great advantages of easier application and less dependence of the quality of the paint job upon the dryness of the surface. Their disadvantages are chiefly such as can be avoided by remembering that they are water suspensions. Therefore, their container should not be stored in unheated places subject to freezing temperatures, and thinning should not be done, except insofar as provided by the directions on the container. They are widely used as interior paints and masonry paints, and formulas of this type are given later in this chapter. Because of the complex character of their dispersed systems, they are commonly not tinted, but are manufactured in the desired colors and shades. A representative formula for a water-resin emulsion paint for exterior wooden surfaces is the following (Wood Paint §14).

Wood Paint §14

Synthetic Resins—Water Emulsion Type

General Exterior Use

Titanium Dioxide	200 g.
Zinc Oxide	120 g.
Lithopone	60 g.
Whiting	80 g.
Fine-Ground Silica	60 g.
Sodium Silicate	80 g.
*Surfynol 104	3 g.
**Acrylic Emulsion	240 ml.
Water	560 ml.

* Trade-mark product of Air Reduction Co., 60 East 42 St., New York 17.
** Trade-mark product of American Resinous Chemical Corp., 103 Foster St., Peabody, Mass.

Directions: Dissolve the sodium silicate in the water. Pour the Acrylic emulsion in the chamber to be used for mixing, and add with thorough stirring the Surfynol, the water solution of sodium silicate, and then the pigments and fillers (the first five items).

Interior Wooden Surfaces

In discussing the painting of interior wooden surfaces, the first formulas to be given will be those of the pigment-oil-drier type, using white lead as the pigment. The tinting colors table already given for exterior oil paints may also be used here. In fact, it can be used for much deeper colors, by replacing practically all the white pigments by the color pigments, if desired, because interior paints do not require the film strength that is imparted by high lead (or zinc or titanium). Note that in interior paints, except for priming or gloss coats, less oil and more pigment is used than in exterior paints.

Wood Paint §15

Oil-Pigment-Drier Type

Interior—First Coat—New Wood

Titanium Dioxide	100 g.
Zinc Oxide	150 g.
Lithopone	150 g.
Calcium Carbonate	100 g.
Raw Linseed Oil	200 ml.
Turpentine	480 ml.
Japan Drier	15 g.

Directions: If the pigments (the first four ingredients) are obtained in dry form they should be ground in the oil, after which the drier and turpentine are stirred in and thoroughly mixed. If you can obtain these pigments in the ground-in-oil form, then of course, you can do without the grinding operation. If not, you can replace all four of the pigments with twice their total weight of white lead ground-in-oil. The all-white-lead product is less desirable, especially for use in kitchens, because it tends to darken under action of the hydrogen sulfide in the atmosphere.

Wood Paint §16

Oil-Pigment-Drier Type

Interior—Second Coat New Wood

Titanium Dioxide	150 g
Zinc Oxide	225 g.
Lithopone	225 g.
Calcium Carbonate	150 g.
Raw Linseed Oil	250 ml.
Turpentine	330 ml.
Japan Drier	20 g.

Directions: The same as Wood Paint §14.

Wood Paint §17

Oil-Pigment-Drier Type

Interior—Third Coat (Gloss)—New Wood

Titanium Dioxide	150 g.
Zinc Oxide	225 g.
Lithopone	225 g.
Calcium Carbonate	150 g.
Raw Linseed Oil	500 ml.
Turpentine	50 ml.
Japan Drier	20 g.

Directions: The same as Wood Paint §14.

Wood Paint §18

Oil-Pigment-Drier Type

Interior—Third Coat (Flat)—New Wood

Titanium Dioxide	150 g.
Zinc Oxide	225 g.
Lithopone	225 g.
Calcium Carbonate	150 g.
Raw Linseed Oil	50 ml.
Marine Spar Varnish (See Varnish §1, Chapter 2)	25 ml.
Turpentine	400 ml.
Japan Drier	10 g.

Directions: The same as Wood Paint §14.

Wood Paint §19

Oil-Pigment-Drier Type

Interior—First Coat—Painted Wood

Titanium Dioxide	150 g.
Zinc Oxide	225 g.
Lithopone	225 g.
Calcium Carbonate	150 g.
Raw Linseed Oil	160 ml.
Turpentine	400 ml.
Japan Drier	20 g.

Directions: The same as Wood Paint §14. For the second coat, if desired, on painted interior woodwork, use Formula §16 or §17 given for the third coat on new wood.

Wood Paint §20

White Interior Resin Paint

Lithopone	100 g.
Zinc Oxide	200 g.
Titanium Dioxide	200 g.
*Beckosol Alkyd Resin in Linseed Oil	200 g.
**Nuodex	15 g.
Linseed Oil	300 g.
Naphtha	25 ml.

* Trade-mark product of Reichhold Chemicals Inc., 525 N. Broadway, White Plains, N.Y.
** Trade-mark product of Nuodex Products Inc., 830 Magnolia Ave., Elizabeth, N.J.

Directions: Grind the pigments—(the lithopone, zinc oxide and titanium dioxide) in the linseed oil; or obtain these pigments in ground-in-oil form and stir into oil until thoroughly mixed. If the latter method is used, use greater weights of the ground-in-oil pigments to allow for the weight of their oil, and also reduce the above quantity of linseed oil to be used. When pigment-oil mixture is uniform, add the resin, the Nuodex and finally the naphtha, stirring after each addition until uniform.

Precautions: Naphtha is inflammable.

Wood Paint §21

White Interior Resin Paint

Titanium Dioxide	220 g.
Ground Silicon Dioxide	67 g.
Lithopone	64 g.
Ground Mica	43 g.
Diethylene Glycol	6 g.
*Tamol	6 g.
Water	160 ml.
*Rhoplex AC-33	430 g.
Ammonium Hydroxide	As in directions

* Trade-mark product of Rohm and Haas Co., 222 West Washington Sq., Philadelphia 5, Pa.

Directions: Dissolve the diethylene glycol and the Tamol in the water. Stir, or preferably grind the first four ingredients into the water solution. 'Then mix in the Rhoplex. Finally add *just enough* ammonium hydroxide (concentrated) to give an alkaline reaction with thymolphthalein indicator paper. (To avoid excess of ammonium hydroxide, add it until the product gives an alkaline reaction with phenolphthalein paper, and then add it very slowly until thymolphthalein change begins.)

Wood Paint §22

Red Interior Latex-Base Paint

Step *a*—Preparation of Casein Ammoniate Solution

[1]"PMX" Special Casein	25 g.
Ammonium Hydroxide 26%	2.5 ml.
[2]Dowicides A and G	2.5 ml.
Water	125 ml.

Step *b*

[3]Rutile Titania, Ti-Rure R-510	18 g.
[4]Lithopone, Albalith #332	196 g.
[5]Calcium Carbonate, Atomite	48 g.
[6]Clay ASP-400	62 g.
[7]Silica, Celite 281	81 g.
[8]Toluidine Red Toner RS-3340	18 g.
[9]Surfynol 104	2 g.
Casein Ammoniate Solution	155 g.
(Prepared in Step *a*)	
[10]Latex, Butaprene PL-11, 49% N.V. . . .	536 g.
Ethylene Glycol	12 ml.
Water	248 ml.

[1] Trade-mark product of Borden Co., 350 Madison Ave., New York 17, N.Y.

[2] Trade-mark product of Dow Chemical Co., Midland, Mich.

[3] Trade-mark product of E. I. du Pont de Nemours & Co., Wilmington, Del.

[4] Trade-mark product of New Jersey Zinc Co., 160 Front St., New York 38, N.Y.

[5] Trade-mark product of Whittaker Clark & Daniels Inc., 260 West Broadway, New York 13, N.Y.

[6] Trade-mark product of Minerals and Chemical Corp. of America, 50 East 42 St., New York 17, N.Y.

[7] Trade-mark product of Johns Manville Corp., 22 East 40 St., New York 17, N.Y.

[8] Trade-mark product of Standard Ultramarine & Color Co., 24 and 5 Avenues, Huntington, W.Va.

[9] Trade-mark product of Air Reduction Co. (The Surfynol is used as a 50% by weight solution in ethylene glycol), 60 East 42 St., New York 17, N.Y.

[10] Trade-mark product of Firestone Plastics Co., 1200 Firestone Parkway, Akron 17, Ohio.

Directions: The first step in the preparation of this paint is to produce the casein ammoniate solution. Pour the water and the ammonium hydroxide into the mixer. Stir thoroughly and add the casein slowly, continuing the stirring throughout the entire preparation of the paint. When the casein has formed a uniform mixture, add the "Dowicides." When the casein solution has thus been prepared, start step *b* in another mixer (you may, of course, remove the casein solution from the mixer and store it in a container).

Begin step *b* by pouring the latex into a grinder and starting the drive, then add in order the "Surfynol," ethylene glycol and the water, and the casein ammoniate solution prepared in step *a*, then add slowly, while grinding, the lithopone, the clay, the calcium carbonate, titania and the toluidine red toner.

Wood Paint §23
White Latex Paint

Step *a*

*PMX Special Casein	10 g.
Potassium Hydroxide	1.0 g.
**Dowicides A and G	1.5 g.
Water	60 ml.

Step *b*

Titanium Dioxide	200 g.
Lithopone	87 g.
Mica (Very fine grind)	48 g.
Potassium Tripolyphosphate	10.5 g.
Water	175 ml.

Step *c*

**Dowicides A and G	3 g.
**Dow Latex 762-W (48% Solids) . . .	340 ml.
Potassium Hydroxide (10% solution in water)	As directed

* Trade-mark product of Borden Company, 350 Madison Ave., New York 17, N.Y.
** Trade-mark product of Dow Chemical Co., Midland, Michigan.

Directions: Step *a*. Dissolve the potassium hydroxide (1 g.) in the 60 ml. water. Pour into a mixer, and stir in casein slowly. When a uniform mixture has been formed, add the Dowicides with continued stirring.

Step *b*. Divide the solution just prepared in Step *a* into two equal parts. To one part, add in order the ingredients listed under Step *b* in the formula. Grind thoroughly, and then add the other part remaining of the solution prepared in Step *a*.

Step *c*. To this product, add the 3 g. of Dowicides and the Dow Latex, mixing until uniform. Then add potassium hydroxide solution slowly, with stirring, until product gives alkaline reaction with phenolphthalein paper; then add *just enough* additional potassium hydroxide solution to give *beginning* of color change to alkaline with thymolphthalein indicator paper.

Precautions: Potassium hydroxide and its solutions destroy human tissue.

Wood Paint §24
White Latex Paint

Lithopone	330 g.
China Clay	165 g.
Titanium Dioxide	55 g.
*Methocel (4% solution in water)	190 ml.
*Dow Latex 512 (50% solids)	220 g.
*Dowicide G.	22 g.
Tributyl Phosphate	5 g.
**Tergitol 7	5 g.
Monoethanolamine Oleate	3 g.
Ethyl Alcohol	3 g.
Pine Oil	2 g.

* Trade-mark product of Dow Chemical Co., Midland, Michigan.
** Trade-mark product of Union Carbide Corp., 30 East 42 St., New York 17, N.Y.

Directions: Grind together the first three ingredients, then stir in the Latex, Dowicide, and the Methocel Solution. Mix the remaining ingredients and add with stirring.

Wood Paint §25
Semi-Gloss Latex White

Step a

Soybean Solution (in water)	20 ml.
Ammonium Hydroxide (concentrated)	1.5 ml.
Sodium Pentachlorophenate	3.5 g.
Water	110 ml.

Step b

Titanium Dioxide	225 g.
Lithopone	65 g.
Mica	35 g.
Tetrasodium Pyrophosphate	1.5 g.
*Duponol WA	1.0 g.
Water	100 ml.

Step c

Ammonium Alginate	1.0 g.
Sodium Pentachlorophenate	0.5 g.
Water	50 ml.

* Trade-mark product of E. I. du Pont de Nemours & Co., Wilmington, Delaware.

**Chemigum 101 (55% solids) . . . . . 350 ml.
Water . . . . 100 ml.

** Trade-mark product of Goodyear Tire & Rubber Co., 1144 E. Market St., Akron 16, Ohio.

Directions: Prepare *a* by adding first ingredient, with stirring, to a mixture of the last three. Prepare *b* by grinding pigments (first three ingredients) in water, adding other two ingredients as grinding proceeds. Then stir *a* into *b*. Prepare *c* by mixing the three ingredients, and stir into mixture of *a* and *b*, followed by the Chemigum and the water.

Wood Paint §26

Green Exterior Resin Paint for Trim

Chrome Green . . . . 180 g.
White Lead . . . . 90 g.
Zinc Oxide . . . . 90 g.
*Rezyl Alkyd Resin in Linseed Oil . . . . 300 g.
**Nuodex . . . . 15 g.
Linseed Oil . . . . 300 g.
Naphtha . . . . 25 ml.

* Trade-mark product of American Cyanamid Co., 30 Rockefeller Plaza, New York 20, N.Y.
** Trade-mark product of Nuodex Products, Inc., 830 Magnolia Ave., Elizabeth, N.J.

Directions: The same as Wood Paint §20.

Metal Painting

As has already been stressed earlier in this chapter in regard to lacquering of metal, a clean surface is most important. See Chapter 4 for suitable formulas for this purpose. Remember also that clean means free from scale, rust, grease, and other foreign impurities; it does not mean smooth. Metals such as cast iron, which have a rough surface, provide a better "anchorage" for a paint film than polished metals. However, in repainting be sure to knock off all loose paint film, by use of a wire brush or other means. Remember also that for maximum durability of finish, a primer should be applied. These primers have become quite modified from the simple priming coat of paint given in Metal Paint §1, especially in factory finishing of metal surfaces. The new primers are formulated with various high polymers, as is shown by the following formula.

Metal Primer §1

Step *a*

*Butvar B-76	90 g.
**Basic Zinc Chromate Y563D	87 g.
***Asbestine	13 g.
****Lampblack BTA	1 g.
Butyl Alcohol	200 g.
Ethyl Alcohol 2B	620 g.

Step *b*

Phosphoric Acid 85%	45 g.
Water	40 g.
Ethyl Alcohol	165 g.

* Trade-mark product of Shawinigan Resins Corp., Springfield 1, Mass.
** Trade-mark product of E. I. duPont de Nemours Co., Wilmington 98, Del.
*** Trade-mark product of International Talc Co.
**** Trade-mark product of Monsanto Chemical Co., 1700 S. Second St., St. Louis, Missouri.

Directions: Grind together ingredients of Step *a;* then mix in a separate container those for Step *b*. The two parts are kept separate until the product is to be used, when they are mixed in the ratio of 1:1 parts by volume (for spraying). Formulated for iron; if used for aluminum, reduce phosphoric acid to 36 g.

Metal Primer §2

Resin Type

*Vinylite Resin A (40% solution in methyl isopropyl ketone)	170 g.
Red Lead Ground in Oil	200 g.
Methyl Isobutyl Ketone	350 g.
Toluene	220 g.
Xylene	60 g.

* Trade-mark of Union Carbide Corp., 30 East 32 St., New York 17, N.Y.

Directions: Add the resin and 100 g. of the methyl isobutyl ketone to the pigment and mix thoroughly. Then add slowly the remainder of the methyl isobutyl ketone and the other ingredients in order, continuing the mixing throughout.

Metal Paint §1

Oil-Pigment Primer (First Coat)

Red Lead Ground in Oil	1250 g.
Raw Linseed Oil	450 ml.
Turpentine	100 ml.
Japan Drier	100 g.

Directions: Add oil slowly to red lead (in large container or mixer) with vigorous stirring until smooth mixture is obtained. Then add more rapidly, but with continued stirring, remainder of oil, drier and turpentine.

Metal Paint §2

Second Coat—Black

Red Lead Ground in Oil	450 g.
Lampblack Ground in Oil	280 g.
Prussian Blue Ground in Oil	80 g.
Raw Linseed Oil	350 ml.
Turpentine	200 ml.
Japan Drier	50 g.

Directions: The same as Metal Paint §1.

Metal Paint §3

Second Coat—Light

White Lead Ground in Oil	1850 g.
Raw Linseed Oil	500 ml.
Turpentine	20 ml.
Japan Drier	20 g.

Directions: The same as Metal Paint §1.

Metal Paint §4

Anti-Corrosive Paint for Severe Exposure Conditions

Zinc Oxide, Fine Ground	640 g.
Zinc Dust	220 g.
Shellac	320 g.
Pine Oil	160 ml.
Ethyl Alcohol	400 ml.

Directions: Soak the shellac in the alcohol for several hours, and then stir until solution is complete, warming if necessary wi+h hot water. Stir in slowly the pine oil, zinc oxide, and zinc dust.

Precaution: Do not warm with direct fire, because of low boiling point and inflammability of alcohol.

Masonry, Brickwork and Plaster Painting

Oil-medium paints are still used extensively for painting masonry, brickwork, and plaster. However, in recent years the use of water-medium paints in this field has been increasing rapidly, especially for masonry. By formulating them properly coatings may be obtained that are fully as durable, and easier to apply than the oil base products, especially because they do not require that the surfaces be dry to insure good results. Therefore, a number of formulas of this type are included in this section. It also contains a few whitewash formulas, which are intended for use, of course, where low cost is the prime consideration, and durability is not important.

Masonry Paint §1

Oil-Medium, General Purpose White First Coat*

White Lead Ground in Oil	1150 g.
Boiled Linseed Oil	400 ml.
Spar Varnish (See Varnish §1, Chapter 2) .	80 ml.
Turpentine	100 ml.
Japan Drier	15 ml.

* For tinting oil-medium masonry paints, see list of colors given earlier in this Chapter.

Directions: Add the oil slowly to the white lead with vigorous stirring until smooth mixture is obtained. Then stir in slowly the varnish, drier, and turpentine.

Masonry Paint §2

Oil-Medium, General Purpose White, Second Coat

White Lead Ground in Oil	1600 g.
Boiled Linseed Oil	350 ml.
Turpentine	140 ml.
Japan Drier	15 ml.

Directions: The same as Masonry Paint §1.

Masonry Paint §3

Oil-Medium, General Purpose White, Third Coat (Flat)

White Lead Ground in Oil	1875 g.
Boiled Linseed Oil	50 ml.
Spar Varnish (See Varnish §1, Chapter 2) .	125 ml.
Turpentine	210 ml.
Japan Drier	5 ml.

Directions: The same as Masonry Paint §1.

Masonry Paint §4

Oil-Medium, General Purpose White, Third Coat (Glossy)

White Lead Ground in Oil	1875 g.
Boiled Linseed Oil	500 ml.
Turpentine	40 ml.
Japan Drier	20 g.

Directions: The same as Masonry Paint §1.

Masonry Paint §5

Water-Medium General Purpose White

Titanium Oxide	850 g.
Asbestine	500 g.
Cobalt Lineoleate Drier (6% cobalt) . . .	10 g.
*Beckosol Emulsion	500 ml.
Water	250 ml.

* Trade-mark product of Reichhold Chemicals, Inc., White Plains, New York.

Directions: The preparation of this product requires heavy stirring action because it is finished in a paste form. The water is added to the Beckosol emulsion, and then the titanium oxide and asbestine are stirred in, or preferably ground into the mixture. The drier is added during the later stages of stirring or grinding. A good proportion to use in painting is about one part of this paste to five parts of water. It can be applied to wet surfaces.

Masonry Paint §6

Water-Medium General Purpose, Lemon Yellow

Chrome Yellow	500 g.
Asbestine	450 g.
Cobalt Lineoleate Drier (6% cobalt)	10 g.
*Beckosol Emulsion	800 ml.
Water	100 ml.

Directions: The same as Masonry Paint §5.

Masonry Paint §7

Water-Medium, General Purpose Red

Iron Oxide Pigment Red	660 g.
Asbestine	400 g.
Cobalt Lineoleate Drier (6% cobalt)	10 g.
*Beckosol Emulsion	800 g.
Water	100 ml.

Directions: The same as Masonry Paint §5.

Masonry Paint §8

Water-Medium General Purpose Green

Chromium Oxide	600 g.
Asbestine	575 g.
Cobalt Lineoleate Drier (6% cobalt)	10 g.
*Beckosol Emulsion	800 ml.
Water	100 ml.

Directions: The same as Masonry Paint §5.

Stucco Paint

White Resin Type

Magnesium Silicate	150 g.
Titanium Dioxide	150 g.
Zinc Oxide	100 g.
Infusorial Earth	60 g.
*Pliolite S-3	80 g.
**Chlorofin	40 g.
***Arochlor	40 g.
Naphtha	430 ml.

* Trade-mark product of Goodyear Tire & Rubber Co., 1144 E. Market St., Akron, Ohio.
** Trade-mark product of Hercules Powder Co., 900 Market St., Wilmington, Del.
*** Trade-mark product of Monsanto Chemical Co., 1700 S. 2nd St., St. Louis, Mo.

Directions: Grind together all ingredients except the naphtha; add that when the ground mixture is uniform.

Concrete Floor Paint §1

Oil-Medium White, First Coat

White Lead, Ground in Oil	1200 g.
Raw Linseed Oil	315 ml.
Spar Varnish (Varnish Formula §1, Chapter 2)	210 ml.
Turpentine	155 ml.
Japan Drier	15 ml.

Directions: Place white lead in large container, add oil slowly with vigorous stirring until a smooth mixture is obtained. Then add varnish, turpentine, and drier, with continued stirring.

Concrete Floor Paint §2

Oil-Medium White, Second Coat

White Lead, Ground in Oil	1725 g.
Raw Linseed Oil	115 ml.
Turpentine	310 ml.
Japan Drier	50 ml.

Directions: The same as Concrete Floor Paint §1.

Concrete Floor Paint §3

Rubber Latex Type

*Pliolite-Pigment Combination	450 g.
**Chlorofin 42	20 g.
Tung Oil	10 g
Naphtha	500 ml.

   * Pliolite is a trade-mark product of the Goodyear Rubber Co., 1144 East Market St., Akron, Ohio. For use in concrete coatings, it is obtained in combination with pigments, such as titanium dioxide, china clay, chrome yellow, red iron oxide, Prussian blue, chrome green, etc., or with proportioned pigment mixes.
   ** Trade-mark product of Hercules Powder Co., 900 Market St., Wilmington, Delaware.

Directions: Mix until uniform.

Concrete Floor Paint §4
Red Resin Type

Iron Oxide . . . . 175 g.
Zinc Oxide . . . . 25 g.
*Gelva . . . . 400 g.
Chlorinated Rubber . . . . 100 g.
**Arochlor . . . . 100 g.
***Butyl Cellosolve . . . . 30 g.
Xylene . . . . 20 g.
Naphtha . . . . 150 g.

* Trade-mark product of Shawinigan Products Corp., 350 Fifth Ave., New York, 1, N.Y.
** Trade-mark product of Monsanto Chemical Co., 1700 S. Second St., St. Louis, Mo.
*** Trade-mark product of Union Carbide Corp., 30 E. 42nd St., New York 17, N.Y.

Directions: Grind the pigments, Gelva, chlorinated rubber, Arochlor and Butyl Cellosolve. When uniform, add the naphtha and xylene, and stir until uniform again.

Note: For a white paint, replace the iron oxide with titanium dioxide. For a gray paint, use titanium dioxide also, but add enough carbon black during mixing to yield the shade of gray desired.

Brick Paint §1
Oil-Medium Red Brick Paint—First Coat

Venetian Red Ground in Oil . . . . 300 g.
Yellow Ochre Ground in Oil . . . . 300 g.
Raw Linseed Oil . . . . 525 ml.
Turpentine . . . . 25 ml.
Japan Drier . . . . 35 g.

Directions: Place pigments in large container, stir in oil until uniformly mixed, then add turpentine and drier with continued stirring.

Brick Paint §2
Oil-Medium Red Brick Paint—Second Coat

Venetian Red Ground in Oil . . . . 420 g.
Yellow Ochre Ground in Oil . . . . 420 g.
Raw Linseed Oil . . . . 460 ml.
Turpentine . . . . 20 ml.
Japan Drier . . . . 30 g.

Directions: The same as Brick Paint §1.

Brick Paint §3

Oil-Medium Red Brick Paint—Third Coat

Venetian Red Ground in Oil	500 g.
Yellow Ochre Ground in Oil	500 g.
Raw Linseed Oil	50 ml.
Turpentine	270 ml.

Directions: The same as Brick Paint §1.

Asbestos Shingle Paint

White Rubber Resin Type

Titanium Dioxide	150 g.
Zinc Oxide	50 g.
Infusorial Earth	125 g.
*Gelva	300 g.
Chlorinated Rubber	80 g.
**Arochlor	80 g.
***Butyl Cellosolve	40 g.
Xylene	30 g.
Naphtha	150 g.

* Trade-mark product of Shawinigan Products Corp., 350 Fifth Ave., New York 1, N.Y.
** Trade-mark product of Monsanto Chemical Co., 1700 S. Second St., St. Louis, Mo.
*** Trade-mark product of Union Carbide Corp., 30 E. 42 St., New York 17, N.Y.

Directions: Grind the pigments, Gelva, chlorinated rubber, Arochlor and Butyl Cellosolve. When uniform, add the naphtha and xylene, and stir until uniform again.

Plaster Paint §1

Oil-Medium White—First Coat—New Plaster*

White Lead Ground in Oil	1875 g.
Raw Linseed Oil	850 ml.
Turpentine	200 ml.
Japan Drier	15 ml.

* This formula, and also §2, 3, and 4 following, are for paint to be applied to new plaster. You should, of course, have left the plaster unpainted for several months to allow setting reaction to go to completion. A further safeguard is to apply a solution made by dissolving 450 g. of zinc sulfate crystals in 1000 ml. of water. It is also necessary to fill cracks —the large ones with plaster, and the smaller ones by a coat of size (obtainable in any paint store).

If you are repainting old plaster only two coats are necessary, so only Formulas §2 and 3, or 2 and 4, should be applied.

Directions: Add the oil slowly to the white lead with vigorous stirring until a uniform mixture is obtained. Then add the turpentine and drier with continued stirring.

Plaster Paint §2

Oil-Medium White—Second Coat—New Plaster

White Lead Ground in Oil	1875 g.
Raw Linseed Oil	210 ml.
Turpentine	250 ml.
Japan Drier	15 ml.

Directions: The same as Plaster Paint §1.

Plaster Paint §3

Oil-Medium White—Third Coat (Flat)
New Plaster

White Lead Ground in Oil	2000 g.
Linseed Oil	25 ml.
Turpentine	400 ml.
Spar Varnish (Varnish §1, Chapter 2)	15 ml.
Japan Drier	15 ml.

Directions: The same as Plaster Paint §1.

Plaster Paint §4

Oil-Medium White—Third Coat (Semi-Gloss)
New Plaster

White Lead Ground in Oil	2250 g.
Linseed Oil	25 ml.
Turpentine	200 ml.
Spar Varnish (Varnish §1, Chapter 2)	100 ml.
Japan Drier	15 ml.

Directions: The same as Plaster Paint §1.

Cold Water Paint §1

Whitewash

Calcium Carbonate, Finely Ground	700 g.
Casein, Very Finely Ground (through 60 mesh)	150 g.
Kaolin, White	150 g.
Sodium Carbonate	30 g.

Directions: All ingredients must be dry and finely ground to obtain proper mixing. First mix thoroughly the calcium carbonate and the casein, then mix in the kaolin and the sodium carbonate. For use, add 2 parts by volume of the dry paint to one part of water, stir thoroughly and allow to stand ½ hour before applying.

Cold Water Paint §2

Zinc-Alum Whitewash

Calcium Hydroxide	600 g.
Zinc Sulfate	10 g.
Sodium Chloride	20 g.
Aluminum Sulfate	20 g.
Skim Milk	150 ml.
Water	850 ml.

Directions: Dissolve the three salts in 100 ml. of the water and add this solution to a well-stirred mixture of the calcium hydroxide and the remainder of the water. (If calcium hydroxide is unavailable, prepare it by slaking 450 g. of quicklime in a somewhat greater quantity of water to allow for evaporation.) Finally, add the skim milk with continued stirring.

Cold Water Paint §3

For Interior Use

Kalsomine

Calcium Carbonate, Fine-Ground	660 g.
Kaolin, White	280 g.
Glue, Fine-Ground	60 g.

Directions: All ingredients must be finely ground. Mix thoroughly the calcium carbonate and the kaolin, then stir in the glue. For use add 2 parts dry paint to one part water (by volume) allow to stand ½ hour before applying.

Cold Water Paint §4

Fire-Resistant Whitewash*

Calcium Carbonate, Fine-Ground	750 g.
Magnesium Oxide, Calcined	100 g.
Casein, Fine Ground	100 g.
Borax, Fine	30 g.
Sodium Carbonate (Soda Ash)	20 g.

* Note that fire-resistant does not mean fireproof.

Directions: To obtain proper mixing, all ingredients must be finely ground. First mix thoroughly the calcium carbonate and the magnesium oxide, then mix in the other ingredients. For use, add 2 parts dry paint to 1 part water (by volume). Allow to stand ½ hour before applying.

Aluminum Paint §1

For Metal Surfaces, General

*Alcoa Aluminum Paste #222	220 g.
Varnish §5 (Chapter 2)	800 ml.
Japan Drier	10 ml.
Boiled Linseed Oil	100 ml.

* Trade-mark product of Aluminum Co. of America, Alcoa Building, Pittsburgh 19, Pa.

Directions: Mix the varnish and oil, and add to the aluminum paste in several lots, stirring thoroughly and breaking up lumps between additions. Then pour back and forth between the two containers, and finally strain through a fine screen or cheese cloth, adding the drier.

Aluminum Paint §2

For Heated Metal Surfaces

*Alcoa Aluminum Paste	275 g.
Varnish §5 (Chapter 2)	800 ml.
Japan Drier	10 ml.
Boiled Linseed Oil	100 ml.

* Trade-mark product of Aluminum Company of America, Alcoa Building, Pittsburgh 19, Pa.

Directions: The same as Aluminum Paint §1.

Aluminum Paint §3

For Wood, Exterior

*Alcoa Aluminum Paste	220 g.
Varnish §5 (Chapter 2)	700 ml.
Japan Drier	15 ml.
Boiled Linseed Oil	150 ml.

* Trade-mark product of Aluminum Co. of America, Alcoa Building, Pittsburgh 19, Pa.

Directions: The same as Aluminum Paint §1.

Aluminum Paint §4

For Wood, Interior

*Alcoa Aluminum Paste . . . . 220 g.
Varnish §5 (Chapter 2) . . . . 800 ml.

   * Trade-mark product of Aluminum Co. of America, Alcoa Building, Pittsburgh 19, Pa.

Directions: The same as Aluminum Paint §1.

Tinting Pigments for Aluminum Paint

Pigment	*Color*
Carbon Black	Gun Metal Gray
Lead Carbonate	Battleship Gray
Chrome Green	Medium Green
Chrome Yellow	Light Green
Yellow Ochre	Light Yellow
Toluidine Red	Rose
Prussian Blue	Deep Blue

Specialty Paint §1

Fluorescent Paint*

Zinc Sulfide, Fluorescent . . . . 380 g.
Zinc Palmitate . . . . 10 g.
Alkyd Resin Solution . . . . 400 ml.
**Solvesso . . . . 300 ml.

   * Fluorescent paints are usually of relatively short life, and are used where repainting from time to time is not too objectionable.
   ** Trade-mark product of Standard Oil Co. of New Jersey, 30 Rockefeller Plaza, New York 20, N.Y.

Directions: Mix the zinc sulfide, zinc palmitate, and the alkyd resin solution. Then stir in the Solvesso. This paint must be prepared fresh, and should be applied to a white, glossy surface.

Specialty Paint §2

Fluorescent Paint

Calcium Sulfide, Fluorescent . . . . . . 420 g.
Calcium Stearate . . . . 15 g.
*Durez Resin Solution . . . . 350 ml.
Naphtha . . . . 200 ml.

   * Trade-mark product Durez Plastics Div., Hooker Electrochemical Co., 5 Walck Road, North Tonawanda, N.Y.

Directions: The same as Specialty Paint §1. Note that this paint may be formulated with any other fluorescent pigments available, such as the calcium molybdate, zinc sulfide, zinc borate, the silicates of magnesium and cadmium and the tungstates of zinc and cadmium. To render these compounds fluorescent, they should be prepared from the oxides of the constituent elements by heating at a high temperature, beyond that available without special apparatus. Therefore, they cannot be prepared on a small scale, and should be purchased in the fluorescent form.

Specialty Paint §3
Fire Resistant Paint

White Lead Ground in Oil	380 g.
Borax	300 g.
Raw Linseed Oil	270 ml.
Turpentine	50 ml.
Japan Drier	15 g.

Directions: Work the oil into the white lead. When uniform, stir in the other three ingredients in order. This paint does its action by the formation of blisters at high temperatures; the blisters serving to insulate the surface below the paint for a time.

Specialty Paint §4
Chlorinated Rubber Paint—Red

*Parlon Solution (40%)	220 g.
Tricresyl Phosphate	35 g.
Tributyl Phosphate	25 g.
Iron Oxide	110 g.
Toluene	600 ml.

* Trade-mark product of Hercules Powder Co., 900 Market St., Wilmington, Del.

Directions: Stir the first three ingredients together until uniformly mixed. Then grind in the iron oxide and add the toluene.

Specialty Paint §5

Chlorinated Rubber Paint—White

*Parlon	65 g.
**Rezyl 807	200 g.
Titanium Dioxide	250 g.
Zinc Naphthenate	725 g.
Toluene	200 ml.
Naphtha	300 ml.

* Trade-mark product of Hercules Powder Co., 900 Market St., Wilmington, Delaware.
** Trade-mark product of American Cyanamid Co., 30 Rockefeller Plaza, New York 20, N.Y.

Directions: Grind together the first four ingredients with 100 ml. of the toluene. When uniform, fine-grind has been obtained stir in the remainder of the toluene and the naphtha.

Specialty Paint §6

Chlorinated Rubber Paint—Black

*Parlon	100 g.
**Rezyl 869	250 g.
Carbon Black	25 g.
Zinc Naphthenate	10 g.
Toluene	350 ml.
Naphtha	250 ml.

* Trade-mark product of Hercules Powder Co., 900 Market St., Wilmington, Delaware.
** Trade-mark product of American Cyanamid Co., 30 Rockefeller Plaza, New York 20, N.Y.

Directions: The same as Specialty Paint §5.

Painting Adjuvants

A. Paint Removers

The many chemical agents which will remove paint or varnish films may be divided into two great classes; the alkalies and the organic solvents. The alkalies owe this action to their chemical reaction with the oxidized oil, oleoresin, or other organic substance that forms the binding element in the paint film. On the other hand, the organic solvents exert a solvent action upon the film. Therefore, the paint-removing action of the alkalies is not usually as quick and complete as that of the organic solvents. Moreover, the alkaline preparations, which include water solutions of sodium hydroxide (lye), trisodium phosphate and sodium carbonate (washing soda) are corrosive to the skin and hazardous to the eyes, and, therefore, are going out of use.

Paint Remover §1

Paraffin Wax	60 g.
Alcohol (denatured)	120 ml.
Butyl Alcohol	360 ml.
Benzene	480 ml.

Directions: Mix the three liquids and dissolve the paraffin in the mixture. The butyl alcohol and benzene may be obtained from any supply house. Be sure to specify the benzene carefully; it is a coal-tar solvent (other name benzol), and should not be confused with benzine, which is a petroleum product.

In using this remover, apply at least two coats to a small area of the surface, working the second coat vigorously with a brush. Allow to stand 5-7 minutes, then peel off the paint with a putty knife. If it does not peel readily, apply more remover. Work only a small area at a time, removing any paint that does not peel, by using fine steel wool. In grooves, recessed surfaces and other places difficult to reach, use the steel wool or, if that fails, a stiff-haired brush. It should be remembered, however, that paint remover cannot remove paint from the smaller pores of the wood, in which it remains as a slight color after the remover has done its work. The final cleaning must be done mechanically, usually by a sanding operation.

Paint Remover §2

Paraffin Wax	60 g.
Alcohol (denatured)	250 ml.
Acetone	250 ml.
Benzene	500 ml.

Directions: The same as for Paint Remover §1.

Paint Remover §3
Especially Effective for Varnishes and Lacquers

Paraffin Wax	50 g.
Butyl Acetate	200 ml.
Ethyl Acetate	300 ml.
Benzene	500 ml.

Directions: The same as for Paint Remover §1.

Paint Remover §4

Ethyl Acetate	120 ml.
Methylene Chloride	430 ml.
Alcohol	110 ml.
Polyvinyl Acetate Resin	40 ml.
Mica (powder)	330 g.

Directions: Mix the first three ingredients and dissolve the resin in them; then stir in the powdered mica. This product substitutes mica for the wax used more generally in paint removers and so has advantages in some applications where a waxy residue is undesirable.

Paint Remover §5

Cellulose Acetate—Scrape Off Type

Methylene Chloride	958 ml.
Cellulose Acetate	28 g.
*Span 60	14 g.

* Trade-mark product of the Atlas Powder Co., Wilmington 99, Delaware.

Directions: Stir the cellulose acetate and methylene chloride together until uniform, and dissolve the Span in the mixture.

Paint Remover §6

Emulsifiable Type

Nitropropane	270 ml.
Methyl Amyl Ketone	270 ml.
Pine Oil	30 ml.
Water	390 ml.
*Span 40	25 g.
*Tween 40	15 g.

* Trade-mark products of the Atlas Powder Co., Wilmington 99, Delaware.

Directions: Stir the emulsifiers (last two ingredients) in the water until dispersed. Mix the first three ingredients, and add to dispersion with continued stirring.

Paint Brush Cleaner*

Alcohol	125 ml.
Ammonium Hydroxide (28% solution in water)	125 ml.
Oleic Acid	300 ml.
Kerosene	450 ml.

> * Note that this cleaner is intended for use on brushes in which the paint has been allowed to harden. In ordinary practice, the paint is removed from the brush while still wet by use of the same medium as that in the paint, or a cheaper, compatible one. Many household dish-washing detergents are useful in removing last traces of oils from brushes, but should be at once rinsed out thoroughly with cold water.

Directions: Mix the oleic acid and the kerosene, then add slowly and with stirring a mixture of the alcohol and ammonium hydroxide solution. This cleaning solution is formulated to use for paint brushes which have been left uncleaned after use so long that the paint has partly dried, and ordinary methods (benzene or turpentine or detergents) are ineffective. The brushes should be soaked in above solution for 48 hours, then thoroughly rinsed in benzine (or other petroleum solvent).

Paperhangers' Paste §1

General

Flour (fine)	250 g.
Rosin (ground)	10 g.
Water	1000 ml.

Directions: Stir the flour into 200 ml. of the water until uniform. Then stir in the rosin slowly. Heat the remainder of water to 203°F. (95°C.) and add the other mixture to it with stirring.

Paperhangers' Paste §2

Strong

Flour	200 g.
Fish Glue	50 g.
Turpentine	25 ml.
Water	975 ml.

Directions: Add the glue to 100 ml. of the water and let stand for 12 hours. Then heat slowly, stirring until uniform, and then add the turpentine. Stir the flour into 200 ml. of the water until uniform and pour into the remainder of the water heated to 203°F. (95°C.) ; start stirring and add the glue-turpentine mixture.

Chapter 4

FORMULAS FOR METAL SURFACES

The Metal Surface

Surfaces of metals which have not been coated or otherwise treated are usually found to have acquired various deposits. These may be the result of the handling the surface has undergone since it was made, and consist of various kinds of solid dirt, or greasy and oily films. Deposits are produced on metal surfaces by the atmosphere, which may also deposit solid particles of dust or soot, or oily films. By far the most common of the atmospheric effects, however, is the scale or film which is formed by chemical reaction between substances in the air and the metal surface.

There are several substances in the atmosphere which react with metals. Oxygen, water vapor and carbon dioxide are always present and are the chief agents in atmospheric corrosion, although other more variable or occasional atmospheric substances often have significant effects. For example, silver is classed with gold and platinum as a "noble" metal in that it is not subject to ordinary atmospheric corrosion by the three substances mentioned; however, the hydrogen sulfide, whose presence in the air is due to burning of sulfur-containing fuels (or boiling of sulfur-containing vegetables) forms the familiar dark coating on silver that requires removal.

Most corrosion films require removal before the metal surface can be refinished, and some finishing processes, such as electroplating, require such freedom from these films (as well as from grease or any other foreign substance) that the cleaning operations on surfaces to be electroplated are usually done immediately before the plating. On the other hand, some corrosion films are desirable for certain purposes. It all depends upon the finish that is desired, and upon the character of the corrosion film formed by the particular metal or alloy. Aluminum, for example, which is a reactive metal, owes its widespread use for utensils and structures to the fact that it forms with atmospheric oxygen a tight, adherent film that protects it from further corrosion. Rather than being detrimental, such films are valuable for many uses, and in fact, are intentionally produced by certain metal protection methods which are described in this chapter.

Since, however, many finishing operations require preliminary freeing of metallic surfaces from corrosion films and the dirt and grease that may be associated with them, this chapter begins by giving formulas for their removal. These formulas are of four kinds, to be used as necessary, (1) Grease Removers; (2) Soak Cleaners; (3) Pickling (or Scaling) Solutions and (4) Bright-Dip Solutions. The bright-dip solutions are used primarily in cases where a brighter metal surface is desired than would be obtained by use of a pickling solution. The bright-dip solution may follow the pickling process or replace it; in any event the bright-dips for all the noble metals are such strong acids that their use is hazardous, and the formulas given here are in quantities to make 50 ml., instead of the approximately 1000 ml. or 1000 g. that is standard for formulas elsewhere in this book.

Note also that the use of bright-dips for electroplating have been largely superseded by the use of electrolytic cleaning processes which are described later in this chapter.

Grease Remover §1

Carbon Tetrachloride	600 ml.
Naphtha	400 ml.

Directions: Mix thoroughly.

Precautions: Naphtha is a gasoline-fraction, so handle accordingly. Carbon tetrachloride is poisonous to skin and tissues, and its vapor is poisonous on inhalation.

Grease Remover §2

Trichloroethylene	900 ml.
Carbon Tetrachloride	100 ml.

Directions: Mix thoroughly. A somewhat more effective solvent than Grease Remover §1, though trichloroethylene is somewhat less widely available.

Precautions: Poisonous to skin and tissues, and on inhalation.

Grease Remover §3

Sodium Carbonate (soda ash)	300 g.
Trisodium Phosphate	300 g.
Sodium Silicate	100 g.
Borax	100 g.
Powdered Silica	200 g.

Directions: Mix thoroughly by stirring together or tumbling in barrel. To use, add to water (1 part to 6), and stir in vessel containing objects to be cleaned, or scrub surface with this solution.

Precautions: Strong alkalies, corrosive to skin. Wear goggles for scrubbing.

Metal Soak Cleaner §1

Alkaline

Sodium Metasilicate, $5H_2O$	360 g.
Trisodium Phosphate	180 g.
Soda Ash	140 g.
Sodium Bicarbonate	120 g.
*Kreelon 4D	120 g.
*Pluronic	80 g.

* Trade-mark product of Wyandotte Chemicals Corp., Wyandotte, Michigan.

Directions: Mix in above order, and use in water solution.

Metal Soak Cleaner §2

Soap-Based Alkaline

Sodium Metasilicate, $5H_2O$	500 g.
Sodium Hydroxide	200 g.
Tetrasodium Pyrophosphate	80 g.
*Pluronic	30 g.
Tall Oil or Rosin Soap	80 g.
Soda Ash	110 g.

* Trade-mark product of Wyandotte Chemical Corp., Wyandotte, Michigan.

Directions: Mix in above order, and use in water solution.

Precautions: While several of the above ingredients injure skin, sodium hydroxide is particularly hazardous. It should be purchased in flake or pellet form.

Metal Pickling Solution §1

For Silver, Copper, and Brass

Concentrated Sulfuric Acid	100 ml.
Water	900 ml.

Directions: Pour the acid slowly into the water with constant stirring, in a glass or porcelain container. Place the work in the solution with tongs or wire of copper or other resistant metal. (Do not use iron tools.) The most convenient means of handling very small work is the wire-mesh basket. It may be made conveniently from a 5-inch circle of fine-mesh copper screening, which should be annealed over a low flame to soften it for this service. After cooling, it is worked with the fingers into bowl-shape, and attached by means of fine copper wire on to a circular ring of heavy copper wire (#10 gauge will do). The ring is attached at opposite ends of a diameter to a loop of heavy copper wire, by which the basket can be hung from a wooden stick resting on the edges of the acid solution container. Leave the work in the solution until it is clean; if the film on the metal does not dissolve, heat the solution, if necessary, to a boiling point. When removing the work, transfer it to a glass or porcelain container of water placed alongside of the acid bath (to avoid dripping acid on the floor). Then wash thoroughly under running water. Allow the work to dry in air, without heating. The natural copper color will appear and should be brightened by scouring with fine pumice or steel wool.

Note that silver surfaces may emerge from the solution covered by a dead-white film, which should be removed by rubbing with fine pumice.

Precautions: Sulfuric acid is extremely destructive to most substances, especially human tissue. It tends to spatter when mixed with water, so wear goggles and rubber gloves. If this acid or any others, come into contact with skin, clothes, etc., flood with water instantly and keep washing until all traces are removed.

Metal Pickling Solution §2
Iron and Other Base Metals

Concentrated Sulfuric Acid . . . . . .   50 ml.
Water   .   .   .   . 950 ml.

Directions: The same as Pickling Solution §1.
Precautions: The same as Pickling Solution §1.

Metal Pickling Solution §3
For Gold

Concentrated Nitric Acid . . . . 100 ml.
Water   .   .   .   . 900 ml.

Directions: The same as for Pickling Solution §1 for Copper, except that in using the §3 Solution, it is important that the gold be 14 karat or over (pure gold is 24 karat) because the gold alloys of less than 14 karat purity have so much base metal that they react too actively with this §3 Solution. Such lower gold-content alloys should be pickled in §1 Pickling Solution for Copper, or in Pickling Solution §4 for Gold Alloys (below 14 karat).

Precautions: The same as Pickling Solution §1.

Metal Pickling Solution §4

For Gold Alloys (Below 14 Karat)

Sodium Bichromate	20 g.
Concentrated Sulfuric Acid . . .	100 ml.
Water	1000 ml. (1 liter)

Directions: Dissolve the sodium bichromate in the water, and then add the acid slowly, with constant stirring; then follow directions for Pickling Solution §1.

Precautions: The same as Pickling Solution §1.

"Bright-Dip" Solutions

The trade term "bright-dip" is applied to very strong acid solutions used for the thorough cleaning of metal surfaces prior to such operations as electroplating, enameling, oxidizing, and other operations which require an exceptionally clean, flat surface. Because of the strength of the acid solutions used, the utmost care should be taken to observe the precautions suggested earlier in the book for working with hazardous chemicals. Work with "bright-dip" solutions should never be undertaken without using rubber gloves and goggles. Take great care to avoid spillage of chemicals or inhalation of their fumes.

"Bright-Dip" Solution §1

For Jewelry

Concentrated Sulfuric Acid	25 ml.
Concentrated Nitric Acid	25 ml.

Directions: Pour the nitric acid slowly into the sulfuric acid, with constant stirring, in a glass or porcelain container. Leave the work in the solution only long enough to obtain the desired bright surface. Even for the less reactive metals, such as platinum and gold, 30 seconds is usually long enough, and that period might damage fine edges on articles of copper or silver. Arrange the solution container so that, immediately upon removal from the acid, the work can be washed thoroughly in cold running water, then dried.

Precautions: Read carefully paragraph headed *"Bright-Dip" Solutions.*

"Bright-Dip" Solution §2

For Jewelry

Concentrated Sulfuric Acid	35 ml.
Concentrated Nitric Acid	15 ml.

Directions: The same as for "Bright-Dip" Solution §1 except that this solution §2 is slightly less active than §1, and preferable for the more reactive metals (i.e. §1 is better for platinum and gold).

Precautions: Read carefully paragraph headed *"Bright-Dip" Solutions.*

"Bright-Dip" Solution §3

Iron and Most Base Metals

Concentrated Sulfuric Acid	3 ml.
Concentrated Nitric Acid	3 ml.
Metallic Zinc	½ g.
Water	44 ml.

Directions: Add the sulfuric acid slowly to the water, with constant stirring; when the mixture has cooled, add the zinc slowly. The nitric acid is added last. This pickling solution leaves the iron surface quite bright.

Precautions: See Bright-Dip Solution §1 for method of use, and entry under *"Bright-Dip Solutions,"* for safety precautions. In addition, the addition of zinc above causes evolution of hydrogen, a gas that burns or explodes if ignited by flames, lit cigarettes, etc.

"Bright-Dip" Solution §4

Brass and Bronze

Concentrated Sulfuric Acid	22 ml.
Concentrated Nitric Acid	4 ml.
Concentrated Hydrochloric Acid	1 ml.
Water	23 ml.

Directions: Add the sulfuric acid slowly to the water with constant stirring. Then add the nitric acid, followed by the hydrochloric acid, in the same manner.

Precautions: Read carefully paragraph headed *"Bright-Dip" Solutions.*

Metal Finishing and Coloring Solutions

Since so many metals undergo surface discoloration on exposure to the atmosphere, the surfaces of such metals require some treatment to prevent this corrosion. That treatment may be the application of a paint or lacquer, for which formulas have already been given in Chapter 3. It may be the deposition of a film of a more resistant metal, which is discussed later in this chapter under Electroplating. Still another method is the formation by chemical treatment of an oxidation coating upon its surface. These coatings may be primarily decorative or primarily protective, and the former may be merely a sheen (i.e. satin finish) or a color. Therefore, the next group of formulas will be the Satin Finish Solutions, the Metal Coloring Solutions, and the Metal Protective Solutions.

Note: For coloring aluminum dye colors (i.e. yellow, red, green, blue, etc.) see Electrolytic Protective Solution §2 on Page 120.

Satin Finish Solution §1

General

Concentrated Hydrofluoric Acid	12 ml.
Water	38 ml.

Directions: Pour the acid slowly into the water, with constant stirring in a glass or porcelain container which has been thickly coated with black asphaltum varnish (commonly obtainable in paint stores). Dip the work into the solution by holding it in copper tongs, or suspending it by a heavy copper wire, or in a copper-mesh basket, as described for Metal Pickling Solution §1.

The satin finish is similar in appearance to a wire-brush finish and may readily be imparted to silver, copper, brass, bronze, and other metals and alloys. It is not an oxidized finish, and while attractive, does not possess the added durability (over that of the original metal) of that type of finish. However, it may be used after an oxidizing process to produce a combined effect.

Precaution: These strong acids are extremely injurious to human tissues. The use of rubber gloves, goggles, and great care is imperative.

Satin Finish Solution §2

General

Concentrated Hydrofluoric Acid	10 ml.
Concentrated Nitric Acid	5 ml.
Water	35 ml.

Directions: Pour the hydrofluoric acid slowly into the water, and then add the nitric acid, also slowly and with constant stirring. The remaining directions and *precautions* are the same as for Satin Finish Solution §1.

Satin Finish Solution §3
Silver

Concentrated Hydrofluoric Acid . . . . . 10 ml.
Concentrated Nitric Acid . . . . 5 ml.
Concentrated Hydrochloric Acid . . . . . 2 ml.
Water . . . . 33 ml.

Directions: Pour the hydrofluoric acid, then the hydrochloric acid, and finally the nitric acid, slowly into the water, all with constant stirring. The remaining directions and *precautions* are the same as for Satin Finish Solution §1.

Satin Finish Solution §4
Gold

Concentrated Nitric Acid . . . . 25 ml.
Concentrated Hydrofluoric Acid . . . . . 25 ml.
Metallic Zinc . . . . 1.5 g.

Directions: Add the zinc to the hydrofluoric acid when it has dissolved, pour in the nitric acid slowly and with stirring. This solution gives to brass the surface appearance of gold. The articles to be finished are suspended in the solution by copper wire or basket (see Pickling Solution for Copper §1 for detailed directions) until the metal has acquired the desired surface appearance, then it is removed and washed thoroughly in running water.
Precautions: See Satin Finish Solution §1.

Metal Coloring Solution §1
Blue-Black to Black Finish on Silver

Potassium Sulfide . . . . 30 g.
Concentrated Ammonium Hydroxide . . . 5 ml.
Water . . . . 1000 ml.

Directions: Heat the water, dissolve the potassium sulfide, and add the ammonium hydroxide. Dip the metal surface in hot water, then in the hot coloring solution until the desired color has been obtained. Wash in running water and dry in air current from fan.
Precautions: Avoid contact with skin and inhalation of fumes.

Metal Coloring Solution §2
Brown Finish on Silver

Ammonium Chloride	100 g.
Cupric Sulfate	100 g.
Dilute Acetic Acid	1000 ml.

Directions: Dissolve the solids in the liquid. Dip the metal surface in hot water, then in the hot coloring solution until the desired color has been obtained. Wash in running water and dry in air current from fan.

Metal Coloring Solution §3
Brown Finish on Copper

Potassium Oxalate	60 g.
Arsenic Sulfide	15 g.
Water	1000 ml.

Directions: The same as for Metal Coloring Solution §2.
Precautions: Potassium oxalate and arsenic sulfide are highly poisonous.

Metal Coloring Solution §4
Gray Finish on Copper

Arsenic Chloride	60 g.
Water	1000 ml.

Directions: The same as for Metal Coloring Solution §2.
Precautions: Arsenic chloride is very poisonous; be especially careful of fumes.

Metal Coloring Solution §5
Various Colors on Copper

Sodium Thiosulfate	40 g.
Lead Acetate	20 g.
Water	1000 ml.

Directions: Dissolve the sodium thiosulfate in the water, then the lead acetate. Heat to boiling. Dip the metal surfaces to be colored; they will undergo a series of color changes, becoming successively gray, purple, maroon, red, and blue-brown; then the work should be removed and washed in running water as soon as the desired color is obtained. While this solution is not as easy to use as those that produce only one color-tone, practice in its use will yield reasonably consistent results.
Precautions: Lead acetate is poisonous.

Metal Coloring Solution §6
Bronze Finish on Copper

Ferric Nitrate . . . .   45 g.
Potassium Thiocyanate . . . . . .   15 g.
Water . . . .   1000 ml.

Directions: The same as for Metal Coloring Solution §2.

Metal Coloring Solution §7
Golden-Bronze Finish on Brass

Potassium Nitrate   . . . . .   670 g.
Concentrated Sulfuric Acid . . .   1000 ml. (1 liter)
Concentrated Nitric Acid   . . .   125 ml.
Concentrated Hydrochloric Acid .   125 ml.

Directions: Add the potassium nitrate slowly and with constant stirring, to the concentrated sulfuric acid, then slowly add the nitric acid, and the hydrochloric acid. This solution is very corrosive, and immersion in it for a matter of seconds should produce the desired finish on the metal surface, which should then be thoroughly washed in running water and allowed to dry in air.

Precautions: Acids very corrosive; use rubber gloves and goggles.

Metal Coloring Solution §8
Green Tone on Brass

Ammonium Chloride   . . . .   115 g.
Cupric Sulfate . . . .   115 g.
Water . . . .   1000 ml.

Directions: Heat the water to boiling and dissolve the salts in it. Apply it while hot to the work by means of a stiff brush. Wash in running water and allow to dry in air.

Metal Coloring Solution §9
Red to Brown Finish on Brass

Ferric Nitrate . . . .   120 g.
Sodium Thiosulfate . . . .   120 g.
Water . . . .   1000 ml.

Directions: Dissolve the ferric nitrate in the water, then the sodium thiosulfate. Swab or immerse the metal surface, wash, and dry. Colors ranging from medium red to medium brown can be obtained by suitable timing of the duration of immersion.

Metal Coloring Solution §10
Blue Finish on Brass

Cupric Sulfate	60 g.
Sodium Thiosulfate	40 g.
Sodium-Potassium Tartrate (cream of tartar)	20 g.
Water	1000 ml.

Directions: Dissolve the salts in the water in the above order and dip the work into the warm solution until the desired blue shade has been reached. Wash and dry.

Metal Coloring Solutions §11
Antique-Green Patina on Copper, Brass, or Bronze

The antique-green finish on copper and its alloys is desired in many articles, especially those used out-of-doors, such as roofing, statuary, weather-vanes, etc. Therefore, a number of solutions have been developed to produce this finish. The selection of the one best suited to a particular alloy or shape of surface must be made by trial, although any one of these four solutions is reasonably dependable.

Potassium Sodium Tartrate (cream of tartar)	240 g.
Ammonium Chloride	80 g.
Cupric Nitrate	600 g.
Sodium Chloride (table salt)	240 g.
Water	1000 ml.

Directions: Heat the water to boiling, dissolve the salts in it, apply the hot solution to the metal with a swab. When the desired color has been obtained, wash, and dry.

Metal Coloring Solution §12

Antique-Green Patina on Copper, Brass, or Bronze

Potassium Sodium Tartrate (cream of tartar)	90 g.
Cupric Acetate	450 g.
Sodium Chloride (table salt)	90 g.
Acetic Acid (25%)	1000 ml.

Directions: Dissolve the salts in the acid and swab or wire-brush this solution on the metal surface. When the desired color has been obtained, wash, and dry.

Metal Coloring Solution §13

Antique-Green Patina on Copper, Brass, or Bronze

Potassium Sodium Tartrate (cream of tartar)	120 g.
Ammonium Chloride	300 g.
Basic Cupric Acetate	180 g.
Ferric Chloride	60 g.
Sodium Chloride (table salt)	240 g.
Water	1000 ml.

Directions: The same as for Metal Coloring Solution §12.

Metal Coloring Solution §14

Steel-Gray Tone on Aluminum

Zinc Chloride	225 g.
Cupric Sulphate	25 g.
Water	1000 ml.

Directions: Heat water to boiling and dissolve the salts in it. Immerse the aluminum articles until the desired shade is obtained. Wash in a 2% solution in water of sodium hydroxide, then thoroughly in running water. Then dry in air.

Metal Coloring Solution §15

Orange Tone on Copper, Bronze, and Brass

Cupric Acetate	100 g.
Water	1000 ml.

Directions: Dissolve the cupric acetate in the water and immerse the article to be colored, or coat its surface with the solution. A few seconds action will usually yield the desired shade. Wash the surface immediately and dry.

Metal Coloring Solution §16

Violet Tone on Copper, Bronze, and Brass

Antimony Chloride	150 g.
Water	1000 ml.

Directions: The same as for Metal Coloring Solution §15, except that heating to 70°C (158°F) is necessary as a final operation to develop the color.
Precautions: Antimony chloride is poisonous; and fumes.

Metal Coloring Solution §17

Red Tone on Gold

Potassium Sulfide	60 g.
Concentrated Ammonium Hydroxide . . .	10 ml.
Water	1000 ml.

Directions: Heat the water, dissolve the potassium sulfide in it, and add the ammonium hydroxide. Heat the gold article and apply the hot solution to it with a soft brush, leaving it on the surface until the desired shade has developed. Wash in water and dry.
Precautions: Avoid contact with skin and inhalation of fumes.

Metal Coloring Solution §18

Black Finish on Iron

Cupric Sulfate	50 g.
Concentrated Nitric Acid	100 ml.
Alcohol	250 ml.
Water	600 ml.

Directions: Dissolve the cupric sulfate in the water, add the nitric acid slowly, then the alcohol. Apply this solution lightly and uniformly to the surface to be blackened; when dry, polish with a woolen pad.
Precautions: Strong acid; fumes; use rubber gloves and goggles.

Metal Coloring Solution §19

Brown Finish on Iron

Tincture Ferric Chloride	40 ml.
Tincture Ethyl Nitrate (sweet spirits of nitre)	40 ml.
Concentrated Nitric Acid	20 ml.
Cupric Sulfate	30 g.
Mercuric Chloride	40 g.
Alcohol	40 ml.
Water	1000 ml.

Directions: Dissolve the mercuric chloride and the cupric sulfate in the water (warmed); add in order the nitric acid, the alcohol, the tincture ferric chloride and finally the sweet spirits of nitre. Apply the solution lightly and uniformly with a pad of glass wool to the surface to be colored and allow to dry in air for 24 hours. Finally wash in hot water, dry in an air current, and coat with oil or lacquer. This formula which has long been used for coloring the external surface of gun barrels has the advantage that the ingredients are usually available in drug stores.

Precautions: Nitric acid is destructive to tissue; cupric and mercuric salts are poisonous.

Metal Coloring Solution §20

Blue Finish on Iron

Ferric Chloride	200 g.
Antimony Chloride	200 g.
Gallic Acid	100 g.
Water	900 ml.

Directions: Dissolve in order the ferric chloride, antimony chloride, and gallic acid in the water. Then follow directions for Metal Coloring Solution §19.

Precautions: Antimony chloride is poisonous; and fumes.

Metal Coloring Solution §21

Rose Color on Zinc

Cupric Chloride	300 g.
Water	1000 ml.

Directions: Dissolve the salt in the hot water; immerse the surface to be colored in the hot solution for a few seconds. Wash, dry, dip in alcohol, and finally dry in a current of warm air.

Metal Coloring Solution §22

Black Tone on Zinc

Nickel Ammonium Sulfate	100 g.
Concentrated Sulfuric Acid	10 ml.
Water	900 ml.

Directions: Add the sulfuric acid slowly to 100 ml. of the water. Dissolve the salt in the remainder of the water and slowly add the diluted acid. Dip the surface to be colored in this solution for a few seconds, wash, and dry. This color bronzes beautifully when the surface is burnished.

Precautions: Avoid contact with skin.

Metal Coloring Solution §23

Green Patina on Zinc

Sodium Thiosulfate	100 g.
Concentrated Sulfuric Acid	30 ml.
Water	1000 ml.

Directions: Dissolve the salt in 300 ml. of the water; add the acid slowly to the remainder of the water; mix the solutions. Filter off the precipitated sulfur and immerse the surface to be colored in the solution (warmed), until the desired color has been obtained. Wash and dry.

Precautions: Avoid contact with skin.

Metal Coloring Solution §24

Slate Gray on Zinc

Potassium Iodide	700 g.
Iodine	70 g.
Water	1000 ml.

Directions: Dissolve the potassium iodide in the water, then add the iodine with stirring. Then follow directions for metal coloring solution §19.

Metal Coloring Solution §25

Bronze Finish on Zinc

Ammonium Chloride	30 g.
Potassium Oxalate	10 g.
Acetic Acid (2% solution in water) . . .	1000 ml.

Directions: Dissolve the potassium oxalate and ammonium chloride in the dilute acetic acid, and apply to the surface of the metal with a cloth or brush. Allow to dry. This solution is weak (but very poisonous) so several applications may be necessary to produce the desired finish.

** Metal Protective Solution

Phosphoric Acid	72 ml.
Sodium Dichromate	8 g.
*Cellosolve	100 ml.
Caramel Solution	10 ml.
Water	900 ml.

* Cellosolve is a trade-mark product of the Union Carbide Corp., 30 East 42nd St., New York City 17, N.Y.
** For other protective solutions, see Electrolytic Protective Solutions, later in Chapter.

Directions: Dissolve the sodium dichromate in the water, and add the other ingredients. Apply this solution to the thoroughly-cleaned metal surface, or dip the metal article in it. After 10 minutes wash, dry, and apply finish.

Metallizing Formulas

The improvement in appearance and durability of surfaces, especially base-metal surfaces, by application of a film of another metal is often so great that many processes have been devised for the purpose. Electroplating, which is discussed in the next section, is one of the most effective and widely-used of these processes. Among the many other processes are the metallizing solutions and pastes which, by chemical action alone, deposit a metallic film upon a surface. Such films cannot be very durable under ordinary conditions of exposure and consequently their field of usefulness is limited to special applications, as in producing certain articles of less-expensive jewelry, picture frames, etc.

Metallizing Formula §1
For Depositing Gold Film

Potassium Gold Chloride	20 g.
Potassium Carbonate	90 g.
Water	1000 ml.

Directions: Heat the water nearly to boiling and dissolve the potassium carbonate in it, then the potassium gold chloride. Immerse the (thoroughly-cleaned) article or surface to be metallized with gold in the hot solution. Since potassium gold chloride is not readily available, it may be prepared in solution by mixing 250 ml. each of concentrated nitric and concentrated hydrochloric acids, dissolving 10 g. of gold in the mixture, and then neutralizing by the slow and cautious addition of potassium carbonate until foaming is no longer produced by further additions. This will require 325 to 350 g. of potassium carbonate. When the reaction is complete, dilute with water to a volume of 1000 ml. Heat the solution, add 90 g. more of potassium carbonate, and immerse the article to be metallized.

Metallizing Formula §2

For Depositing Silver Film

Silver	600 g.
Concentrated Nitric Acid	600 g.
Sodium-Potassium Tartrate (cream of tartar)	800-1200 g.

Directions: Dissolve the silver in the nitric acid by gentle heating. Add enough cream of tartar to form a thin paste. To apply, rub onto the surface to be silvered, using a pad of glass wool, until a satisfactory coating appears.

Precautions: Nitric acid is highly destructive to tissue, and fumes strongly when acting upon silver. This solution should be prepared out-of-doors, or with adequate exhaust of air.

Metallizing Formula §3

For Depositing Zinc Film

Powdered Zinc	450 g.
Powdered Calcium Carbonate (chalk or whiting)	350 g.
Powdered Ammonium Sulfate	150 g.
Powdered Magnesium Metal	50 g.

Directions: Mix the ingredients in the order above and rub the mixture vigorously onto the surface with a soft pad which is kept thoroughly wet with water.

Metallizing Formula §4

For Depositing Tin Film

Stannous Chloride	150 g.
Powdered Calcium Carbonate (chalk or whiting)	650 g.
Powdered Ammonium Sulfate	150 g.
Powdered Magnesium Metal	50 g

Directions: The same as for Metallizing Formula §3.

Metallizing Formula §5
For Depositing Nickel Film

Nickel Ammonium Sulfate	600 g.
Powdered Calcium Carbonate (chalk or whiting)	350 g.
Powdered Magnesium Metal	50 g.

Directions: The same as for Metallizing Formula §3.

Electroplating Methods

The usefulness of these methods is great enough to justify their inclusion in this general-purpose book, even though they cannot be used without certain special equipment. Its size and cost depends, of course, upon the scale upon which the work is done, but the operations cannot be conducted upon any scale without certain essential elements of equipment.

The actual container for the electroplating operation is not so serious a problem. Rectangular glass vessels will do for small-scale work and asphalt-lined wooden tanks for medium scale, although for some solutions a lead lining is preferred in the trade. In any case, the wooden tank should be tight at its joints, because some metals plate best with cyanide solutions, which certainly should not be allowed to leak.

The essential elements are electrical and consist primarily of a source of low voltage (6 volts) D.C. electric current, with means for measuring and controlling it. While the ideal source of such current for work in volume is a motor-generator set, you can obtain from a large electrical supply or chemical apparatus company other apparatus for transforming and rectifying the 110 volt (or 220 volt) A.C. in most lines to the 6-volt D.C. you need. From the same source you can obtain the necessary auxiliary equipment, such as ammeters and voltmeters for measuring current and voltage, and rheostats or even more economical means of controlling the current to the individual cell or cells. The need for this control is emphasized by the fact that every plating formula includes the current density (current per unit area of surface to be plated) as definitely as it does the ingredients of the solution. In fact, the quality of the plated coating depends upon the current density, and proper control is a most important factor in determining whether the plated coating is firmly adherent, or so loose and spongy as to be useless.

Another factor is, of course, the cleanness of the surface on which you deposit the metal. You can effect this cleaning by use of the pickling formulas given earlier in this chapter. However, since the surface should be cleaned immediately prior to the time it is to be plated, there has grown up increasing use of the electrolytic process itself as a method of cleaning. One such type of process is to connect the article to be plated in the cell just as if it were to be plated, and to fill the cell with a solution which cleans the article by a combined process of chemical dissolving of the scale on the surface, and by the evolution of bubbles of hydrogen (formed by electrolysis of the cleaning solution) on the surface. There are, of course, other more complex methods of electrolytic cleaning, but the one just described is the least complicated, and formulas for Electrolytic Cleaning Solutions will be given before the Electroplating Solutions.

It should also be emphasized that this one cleaning operation is not the only step preliminary to plating. It is often preceded by polishing, by washing with organic solvents to remove grease (See Grease Removers at start of this Chapter); and it is sometimes followed by other washes before plating. After plating, also, the coating must be thoroughly freed of all solution and often buffed or polished as well.

As a solution is used for plating, it naturally undergoes changes in composition. Those that are essentially depletion of the ions of the plating metal can be overcome by additions. Another kind of change that often occurs is in acidity. This is more serious, because it threatens not only the quality of the work, but the health, or even the lives of the workers. For if cyanide solutions become too acid, hydrogen cyanide is evolved. Therefore, another necessary control is that of acidity (usually expressed in pH). Remember that the *higher* the pH, the lower the acidity; while falling pH means increasing acidity.

Electrolytic Cleaning Solution §1

General

Sodium Carbonate	50 g.
Sodium Hydroxide	15 g.
Sodium Cyanide	10 g.
Water	1000 ml.

Current Density: 30-35 amperes per sq. ft.

Anode: Iron Bar (If an iron cleaning tank is used, it may be made the anode by connecting the circuit accordingly).

Temperature of Bath: 156°F (70°C)

Directions: Dissolve the salts in the water. Heat the solution in the iron tank, preferably with an immersion heater or steam coil. When up to temperature, turn on the current, and adjust it to the above density.

Precautions: Sodium cyanide is intensely poisonous (like all cyanides). The amount entering the body through a cut may be fatal. Never add acid to a cyanide solution, because then hydrogen cyanide will be evolved, which is rapidly fatal upon inhalation. (It is used in gas chambers.) For this reason, and because electrolytic systems often evolve inflammable hydrogen gas, as in the above cleaning process, all electrolytic equipment should be provided with exhaust fans.

Electrolytic Cleaning Solution §2

For Removing Scale from Iron or Steel

Concentrated Sulfuric Acid . . . . . . 160 ml.
Water . . . . 840 ml.
   Current Density: 60 amperes per sq. ft.
   Anode: Iron (see note on previous formula)
   Temperature: 140°F (60°C)

Directions: Add the acid slowly to the water with constant stirring. Heat the solution to above temperature with immersion heater or steam coil. Adjust current to above value. Remove work as soon as descaled to minimize loss of metal.

Precautions: Sulfuric acid is very corrosive to tissues. Avoid spattering and wear goggles.

Electrolytic Cleaning Solution §3

For Brass

Concentrated Sulfuric Acid   . . . . . 380 ml.
Concentrated Nitric Acid . . . . 72 ml.
Concentrated Hydrochloric Acid . . . . . 4 ml.
Water . . . . 444 ml.
   Current Density: 30 amperes per sq. ft.
   Anode: Carbon
   Temperature: 90°F (32°C)

Directions: The same as Electrolytic Cleaning Solution §2.

Electroplating Solution §1

Plating Copper

Copper Sulfate (blue) . . . . 16 g.
Sodium Oxalate . . . . 12 g.
Sodium Sulfate . . . . 15 g.
Boric Acid . . . . 20 g.
Water . . . . 980 ml.
   Current Density: 10 amperes per sq. ft.
   Anode: Copper
   Temperature: 70°F (21°C)

Directions: Heat 100 ml. of the water to 176°F (80°C) and dissolve in it the sodium oxalate. Heat 40 ml. of the water to the same temperature and dissolve the copper sulfate in it. Add the copper sulfate solution to the sodium oxalate solution. Dissolve the boric acid and sodium sulfate in the remainder of the water and add the solution to the hot mixed solution.

Precautions: Copper salts and oxalates are poisonous.

Electroplating Solution §2

Plating Copper

Copper Cyanide	100 g.
Sodium Cyanide	115 g.
Sodium Hydroxide	40 g.
*Penetronyx D-30	5 ml.
Water	1000 ml.

Current Density: 3 amperes per sq. ft.
Anode: Copper
Temperature: 122°F (50°C)

* Penetronyx is a trade-mark additive for electroplating baths, made by the Onyx Oil and Chemical Co., Jersey City 2, N.J. The use of such additives is an important aid in modern plating processes.

Directions: Dissolve the sodium hydroxide in 100 ml. of the water in a separate glass container with stirring. (Do not spatter.) Dissolve the sodium cyanide in the other 900 ml. of water, then add the sodium hydroxide solution and dissolve in that solution the copper cyanide. Finally add the Penetronyx. Its purpose is to improve the smoothness and brightness of the copper deposit, which may otherwise require buffing, particularly at higher current densities than that recommended above, which are often used in commercial work.

Precautions: The cyanides are extremely poisonous, so that the amount absorbed through a cut in the skin may be fatal. Moreover, all articles plated by them should be washed with water, alkaline detergent solutions, and water again, until all traces are safely removed. Furthermore, cyanide solutions should never become acid, because they evolve hydrogen cyanide. All electroplating cells should be provided with exhaust fans, discharging at a distance.

Electroplating Solution §3
Cadmium Plating

Sodium Cyanide	120 g.
Cadmium Oxide	45 g.
Sodium Sulfate (anhydrous)	50 g.
*Penetronyx D-30	7 ml.
Water	1000 ml.

Density: 30 amperes per sq. ft.
Anode: Cadmium**
Temperature: 70°F (21°C)

* Trade-mark additive for electroplating baths, made by
Onyx Oil and Chemical Co., Jersey City 2, N.J.
** Better results in cadmium plating are obtainable by
use of special anodes and patented processes such as the
Udylite Process licensed by the Udylite Co., Detroit, Michi-
gan and the Cadalyte Process, licensed by Graselli Chemical
Co., Cleveland, Ohio.

Directions: Follow directions and precautions for Electroplating Solution §2, except that the ingredients are dissolved in the water in the
order listed above. Be sure to reread Precautions given for Electroplating
Solution §2.

Electroplating Solution §4
Chromium Plating

Chromic Acid	250 g.
Sodium Sulfate	4 g.
Water	1000 ml.

Current Density: 150 amperes per sq. ft.
Anode: Lead
Temperature: 113°F (45°C)

Directions: Dissolve the solids in the order listed above. Chromium
plating is difficult, partly because the current density must be closely
controlled for good results, and partly because chromium anodes dissolve
too quickly, so that inert (lead) anodes are used. This means that the
concentration of the solution falls and it must be adjusted by addition of
fresh materials. Moreover, chromium plates best on certain other metals
(e.g. copper and nickel). Chromium is so difficult to plate on some metals,
such as zinc and brass, that they are often plated first with nickel, to which
the chromium plate is then applied. Therefore, it is desirable to consult
the Metal and Thermit Corporation of 100 East 42 St., New York 17, N.Y.
which owns patented processes and follow their detailed instructions.

Precautions: Even though chromium salts, while toxic, are not so intensely poisonous as cyanides, the exhaust fans are necessary, *as for all other plating processes.*

Electroplating Solution §5

Cobalt Sulfate (anhydrous)	278 g.
Boric Acid	42 g.
Sodium Chloride	17 g.
*Penetronyx D-30	5 ml.
Water	1000 ml.

    Current Density: 80 amperes per sq. ft.
    Anode: Cobalt
    Temperature: 86°F (30°C)

    * Trade-mark additive for electroplating baths, made by Onyx Oil and Chemical Co., Jersey City 2, N.J.

Directions: Dissolve the ingredients in above order. For precautions, see Electroplating Solution §2.

Electroplating Solution §6
Gold Plating

Potassium Cyanide	15 g.
Gold Cyanide	2½ g.
Water	1000 ml.

    Current Density: 4 amperes per sq. ft.
    Anode: Graphite
    Temperature: 149°F (69°C)

Directions: Dissolve ingredients in above order. Follow directions and precautions for Electroplating Solution #2.

Electroplating Solution §7
Green Gold Plating

Sodium Cyanide	30 g.
Gold Chloride	2½ g.
Silver Chloride	1¼ g.
Water	1000 ml.

    Current Density: 4 amperes per sq. ft.
    Anode: Graphite
    Temperature: 149°F (69°C)

Directions: Dissolve ingredients in above order. Follow directions and precautions for Electroplating Solution §2.

Electroplating Solution §8

Iron Plating (Especially on copper and brass)

Ferrous Chloride Tetrahydrate	310 g.
Calcium Chloride	325 g.
Chromous Chloride	5 g.
Water	1000 ml.

Current Density: 140 amperes per sq. ft.
Temperature: 194°F (90°C)
Anode: Wrought Iron or Low Carbon Steel

Directions: Dissolve ingredients in above order.

Electroplating Solution §9

Indium Plating

Potassium Cyanide	70 g.
Indium Potassium Cyanide	42 g.
*Penetronyx	5 ml.
Water	1000 ml.

Current Density: 6 amperes per sq. ft.
Anode: Indium
Temperature: 140°F (64°C)

* Trade-mark additive for electroplating baths, made by Onyx Oil and Chemical Co., Jersey City 2, N.J.

Directions: Dissolve ingredients in above order. Follow directions and precautions for Electroplating Solution §2.

Electroplating Solution §10

Lead Plating

Lead Fluoborate	150 g.
Fluosilicic Acid	40 g.
Glue	5 g.
Water	1000 ml.

Current Density: 45 amperes per sq. ft.
Anode: Lead
Temperature: 100°F (38°C)

Directions: Dissolve ingredients in above order.

Electroplating Solution §11

Nickel Plating

Nickel Sulfate Heptahydrate	105 g.
Nickel Chloride, Hexahydrate	15 g.
Ammonium Chloride	15 g.
Boric Acid	15 g.
Water	1000 ml.

Current Density: 10 amperes per sq. ft.
Anode: Pure nickel (99%)
Temperature: 77°F (63°C)

Directions: Dissolve the solids in the above order.

Electroplating Solution §12

Platinum or Rhodium Plating

Platinum Diaminonitrite (or rhodium diaminonitrite)	15 g.
Ammonium Nitrate	100 g.
Sodium Nitrite	10 g.
Ammonium Hydroxide	50 ml.
Water	1000 ml.

Current Density: ½ ampere per sq. ft.
Anode: Platinum
Temperature: 194°F (90°C)

Directions: Add the ammonia in the water. Dissolve the three solid ingredients separately in separate portions of this solution, then mix.

Electroplating Solution §13

Dull Silver Plating on Copper, Brass, or Bronze

Potassium Cyanide	37 g.
Potassium Carbonate, Anhydrous	38 g.
Silver Cyanide	35 g.
Sodium Thiosulfate	½ g.
Water	1000 ml.

Current Density: 3 amperes per sq. ft.
Anode: Silver
Temperature: 68°F (20°C)

Directions: Dissolve the salts in order listed above, with directions and precautions for Electroplating Solution §1. However, a preliminary dip which must be used for the articles to be plated consists of 7½ g. of mercuric chloride and 4 g. of ammonium chloride dissolved in a liter of water. Sometimes, it is necessary especially in silver plating such metals as brass and iron to do a preliminary plating operation with a much less concentrated silver solution than that given above for the main plating operation.

Precautions: Read carefully precautions given for Electroplating Solution §2.

Electroplating Solution §14
Bright Silver Plating

Potassium Cyanide . . . .   70 g.
Silver Chloride . . . .   39 g.
Potassium Carbonate . . . .   38 g.
Sodium Thiosulfate . . . .   ½ g.
Water   . . . . 1000 ml.
    Current Density: 3 amperes per sq. ft.
    Anode: Silver
    Temperature: 68°F (20°C)

Directions: The same as Electroplating Solution §13.

Precautions: Read carefully precautions given for Electroplating Solution §2.

Electroplating Solution §15
Tin Plating

Stannous Fluoborate . . . .   200 g.
Fluoboric Acid . . . .   50 g.
Boric Acid . . . .   25 g.
Dextrose . . . .   20 g.
Water   . . . . 1000 ml.
    Current Density: 15 amperes per sq. ft.
    Anode: Tin
    Temperature: 22°F (50°C)

Directions: Dissolve the solids in the water in the above order.

Electroplating Solution §16
Brass Plating

Sodium Cyanide . . . .   54 g.
Sodium Carbonate . . . .   30 g.
Zinc Cyanide . . . .   9 g.
Copper Cyanide . . . .   27 g.
Water   . . . . 1000 ml.
    Current Density: 3 amperes per sq. ft.
    Anode: Brass (about 70% copper; 30% zinc is preferred)
    Temperature: 113°F (45°C)

Directions: Dissolve the salts in the water in the order listed above.

Precautions: Read carefully precautions given for Electroplating Solution §2.

Anodic Coatings

Earlier in this chapter, it was explained how films of oxide (scale and rust) could be removed from metals by connecting them as cathodes in Electrolytic Cleaning Solutions. Conversely, metals that are protected or given desirable decorative coatings by oxide films may have such films developed on them by connecting them as anodes in an electrolytic cell, using an Electrolytic Protective Solution for the purpose.

Electrolytic Protective Solution §1

Protection of Zinc Plates and Castings

> *Yellow Anozinc Compound 50 . . . . .   240 g.
> Water (to make) . . . .   1000 ml.
>   Current Density: 5-50 amperes per sq. ft.
>   Cathode: Steel (The zinc articles form the anode)
>   Temperature: 60-80°F (16-30°C)

Directions: The solution is prepared by dissolving the Yellow Anozinc in water at 150°F, contained in a steel tank, and cooling to room temperature before use. Yellow Anozinc is a trade name product of the Metal and Thermit Corp., 100 East 42 St., New York 17, N.Y. This company gives information for equipment to be used, and other important conditions to be observed (pH, voltage, time, etc.). It also furnishes information on how to obtain a clear coating, as well as a yellow coating on zinc; how to use the Yellow Anozinc compound 51 under other conditions; or the Black Anozinc Compounds where black protective coatings on zinc are desired.

Electrolytic Protective Solution §2

Protection of Aluminum

> Sulfuric Acid, Concentrated . . . . . .   200 ml.
> Water   . . . .   800 ml.
>   Cathode Carbon Potential Across Cell. Start at 0
>   and raise slowly to 30 volts.
>   Time of Treatment: 10-15 minutes
>   Temperature: 60-86°F (19-30°C)

Directions: Add acid slowly to water. This electrolytic action produces a highly absorptive oxide film that readily dyes brilliant colors with coal-tar dyestuffs.

Precautions: Corrosive acid, gloves and goggles preferred.

Metal Polishes and Cleaners

Earlier in this chapter a wide variety of formulas were given for cleaning metal surfaces. These formulas included grease removers, pickling solutions, bright-dips, electrolytic cleaning solutions and others, but all had the common characteristic that they were intended primarily for production cleaning, that is, for use on metal surfaces in the finishing stages of a production process.

There is also, of course, need for metal surface treatment that is primarily of maintenance character, being used on finished metal surfaces to remove the soil acquired in use. The products used for this purpose are, in general, much milder in their action than the production cleaners. These "maintenance cleaners," as they might be called, may be designated as polishes or cleaners, the former containing abrasives, and the latter depending for their action primarily upon their solvent or detergent content, although they may contain relatively soft abrasives. As is apparent from the following formulas, the polishes are applied chiefly to surfaces of metals and alloys which are left "bare," that is, without surface coatings. They are represented by the precious metals, brass, and the relatively-hard electrolytic deposits (chromium, nickel, etc.). On the other hand, the cleaners and polish-cleaners are used on surfaces where scratching by the abrasive is more likely to occur, such as metal surfaces having a protective or decorative oxidative film, or metal surfaces coated with paints, lacquers and other applied finishes. The automobile cleaners and cleaner-polishes are important and somewhat exacting formulations in this category.

Metal Polish §1

Silver and Gold Polish

Sodium Thiosulfate	250 g.
Gelatin	250 g.
*Santomerse 30X	100 g.
Keiselguhr	200 g.
Disodium Phosphate	25 g.
Water	900 ml.

*Trade-mark product of Monsanto Chemical Co.

Directions: Dissolve the gelatin in 600 ml. of the water (estimated). Dissolve the sodium thiosulfate and disodium phosphate in the remainder of the water (300 ml.), and mix the two solutions. Then stir in the Santo-merse, and continue stirring until dissolved, and add the kieselguhr.

Metal Polish §2
Silver Polish

Powdered Soap	50 g.
Precipitated Chalk	350 g.
Gum Camphor	2 g.
Coconut Oil	10 ml.
Ammonium Hydroxide Solution (20% Ammonia)	10 ml.
Alcohol	5 ml.
Water	100 ml.

Directions: Heat the water to boiling, dissolve the soap, add the coconut oil and then the ammonium hydroxide solution. Add the camphor to the alcohol, and when dissolved, add it to the water solution. Then stir in the precipitated chalk.

Metal Polish §3
Metal Polish for Hard Coating, Chromium, Nickel, etc.

Kieselguhr	200 g.
Soap Powder	30 g.
Glycerol Trioleate	50 ml.
Ammonium Hydroxide (12% solution)	30 ml.
Alcohol	150 ml.
Water	550 ml.

Directions: Warm the water and dissolve the soap in it. Then add with stirring the glycerol trioleate, the ammonium hydroxide, the alcohol and finally, the kieselguhr. This product should be shaken before use.

Metal Polish §4
Brass Polish

Oleic Acid	85 ml.
Ammonium Hydroxide Solution (strong)	30 ml.
Naphtha	750 ml.
White Tripoli Powder	180 g.

Directions: Stir the ammonium hydroxide into the oleic acid and continue stirring until mixture is homogeneous in appearance. Then add the naphtha slowly with constant stirring, and finally, stir in the tripoli powder. The final product should be of uniform texture, and should not separate, except on freezing or prolonged standing.

Metal Cleaner §1

Concentrated Industrial Cleaner

Kerosene	900 ml.
*Atlas G-2090	100 g.

* Product of Atlas Powder Co., Wilmington 99, Delaware.

Directions: Mix at room temperature until homogeneous. To use, dilute in ratio of 1 volume of this product with 9 volumes of kerosene. Spray on to the surface to be cleaned, allow to soak for a short time, and flush with water.

Metal Cleaner §2

Emulsion

Kerosene	160 ml.
*Span 20	20 g.
*Tween 20	20 g.
Water	800 ml.

* Trade-mark product of Atlas Powder Co., Wilmington 99, Delaware.

Directions: Mix kerosene and emulsifiers and add water with moderate stirring.

Metal Cleaner §3

Abrasive Cleaning-Polishing Emulsion

Stearic Acid	120 g.
Petrolatum	30 g.
*Span 60	7 g.
*Tween 60	28 g.
Abrasive	300 g.
Water	515 ml.

* Trade-mark product of Atlas Powder Co., Wilmington 99, Delaware.

Directions: Choose an abrasive powder of a material and fineness that will not scratch the particular metal surface to be cleaned. Add the abrasive to a mixture of the first four ingredients which has been heated to 167°F (75°C). Heat water to 176°F (80°C) and add slowly, with stirring, until inversion occurs. (Change of water-in-oil to oil-in-water emulsion.) Then the remaining water may be added quickly. This is a rubbing polish.

Metal Cleaner §4
Solvent Emulsion

Carbon Tetrachloride . . . . 500 ml.
*Span 60 . . . . 30 g.
*Tween 60 . . . . 20 g.
Water . . . . 450 ml.

* Trade-mark product of Atlas Powder Co., Wilmington 99, Delaware.

Directions: Mix the emulsifiers with the carbon tetrachloride and heat to 140°F (60°C). Heat water to 149° F (65°C) and add with moderate stirring.

Precautions: Carbon tetrachloride is poisonous to skin and tissues, and its vapor is poisonous on inhalation.

Metal Cleaner §5
Protective Cleaner

Mineral Oil . . . . 300 ml.
*Span 40 . . . . 30 g.
*Tween 40 . . . . 30 g.
Water . . . . 640 ml.

* Trade-mark product of Atlas Powder Co., Wilmington 99, Delaware.

Directions: Warm oil slightly to dissolve emulsifiers. Add water slowly with moderate stirring until inversion occurs. (For inversion, see Metal Cleaner §3.) Remainder of water may then be added rapidly. This cleaner is intended to leave a protective film of oil upon the metal.

Automobile Cleaner-Polish §1

Mineral Spirits . . . . 409 ml.
*Silicone Oil (L-41, 5000 cskts) . . . . . 15 g.
**Atlas G-2133 . . . . 25 g.
***Gersthofen Wax KPS . . . . 15 g.
Water . . . . 409 ml.
****Celite . . . . 91 g.
Kaolin . . . . 36 g.

* Trade-mark product of Linde Air Products Co., 30 East 42 St., New York 17.
** Product of Atlas Powder Co., Wilmington 99, Delaware.
*** Trade-mark product of Wax & Resin Products Co., 42 Broadway, New York 4.
**** Trade-mark product of Johns Manville Corp., 22 E. 40 St., New York 16.

Directions: Warm (with hot water—no flame) the mineral spirits enough to dissolve the Gersthofen Wax, adding the silicone and Atlas G-2133. Add the water slowly with vigorous stirring until inversion (change of water-in-wax to wax-in-water system) occurs. The remaining water may be added rapidly. The Celite and kaolin are stirred into the completed emulsion.

Precautions: Treat mineral spirits as gasoline.

Automobile Cleaner-Polish §2

*Silicone (DC 200)	40 g.
**Solvesso 100	190 ml.
Kerosene	20 ml.
***Span 20	19 g.
***Tween 20	21 g.
Water	570 ml.
****Celite	140 g.

* Trade-mark product of Linde Air Products Co., 30 East 42 St., New York 17.
** Trade-mark product of Standard Oil Co. of N.J., 30 Rockefeller Plaza, N.Y.
*** Trade-mark product of Atlas Powder Co., Wilmington, 99, Delaware.
**** Trade-mark product of Johns Manville Corp., 22 East 42 St., New York 16.

Directions: Mix the first five ingredients and add about ¼ of the water with vigorous stirring. After inversion (see previous formula) the remainder of the water may be added rapidly. The Celite is added slowly, with continued stirring.

Precautions: Solvesso is an inflammable light petroleum product.

Automobile Cleaner-Polish §3

Cloth Dipping Polish

*Silicone Oil (L-41, 5000 cskts)	40 g.
Mineral Spirits	466 ml.
**Atlas G-2133	25 g.
***Gersthofen Wax KPS	15 g.
Water	454 ml.

* Trade-mark product of Linde Air Products Co., 30 E. 42 St., New York 17.
** Product of Atlas Powder Co., Wilmington 99, Delaware.
*** Trade-mark product of Wax & Rosin Products Co., 42 Broadway, New York.

Directions: Warm mineral spirits enough to dissolve wax, adding other two active ingredients. Then add water slowly with vigorous stirring until inversion (See Metal Cleaner §3) occurs. The remaining water may be added rapidly. This polish should be diluted (about 10 times with water) and a rubbing cloth dipped into this solution.

Precautions: Treat mineral spirits as gasoline.

Automobile Cleaner-Polish §4

"One-Shot" Silicone Type Polish

*Silicone Oil	50 g.
**Crown Wax #23	20 g.
Oleic Acid	20 g.
***Snow Floss	67 g.
***Super Floss	22 g.
****Franklin Clay	22 g.
Morpholine	10 g.
Mineral Spirits	400 ml.
Water	400 ml.

* Trade-mark product of Union Carbide Corp., **30 E. 42** St., N.Y. **17**.
** Trade-mark product of Petrolite Corp., Ltd., Kilgore, Texas.
*** Trade-mark product of Johns Manville Corp., **22 E. 40** St., N.Y. **16**.
**** Trade-mark product of United Clay Mines Corp., **109** Oakland St., Trenton, N.J.

Directions: Warm the wax in 100 ml. of the mineral spirits until dissolved, then add the silicone, oleic acid, and remainder of the solvent and warm to 158°F (70°C). Add the other ingredients to the water in the above order in a separate container, stirring well, and then add the hot wax solution to the water slowly with stirring.

Precautions: Treat mineral spirits as gasoline.

Automobile Cleaner-Polish §5

"One-Shot" Silicone Type Paste

*Silicone Oil	100 g.
Carnauba Wax	70 g.
**Estawax P-25	70 g.
***Microcrystalline Wax (Bee Square Amber)	70 g.
****Cerese Plasticizing Wax D	42 g.
Mineral Spirits	650 ml.

* Trade-mark product of Union Carbide Corp., **30 E. 42** St., New York **17**, N.Y.
** Trade-mark product of Petrolite Corp., Kilgore, Texas.
*** Trade-mark product of Bareco Oil Co., **121** S. Broad St., Philadelphia **7**, Pa.
**** Trade-mark product of Socony Vacuum Co., **26** Broadway, New York, N.Y.

Directions: Heat the waxes, silicone and about 20 per cent of the mineral spirits to 175° (80°C) until all the waxes are melted. The balance of the mineral spirits is then added and the mixture stirred slowly until cooled to 120°F (49°C) then poured and allowed to gel.

Precautions: Treat mineral spirits as gasoline.

Chapter 5

CEMENTS, PLASTER, GLASS
AND RELATED SUBSTANCES

Portland Cement

Portland cement reacts with water to form a matrix of interlacing crystals, into which other solids may be incorporated. The compressive strength of the mass depends upon the proportion of cement, the use of other solids of such sizes that they form a suitably bonded mass with the cement, and the correct proportion of water to react with the cement. If the other solids (called aggregate) are too fine, they will not form strong bonds with the cement; therefore sand, gravel, and crushed stone used in concrete should be free from "fines" and clean of soluble substances which might interfere with the reaction of the concrete with water. However, assuming the elimination of aggregate of very small particle size, some differences in aggregate size help to form more dense concrete. Therefore, it is customary to use at least two sizes—sand and crushed stone, or sand and gravel, the larger size depending upon the scale of work and the dimension of the smallest section to be filled.

Determination of the correct quantity of water to use is more difficult, largely because of the difference in the quantity of water required to wet various aggregates. Therefore, to have the correct quantity of water to react with the cement the total quantity used must be varied. Moreover, for some purposes it is desirable to have a less "stiff" concrete than others. While no rigid rule can be established, the table on page 128 may be found a useful guide.

Waterproofing Concrete

Watertight concrete can be made with Portland cement without special materials if the following essential requirements are observed carefully:

1. Sound, clean aggregates that do not absorb much water.
2. Limited amount of mixing water.
3. Plastic, workable mixtures.
4. Thorough mixing.

Kind of Concrete Work	Mix by Vol. Materials Cubic Feet				Gals. Water per Bag When Mixing	One Bag Batch Makes This Much Concrete, Cu. Ft.	Materials for One Cubic Yard of Concrete			
	Cement Bags	Sand Cu. Ft.	Stone Gravel Cu. Ft.	Work-ability of Mix			Cement Bags	Sand Cu. Ft.	Stone Gravel Cu. Ft.	Gals. Water When Mixing
Footings, Heavy Foundations	1	3.75	5	Stiff	6.4	6.2	4.3	16.3	21.7	27.6
Watertight Construction, Walls	1	2.5	3.5	Med.	5	4.5	6.0	15.0	21.0	30
Driveways Floors Walks — One Course	1	2.5	3	Stiff	4.4	4.1	6.5	16.3	19.5	28.7
Driveways Floors Walks — Two Courses	1	Top 2	0	Stiff	3.6	2.14	12.6	25.2	0	43.3
	1	Bottom 2.5	4	Stiff	4.9	4.8	5.7	14.2	22.8	27.8
Pavements	1	2.2	3.5	Stiff	4.3	4.2	6.4	12.1	22.4	27.5
Watertight Construction for Tanks, Wells	1	2	3	Med.	4.1	3.8	7.1	14.2	21.3	29.3
Cast units like posts, slabs				Wet.	4.9	3.9	6.9	13.8	20.7	33.7
Heavy Duty Floor, Barns, Shops, etc.	1	1.25	2	Stiff	3.4	2.8	9.8	12.3	19.6	33.9
Mortar for Brick, Concrete Blocks	1	6	1 Sack 50 lb. Hydrated Lime	Med.	12.5	5.5	4.9	29.4	5	61.2

5. Proper placing.

6. Favorable curing conditions.

A very dependable method of waterproofing concrete is by the use of a membrane. Membrane waterproofing, when properly done, yields most consistent results. Membrane waterproofing is constructed in place by building up a strong, waterproof, and impermeable blanket of overlapping sheets of tar-saturated, open-mesh fabric, or rag felt. The sheets are coated and cemented together with hot coal-tar pitch. There is always one more application of pitch than the number of sheets, because the work is started and ended with a coat of hot pitch, except when it is necessary to lay a dry sheet on a wet surface in order to start work. Properly constructed membrane waterproofing prevents the entrance of water regardless of hydrostatic head, capillary attraction, concrete cracks, or expansion of joints.

A second method of waterproofing concrete is called integral. It consists of adding a material to the batch as it is being mixed. Formulas for such materials are given below under the name Concrete Integral Waterproofing.

Still a third method of waterproofing concrete may be called surface waterproofing. It is designed primarily to "harden" the surface of the concrete to reduce wear, and is often applied to surfaces subject to heavy traffic. Of course, it affects only the surface to which it is applied, and has no value for underground surfaces, for which the membrane method should be applied. Formulas for concrete surfacing compounds are given under the name Concrete Surfacing.

Concrete Integral Waterproofing §1

Calcium Chloride	250 g.
Sodium Silicate	3 g.*
Ground Silica	3 g.
Water	950 ml.

* Or the equivalent amount of sodium silicate solution, which may be obtained from the Philadelphia Quartz Co., Public Ledger Bldg., Philadelphia, Pa.

Directions: Dissolve the sodium silicate in 100 ml. of the water and stir in the ground silica. Then dissolve the calcium chloride in the remainder of the water and, while it is still hot, add the other mixture with stirring. This makes enough solution for addition to the concrete prepared from 1 bag of cement. Allow for this addition when mixing the concrete; that is, mix the concrete stiff, so that this addition brings it to the consistency desired.

Concrete Integral Waterproofing §2

Ammonium Stearate . . . .   20 g.
Water . . . . 1000 ml.

Directions: This formula is to be used in treating the water to be used in mixing the concrete. Since the above quantities are small, you may prefer to have their English unit equivalents, which are 2 pounds of ammonium stearate to ten gallons of water.

Concrete Surfacing §1

Portland Cement . . . . . 500 g.
Sand . . . . 500 g.
Water . . . . Enough for workable
                        consistency

Directions: Mix the cement and sand, and add just enough water to make the mass workable. This mixture is used as a surface application on stair treads, sidewalks, floors, chimney caps, finished joints in stonework, and other surfaces subject to extreme conditions of wear or exposure. It should not be less than ½″ or more than 1″ thick.

Concrete Surfacing §2

*Sodium Silicate Solution (40°Be) . . . . 200 ml.
Water . . . . 800 ml.

  * Obtainable from the Philadelphia Quartz Company, Public Ledger Bldg., Philadelphia, Pa.

Directions: Mix and stir thoroughly. Apply to surface of concrete every day or two for at least three applications, or until no more solution is absorbed.

Concrete Surfacing §3

Solid

Magnesium Fluosilicate . . . .   500 g.
Zinc Fluosilicate . . . .   250 g.
Calcium Fluosilicate . . . .   250 g.
Water . . . . 1000 ml.

Directions: Sift the three crystalline materials together until they are well mixed. In application, add 250 g. of the above to 1000 ml. of water and spread on the concrete surface with a broom. A preliminary treatment with a weaker solution (100 g. to 1000 ml. of water) will improve results somewhat. If the concrete is old, be sure that it is thoroughly cleaned.

Coloring Concrete

Concrete may readily be colored by the addition of pigments during mixing. Be sure to use only the most stable of the inorganic pigments, to resist the fading action of light, heat, etc. The quantities depend, of course, upon the shade you want. Since this is so different in wet concrete and dry concrete, you should mix a little in advance so you can judge its color after drying for at least twenty-four hours. The table below is given in units of pounds of pigment per bag of cement—for test purposes 1 pound per bag is equivalent to 10 g. of pigment per 1000 g. cement.

| | | Pounds per bag of cement | |
| | | Light Shade | Medium Shade |
Desired Color	Pigment		
Black, Blue-black and Grays	Germantown Lampblack	½	1
	Carbon Black	½	1
	Black Oxide of Manganese	1	2
Blue	Ultramarine Blue	5	9
Brownish Red to Dull Brick Red	Red Oxide of Iron	5	9
Bright Red to Vermilion	Mineral Turkey Red	5	9
Brown to Reddish Brown	Metallic Brown (oxide)	5	9
Buff, Colonial Tint	Yellow Ochre with not less than 15% Yellow Oxide of Iron	5	9
Cream	Small Quantity of Yellow Oxide of Iron		
Green	Chromium Oxide	5	9
	Greenish-blue Ultramarine	6	
Pink	Red Oxide of Iron	4	8

Plaster Formula §1

Plasterer's First Coat (Scratch Coat)

Plaster of Paris	. . . .	320 g.
Sharp Sand	. . . .	640 g.
Hair	. . . .	40 g.
Water	. . . .	sufficient

Directions: Mix the plaster, sand and hair with enough water for proper working consistency, that is, so the material will be stiff enough to hold on the lath, and yet fluid enough to apply. Add water until this consistency is obtained, but work quickly because plaster of Paris sets rapidly.

See Formula §4 for methods of slowing this setting. For coloring the plaster, see list of inorganic pigments given on page 131 for coloring concrete.

Plaster Formula §2

Plasterer's Second Coat (Brown Coat)

Plaster of Paris	250 g.
Sharp Sand	750 g.
Water	sufficient

Directions: The same as Plaster Formula §1.

Plaster Formula §3

Plasterer's Third Coat (Finishing Plaster)

Calcium Hydroxide	700 g.
Plaster of Paris	300 g.
Water	sufficient

Directions: Add water slowly and with stirring to the calcium hydroxide until water is no longer absorbed. Let mixture stand 12 hours. Then add the Plaster of Paris and ½ its weight of water. Stir, and add additional water to give the mass the desired working consistency. Add 15 g. Portland cement just before using.

Plaster Formula §4

Quick-Setting Plaster

Plaster of Paris	350 g.
Calcium Hydroxide	100 g.
Ground Limestone	500 g.
Portland Cement	50 g.

Directions: Mix powders quickly, and keep in a tightly closed drum, or other container until used. Prepare by stirring in water until of desired working consistency.

Plaster Formula §5

Slow-Setting Plaster

Plaster of Paris	350 g.
Calcium Hydroxide	200 g.
Ground Limestone	400 g.
Powdered Acacia (or Glue)	50 g.

Directions: The same as Plaster Formula §4.

Plaster Formula §6

Finishing Plaster Corrective

Finishing plaster sometimes develops soft, chalky areas, due to too rapid drying, especially in dry weather. Such conditions are rectified by moistening with the following solution:

Zinc Sulfate	7 g.
Alum	7 g.
Water	1000 ml.

Directions: Dissolve salts in water.

Plaster Formula §7

Patching Plaster

Plaster of Paris	750 g.
Powdered Acacia (or Powdered Glue)	125 g.
Infusorial Earth	125 g.

Directions: Mix powders dry and package tightly to exclude moisture. To apply, mix with minimum quantity of water to yield mass of suitable working consistency.

Plaster Formula §8

Fluorescent Plaster

Plaster of Paris	950 g.
Zinc Silicate Phosphor	50 g.

Directions: The plaster is preferably not mixed with the phosphor, but the latter is added to the water-plaster mixture before placing, while still plastic. The purpose of this sequence is to have the mass set as quickly after addition of the phosphor as possible, to avoid reorientation of the latter with resulting loss of phosphorescence. The above phosphor gives a green phosphorescence; for a reddish-orange color calcium sulfide phosphor should be used instead.

Stucco

Stucco consists of Portland Cement (sometimes with added plaster of Paris) sand, water and, usually, calcium hydroxide to improve workability. Stucco is usually formulated for fairly rapid setting because it is usually applied to the outside of houses. For this reason also, coloring materials are relatively more important. The pigments used are essentially the same as those listed for cement earlier in this chapter; but the effect upon their shades of the calcium hydroxide in the stucco, and the usual desire for combination colors obtained by mixing them, emphasize the importance of preparing trial batches, which can then be modified until the hue and shade sought have been obtained.

Acid Wash Before Stuccoing

Before applying stucco to old masonry surfaces, a preliminary wash with an acid solution is customarily applied. The usual practice is to apply a wash made by mixing one part by volume of commercial muriatic acid (hydrochloric acid) with ten parts of water (although removal of spots of new concrete or heavy coats of soot and grime requires solutions as strong as one part of acid to 6 parts of water). These solutions should be followed within 10 minutes by thorough washing with water, otherwise the acid will attack the masonry (particularly the mortar). From this statement, the danger to skin, eyes, clothes, etc., can easily be seen. Even with full equipment of goggles, "petroleum jelly" on face and neck, and rubber gloves, this is dangerous work, and should be performed only by mechanical means, as it is done on all larger jobs today.

Mortar

General Bricklaying

Portland Cement	300 g.
Calcium Hydroxide (Hydrated Lime) . . .	300 g.
Sand	1800 g.
Water	1000 ml.

Directions: Mix the three solid materials, and stir in, or hoe in, the water until the desired consistency has been obtained. This depends, of course, upon the type of joints to be filled. If they are large, less water should be used than given above; however, cracks and joints in masonry that is to be very tight, such as chimneys, retaining walls, and cut stone work, must be filled by the mortar. For that purpose, a watery form of the above mixture, called grout, is used. For finishing mortar, see Concrete Surfacing §1.

Glass

The formulas given in this book for use on glass surfaces range from silvering applications to polishes and cleaners, and include putties used to fill joints between glass and other materials.

Glass Metallizing Procedure §1

For Depositing Silver Film on Glass

Solution *a*

Silver Nitrate	7 g.
Potassium Hydroxide	3.5 g.
Dilute Ammonium Hydroxide Solution (2%)	1.0 ml. (about)
Distilled Water	1000 ml.

Directions: Dissolve the silver nitrate in 700 ml. of the water, and the potassium hydroxide in the remaining 300 ml. Add the ammonium hydroxide to the silver solution until the precipitate it forms does not quite redissolve, then add the potassium hydroxide solution and mix thoroughly.

Precautions: Silver nitrate and potassium hydroxide are corrosive.

Solution *b*

Sucrose (ordinary sugar)	4 g.
Alcohol	9 ml.
Concentrated Nitric Acid	0.15 ml.
Distilled Water	50 ml.

Directions: Dissolve the sugar in 35 ml. of the water, then add the alcohol, the nitric acid, and the remainder of the water. This solution should be prepared in advance, so as to stand several days before use. It is then poured into Solution *a*; the mixture is shaken once or twice, and poured onto the (thoroughly clean) glass surface so as to cover it by ½-inch or so over its entire area. It is allowed to stand for several minutes until a uniform light gray deposit has formed on the glass surface, which is rinsed with water, and freed from loose precipitate by means of a soft pad. While drying the morror is placed on edge, and it is then polished with a very soft abrasive.

Glass Metallizing Procedure §2

For Depositing Lead (Black) Film on Glass

Solution *a*

Sodium Hydroxide	6.5 g.
Water	100 ml.

Solution *b*

Thiourea	6 g.
Water	600 ml.

Solution *c*

Lead Acetate	5 g.
Water	150 ml.

Directions: Prepare the solutions separately by dissolving the solids in the water. Mix them in the above order. Heat to 40°C (104°F). Pour the mixture over the glass to be plated, which has been thoroughly cleaned. (Mirror-cleanness may be obtained by washing with soap and water, immersing 3 hours in chemical cleaning mixture, which consists of 500 g. potassium dichromate mixed with 270 ml. concentrated sulfuric acid; then rinsing carefully with water.) After 15 minutes remove the glass from the solution and allow to dry.

Precautions: Lead compounds are poisonous; sulfuric acid and sodium hydroxide are corrosive.

Glass Fluorescent Lacquer

Zinc Orthosilicate	10 g.
Anthracene	10 g.
Eosin	10 g.
Metal Lacquer 1 (Chapter 3)	980 ml.

Directions: Dissolve the anthracene and the dye in the lacquer. This lacquer is used to render Christmas tree ornaments fluorescent.

Glass Cleaning Solution §1
General Surface Cleaner

*Cellosolve	50 ml.
Glycol	50 ml.
Alcohol (95%)	350 ml.
Water	550 ml.

     * Trade-mark product of Union Carbide Corp., 30 E. 42 St., New York, N.Y.

Directions: Mix liquids in above order.

Glass Cleaning Solution §2

*Carboxymethylcellulose (CMC) hv	5 g.
**Onyxol 336	20 g.
Kerosene, refined	180 ml.
Concentrated Ammonium Hydroxide	20 ml.
***Celite	50 g.
Bentonite	20 g.
Water	735 ml.

     * Trade-mark product of Hercules Powder Co., 900 Market St., Wilmington, Delaware.
     ** Trade-mark product of Onyl Oil & Chemical Co., Jersey City 2, N.J.
     *** Trade-mark product of Johns Manville Corp., 22 East 40 St. New York 16.

Directions: Dissolve the CMC by stirring in the water. Add Onyxol, kerosene, and ammonium hydroxide. Sift in Celite and bentonite with stirring. This product gives minimum of powdering, and no residual oily film.

Glass Cleaning Solution §3

Bottle Washing Compound

*Drymet	200 g.
Sodium Hydroxide (Bead form)	700 g.
Sodium Tripolyphosphate	100 g.

* Trade-mark product of Cowles Chemical Co., 7016 Euclid Ave., Cleveland 3, Ohio.

Directions: The three solids must be mixed quickly and packaged in sealed cans or drums because sodium hydroxide becomes wet rapidly with atmospheric moisture. This product should be tried in 1% solution in water in bottle-washing machines and then its strength varied as indicated by experience with the type of bottles to be washed.

Precautions: Very strong alkali, destructive to human tissues—to be used only in machines, and followed by thorough rinsing with dilute acid and/or water.

Glass Cleaning Solution §4

General Household Use

*Tergitol Anionic 7	3 g.
*Carbitol Solvent	77 g.
Isopropanol	350 g.
Water	570 ml.

* Trade-mark product of Union Carbide Corp., 30 East 42 St., New York 17, N.Y.

Directions: Mix the last three ingredients, stir until dissolved, then add the Tergitol, and continue stirring until uniform.

Windshield Defroster

Glycerol	300 ml.
Ethylene Glycol	350 ml.
Ethyl Alcohol	250 ml.
*Aerosol AS Solution	10 ml.
Water	100 ml.

* Trade-mark product of American Cyanamid Company, 30 Rockefeller Plaza, New York 21, N.Y.

Directions: Mix the liquids in above order and apply to inside of windshield to prevent fogging.

Putty §1

Common Glazier's Putty

Whiting (Form of Calcium Carbonate) . . .	700 g.
Boiled Linseed Oil	400 ml.

Directions: Mix the whiting and oil to the consistency of a dough; since the best proportions vary somewhat with the fineness of the whiting, it may be necessary to change them somewhat to obtain the proper consistency.

Putty §2

House Joint-Sealing

Whiting (form of Calcium Carbonate) . . .	500 g.
Asbestos Fiber	200 g.
Boiled Linseed Oil	500 ml.

Directions: Mix the whiting and oil to the consistency of a heavy fluid (by using less whiting than above quantity as necessary) and then stir in the asbestos fiber.

Putty §3

Modern Calking Compound

Asbestos Fiber	200 g.
*Asbestine	200 g.
**Talc	100 g.
Boiled Linseed Oil	350 ml.
***Japan Drier	40 ml.
Kerosene	80 ml.

> * Trade-mark product of International Pulp Co., 90 West St., New York 4, N.Y.
> ** If color is desired, replace the talc by minimum amount of pigment that will yield desired shade
> *** Or zinc naphthenate, 10 g.

Directions: Add the drier to the linseed oil and incorporate the first three ingredients with them by very heavy stirring action, preferably in a sturdy mechanical mixer. The kerosene is to be added to the mixture last.

Putty §4

For Pipe Joints

White Lead Ground in Oil	400 g.
Red Lead Ground in Oil	400 g.
Linseed Oil	200 ml.

Directions: Mix thoroughly.

Putty Softener

For Removing Hardened Putty

Soap Flakes . . . . 100 g.
Sodium Carbonate (Washing Soda) . . . . 250 g.
Calcium Hydroxide . . . . 300 g.
Water . . . . 400 ml.

Directions: Dissolve the washing soda in the water, then stir in the calcium hydroxide and the soap. Apply to putty, and allow several hours to soften.

Precautions: Sodium carbonate is injurious to skin and tissues.

Chapter 6

HOUSEHOLD CLEANING, POLISHING AND RELATED PRODUCTS

The title and organization of this chapter are a natural result of the fact that many products in wide use are formulated primarily to meet the requirements of use in the home. Therefore, it has seemed desirable to group them together, even though this arrangement is not consistent with that followed in the preceding chapters. As a consequence of this necessary inconsistency, you will find furniture polishes in Chapter 2, metal polishes in Chapter 4 and glass polishes in Chapter 5, even though many of them are household products. The use of those cross references, together with the formulas in this chapter, will give you an adequately broad coverage of the maintenance products used within the home.

Dishwashing Powder §1
Alkaline Powder

Sodium Carbonate, Anhydrous	100 g.
Trisodium Phosphate	200 g.
Sodium Metasilicate	300 g.
Tetrasodium Pyrophosphate	400 g.

Directions: Mix fine crystals intimately by sifting.

Dishwashing Powder §2
Soap-Alkaline Powder

Powdered Soap	40 g.
Borax	100 g.
Trisodium Phosphate	860 g.

Directions: Mix intimately by sifting.

140

Dishwashing Powder §3

Soap-Alkaline Powder

Powdered Soap	680 g.
Sodium Carbonate, Anhydrous (Soda Ash) . .	220 g.
Trisodium Phosphate	100 g.

Directions: Mix the powders thoroughly by sifting. The product is a soap-alkaline detergent mixture, for dishwashing or cleaning porcelain or glass surfaces.

Dishwashing Powder §4

Sodium Tripolyphosphate	400 g.
Tetrasodium Pyrophosphate	200 g.
Sodium Carbonate Anhydrous (Soda Ash) . .	200 g.
Sodium Metasilicate Pentahydrate	100 g.
*Surfynol 104	50 g.
**Pluronic F68	50 g.

* Trade-mark product of Air Reduction Co., 60 East 42 St., N.Y. 17, N.Y.
** Trade-mark product of Wyandote Chemical Corp., Wyandote, Michigan.

Directions: Mix ingredients thoroughly in above order.

Dishwashing Powder §5

For Machine Dishwashing

*Drymet	50%
**Glassy Phosphate	50%

* Trade-mark product of Cowles Chemical Co., 7016 Euclid Ave., Cleveland 3, Ohio.
** Trade-mark product of American Resinous Chemical Corp., Peabody, Massachusetts.

Directions: Mix the two ingredients. This product meets hard-water conditions well, in addition to its general effectiveness. For local use, varying degrees of water hardness may be specifically formulated, by varying the above proportions. A lower cost product may be provided by addition of up to 20% soda ash.

Dishwashing Liquid §1

For Glassware

*Supronyx	250 ml.
Water	750 ml.

* Trade-mark product of Onyx Oil and Chemical Co., Jersey City 2, N.J.

Directions: Dissolve the Supronyx in the water. It should be added to dishwashing water, or water to be used in washing windows, glassware, etc., in the proportion of ½ ounce (or 1 tablespoonful) of the above solution per gallon of water.

Dishwashing Liquid §2

*Supronyx	660 ml.
**Ultrawet 60L	340 ml.

    * Trade-mark product of Onyx Oil & Chemical Co., Jersey City 2, N.J.
    ** Trade-mark product of Atlantic Refining Co., 260 S. Broad St., Philadelphia 1, Pa.

Directions: Mix the two products. This product is formulated without added water so it can be used in the proportion of one teaspoonful (⅛ ounce) per gallon of dishwashing water.

Laundry Compound §1

Built Soap (Washing Machines)

*Drymet	400 g.
High Grade Soap (Powdered)	500 g.
Sodium Tripolyphosphate	100 g.

    * Trade-mark product of Cowles Chemical Co., 7016 Euclid Ave., Cleveland 3, Ohio.

Directions: Mix the three solids quickly and package.

Laundry Compound §2

Low Sudsing (Washing Machines)

*Pluronic L62	130 g.
*Kreelon 4D	50 g.
*Carbose D	30 g.
Sodium Metasilicate · $5H_2O$	100 g.
Sodium Tripolyphosphate	200 g.
Sodium Sesquicarbonate	490 g.

    * Trade-mark product of Wyandotte Chemicals Corp., Wyandotte, Michigan.

Directions: Mix quickly and package.

Laundry Compound §3
Low Sudsing (Washing Machines)

*Pluronic F68	90 g.
*Pluronic L62	40 g.
*Kreelon 4D	70 g.
*Carbose D	40 g.
Sodium Metasilicate · 5H$_2$O	100 g.
Sodium Tripolyphosphate	300 g.
Sodium Sesquicarbonate	360 g.

*Trade-mark product of Wyandotte Chemicals Corp., Wyandotte, Michigan.

Directions: Mix quickly all ingredients except Pluronic F68. Then melt that by heating to 140°F (60°C) and spray it on to the formulation. This produces a more free-flowing product.

Laundry Compound §4
Controlled Sudsing (Washing Machines)

Sodium Carbonate	250 g.
Sodium Tripolyphosphate	200 g.
Sodium Sulfate	200 g.
Sodium Silicate	150 g.
*Tergitol Nonionic NPX	130 g.
*Cellosize (Hydroxyethyl Cellulose) WPHS	20 g.
**Silene EF	20 g.
Water	30 ml.

*Trade-mark product of Union Carbide Corp., 30 E. 42 St., New York 17, N.Y.
**Trade-mark product of Columbia Chemicals Division, Pittsburgh Plate Glass Company, Grant Building, Pittsburgh, Pa.

Directions: Mix the Tergitol and the water, and incorporate the remaining ingredients in the above order.

Laundry Compound §5
High Sudsing (Agitator Type Washing Machines)

*Pluronic L64	50 g.
*Kreelon 4D	250 g.
*Carbose D	30 g.
Sodium Metasilicate · 5H$_2$O	100 g.
Sodium Tripolyphosphate	250 g.
Sodium Sesquicarbonate	320 g.

*Trade-mark product of Wyandotte Chemicals Corp., Wyandotte, Michigan.

Directions: Mix quickly all ingredients and package.

Laundry Compound §6
Commercial Laundry Product

*Pluronic L64	100 g.
*Kreelon 4D	200 g.
*Carbose D	30 g.
Sodium Metasilicate · 5H$_2$O	100 g.
Sodium Tripolyphosphate	50 g.
Sodium Carbonate, Anhydrous (Soda Ash)	520 g.

* Trade-mark product of Wyandotte Chemicals Corp., Wyandotte, Michigan.

Directions: Mix quickly all ingredients and package.

Laundry Compound §7
Bluing Detergent

Dodecylbenzene Sulfonate (60%)	275 g.
Sodium Tripolyphosphate	300 g.
Powdered Soap	300 g.
Sodium Silicate	100 g.
Triethanolamine	20 g.
*CMC	5 g.
Prussian Blue	2 g.

* Trade-mark product of Hercules Powder Co., 900 Market St., Wilmington, Delaware.

Directions: Mix in above order.

Laundry Bleach

Bleaching Powder	20 g.
Sodium Carbonate, Anhydrous (Soda Ash)	10 g.
Water	1000 ml.

Directions: Dissolve the soda ash and the bleaching powder separately in 500 ml. of the water and mix the solutions. If necessary, clarify or filter the solution through a plug of glass wool, or other substance unaffected by this solution.

Cleaning Powder
General Purpose

Silica (finely ground)	550 g.
Trisodium Phosphate	400 g.
Sodium Carbonate Anhydrous (Soda Ash) . .	30 g.
Soap Powder	20 g.

Directions: Sift the powders together to mix thoroughly. This product is a typical grit, alkali, and soap cleaner for porcelain, glass, and similar surfaces. It should be used with rubber gloves and general care to protect skin and eyes.

Liquid Soap

Potassium Hydroxide	50 g.
Oleic Acid	200 ml.
Glycerin	200 ml.
Water	550 ml.

Directions: Dissolve the potassium hydroxide in the water; then mix the oleic acid and the glycerin, and add the mixture to the potassium hydroxide solution, heating to 172°F. (78°C.), and stirring until emulsification is complete.

Precautions: Potassium hydroxide is destructive to skin and tissues.

Floor Cleaner §1
For Ceramic Tiles and Concrete Floors

*Tergitol Nonionic NPX	160 g.
Naphtha	570 g.
Water	270 ml.

* Trade-mark product of Union Carbide Corp., 30 East 42 St., New York 17, N.Y.

Directions: Mix the Tergitol in water, add the naphtha and stir until a uniform paste has been obtained. This mixture can be diluted, as desired, with additional water. It is inflammable.

Precautions: Naphtha is a petroleum fraction, and all flames and burning materials (e.g. cigars and cigarettes) should be avoided.

Floor Polish §1

Dry-Polish Floor Polish

Carnauba Wax	100 g.
*Tween 80	30 g.
Water	870 ml.

* Trade-mark product of Atlas Powder Co., Wilmington 99, Delaware.

Note: For furniture polishes, see Chapter 2.

Directions: Heat wax and Tween together to 212°F (100°C) and hold at that temperature while adding water (heated to boiling) slowly with thorough stirring until inversion (change of water-in-wax to wax-in-water system) occurs. Then the remainder of the water may be added rapidly. Rapid cooling with moderate stirring promotes a finely divided emulsion. This formula may be modified to produce a product giving a less slippery and more water resistant finish. (See next formula.)

Floor Polish §2

Dry-Bright Floor Polish
(Resistant to Water Spotting)

Carnauba Wax	50 g.
Candelilla Wax	15 g.
Paraffin	10 g.
Congo Gum	10 g.
*Durez 219	15 g.
**Tween 80	30 g.
Water	870 ml.

* Trade-mark product of Durez Plastics Division, Hooker Electrochemical Co., 5 Walck Road, North Tonawanda, N.Y.
** Trade-mark product of Atlas Powder Co., Wilmington 99, Delaware

Directions: Heat all ingredients except the water together to 212°F (100°C), and hold at that temperature while slowly adding boiling water, with thorough stirring until inversion (change of water-in-wax to wax-in-resin system) occurs. Then the remainder of the water may be added rapidly. Rapid cooling with moderate stirring promotes a finely divided emulsion.

Floor Polish §3

Dry-Bright Floor Polish
(Water Resistant—Removable With Hot
Water or Detergent)

*Polinel Wax	110 g.
**Brij 30	30 g.
Water	860 ml.

* Trade-mark product of Lovell Chemical Co., Nashville, Tenn.
** Trade-mark product of Atlas Powder Co., Wilmington 99, Delaware.

Directions: Heat wax and Brij together to 212°F (100°C) and hold at that temperature while adding water (heated to boiling) slowly with thorough stirring until inversion occurs. Then remainder of water may be added rapidly.

Floor Polish §4

Dry-Bright Floor Polish
(Water Resistant—Removable With Hot
Water or Detergent)

*Gersthofen Wax KPS***	100 g.
**Atlas G-3920	30 g.
Water	870 ml.

* Trade-mark product of the Wax and Rosin Products Co., 42 Broadway New York 4, N.Y.
** Product of the Atlas Powder Co., Wilmington 99, Delaware.

Directions: The same as Floor Polish §2.

Floor Polish §5

Dry-Bright Floor Polish

Carnauba Wax	100 g.
*Tween 20	20 g.
**Atlas G-9446N	30 g.
Water	850 ml.

* Trade-mark product of Atlas Powder Co., Wilmington 99, Delaware.
** Product of the Atlas Powder Co., Wilmington 99, Delaware.

Directions: Heat wax and G-9446N to 100°C. Add two-thirds of the water slowly. Emulsify by adding Tween 20 slowly with agitation. Add balance of water and cool.

Floor Polish §6

Carnauba Wax	60 g.
Candelilla Wax	60 g.
*Tween 20 or Brij 35	2 g.
Triethanolamine	10 g.
Oleic Acid	10 g.
Water	860 ml.

   * Trade-mark products of Atlas Powder Co., Wilmington 99, Delaware.

Directions: The same as Floor Polish §2.

Floor Polish §7

Dry Bright—High Wax Type

Step *a*—Base Emulsion

*R-50 (Microcrystalline Wax plus Rhenolic Resin)	25 g.
*PE-100 Emulsifiable Petroleum Wax . . .	12.5 g.
Carnauba Wax (#3 Refined)	12.5 g.
Oleic Acid	5 g.
**Aminomethylpropanol (AMP)	4.3 g.
Water	400 ml.

Step *b*—Leveling Agent

Shellac	50 g.
Ammonium Hydroxide, Concentrated . . .	4.0 g.
Water	365 ml.

   * Trade-mark product of Petrolite Corp., Kilgore, Texas.
   ** Product of Commercial Solvents Corp., 260 Madison Ave., New York 17, N.Y.

Directions: Blend the waxes and oleic acid in a melt at temperatures up to but not exceeding 270°F (132°C). Cool to 210°F (99°C) with agitation. Add AMP with stirring at 200-210°F (93-99°C). Cool at 200-205°F (93-96°C) for five minutes; then pour the wax melt slowly into the water at 200-210°F (93-99°C) with rapid agitation. When the emulsion has smoothed out, add cold solution of leveling agent during agitation and cooling to room temperature.

Floor Polish §8

Dry Bright—High Resin Type

Step *a*—Base Emulsion

*R-50 (Microcrystalline Wax Plus Phenolic Resin)	50 g.
Oleic Acid	5.5 g.
**Aminomethylpropanol (AMP)	3.8 g.
Water	400 ml.

Step *b*—Leveling Agent

Shellac	50 g.
Ammonium Hydroxide, Concentrated . . .	4.0 g.
Water	365 ml.

* Trade-mark product of Petrolite Corp., Kilgore, Texas.
** Product of Commercial Solvents Corp., 260 Madison Ave., New York 17, N.Y.

Directions: The same as Floor Polish §7.

General Purpose Polish §1

(High Gloss on Furniture, Floors, Leather)

Carnauba Wax	135 g.
*Duponol G	20 g.
Borax	10 g.
Shellac	20 g.
Ammonium Hydroxide (28%)	3 ml.
Water	815 ml.

* Trade-mark product of E. I. du Pont de Nemours & Co., Wilmington 99, Delaware.

Directions: Melt the carnauba wax and Duponol in steam-heated container. Dissolve the borax in 30 ml. of the water and add with vigorous stirring to the melted wax. After mixture has become uniform, cool to room temperature. Add the ammonium hydroxide to the remainder of the water and dissolve the shellac in this solution by heating. When this solution has cooled to room temperature, stir it into the wax emulsion.

General Purpose Polish §2

Concentrate

Paraffin Wax	760 g.
*Duponol G	80 g.
Cetyl Alcohol	160 g.

* Trade-mark product of E. I. du Pont de Nemours, Wilmington 98, Delaware.

Directions: Dissolve the Duponol, paraffin wax, and cetyl alcohol by heating them together in a steam heated container. Polishing emulsions can be prepared from this solution by adding boiling water while stirring at high speed. An emulsion with 17% of the above and 83% water is a creamy white product, whose stiffness may be adjusted by varying the percentage of water.

Leather Polish §1
Liquid Form

Montan Wax	200 g.
Paraffin Wax	160 g.
Stearic Acid	30 g.
Dye	8 g.
Turpentine	600 ml.

Directions: Heat the montan wax, the paraffin wax and the stearic acid in separate containers until molten. Add the paraffin wax cautiously and with stirring to the montax wax, which was previously removed from heat, then to this mixture add cautiously the molten stearic acid. While mixture is still liquid, add the dye, which can be of any color desired, but should be an oil-soluble type. Allow the mixture to cool until solidification begins, and add it slowly and with stirring to the turpentine.

Leather Polish §2
Paste

Montax Wax	120 g.
Carnauba Wax	50 g.
Paraffin Wax	40 g.
*Butyl Cellosolve	25 ml.
Dye	10 g.
Turpentine	550 ml.
Water	400 ml.

* Trade-mark product of the Union Carbide Corp., 30 East 42 St., New York 17, N.Y.

Directions: Heat the montan wax and the carnauba wax in separate containers until molten. Add the carnauba wax cautiously with stirring to the montan wax. Heat the paraffin wax in a separate container and add it slowly to this mixture. Allow to cool until almost solid, and add the Butyl Cellosolve, followed by the turpentine. Then stir in the dye, which should be an oil-soluble type, and finally add the water.

Saddle Soap

Coconut Oil	150 ml.
Palm Oil	150 ml.
Glycerin	60 ml.
Rosin	20 g.
Sodium Hydroxide	60 g.
Whiting (Calcium Carbonate, Powdered)	20 g.
Water	700 ml.

Directions: Mix first four ingredients, and heat to 167°F (75°C) with stirring until uniform. Dissolve sodium hydroxide completely in water, and heat to 167°F. Add slowly to first mixture, with stirring until fully emulsified. Then stir in whiting.

Precautions: Sodium hydroxide is corrosive, and very injurious to skin and tissues.

Shoe Polish §1
Cream Type

Carnauba Wax	65 g.
Paraffin Wax	45 g.
Soap Flakes	45 g.
Turpentine	150 ml.
Water	750 ml.
Color	

Directions: Heat the two waxes in separate containers until they are molten and then add the paraffin wax slowly to the carnauba wax. When this mixture almost is at solidification point, add the turpentine slowly. Dissolve the soap in water, heat to boiling, remove from fire, and add the wax-turpentine solution. Add the dye to the soap solution before waxes and turpentine are incorporated.

To produce the desired shade of color, the following dyes may be combined in the desired proportions:

Acid Black	Black
Bismarck Brown G	Brown
Crocein Scarlet	Red
Orange II	Orange
Metanil Yellow	Yellow

In ordering, specify water soluble colors.

Shoe Polish §2

Wax Type

Microcrystalline Paraffin Wax	200 g.
Carnauba Wax	30 g.
Montan Wax	40 g.
Turpentine	800 ml.
Color	

Directions: Melt first three ingredients, adding each one after other has melted, then add the color. When thoroughly stirred, discontinue heating, and add turpentine slowly, with stirring. To produce the desired shade of color, the following dyes may be combined in the desired proportion:

Nigrosin	Black
Bismarck Brown	Brown
Rhodamin	Red
Chrysoidin	Orange
Auramin	Yellow

In ordering, specify oil-soluble colors.

Shoe Polish §3

Cleaner and Whitener for White Shoes

Carnauba Wax	30 g.
Paraffin Wax	50 g.
Beeswax	50 g.
Turpentine	100 ml.
Stoddard Solvent	150 ml.
*Onyxol 336	50 g.
Water	420 ml.
**Titanox A	150 g.

* Trade-mark product of Onyx Oil & Chemical Co., Jersey City 2, N.J.
** Trade-mark product of Titanium Pigment Corp., 111 Broadway, New York 6, N.Y.

Directions: Melt the three waxes by heating to 176°F (80°C) by steam-heat, and mix the water and Onyxol and heat them to 176°F. Then add the water solution slowly and with stiring to the waxes. After mixture has cooled to 140°F. (60°C), add the turpentine and Stoddard Solvent. Sift in Titanox A and stir until mixture has cooled to room temperature.

Precautions: Stoddard Solvent is a lower boiling petroleum fraction, so observe precautions as with gasoline.

Stove Polish §1

Water Suspension Type

Sodium Carbonate	40 g.
Coconut Oil Soap	100 g.
Diatomaceous Earth	650 g.
Alcohol	100 ml.
Water	300 ml.

Directions: Dissolve the sodium carbonate in the water. Mix this solution and the alcohol, and dissolve the soap in them. Stir the abrasive slowly into the liquid.

Precautions: Sodium carbonate is injurious to animal tissues.

Stove Polish §2

Solution Type

Diatomaceous Earth	400 g.
*Duponol C	10 g.
Alcohol	100 ml.
Water	500 ml.

*Trade-mark product of E. I. du Pont de Nemours & Co., Wilmington 98, Delware.

Directions: Dissolve the Duponol in the water, add the alcohol, and stir in the diatomaceous earth.

Stove Polish §3

Paste

Powdered Pumice	500 g.
Carnauba Wax	200 g.
Stearic Acid	100 g.
Mineral Oil	150 ml.

Directions: Mix the last three ingredients and warm until melted. Stir in the pumice.

Stove Polish §4

Black—Cake Form

Ozokerite	250 g.
Beeswax	150 g.
Rosin	150 g.
Castor Oil	50 ml.
Graphite	300 g.
Carbon Black	100 g.

Directions: Heat the first two ingredients together until melted; then heat the third and fourth ingredients in a second container until they have melted to a clear solution, and add it to the first one. Add the last two ingredients last, with continued stirring. Package before solidification has occurred.

Stove Polish §5

Black—Liquid Form

Beeswax	25 g.
Carnauba Wax	25 g.
Graphite	200 g.
Lampblack	25 g.
*Santomerse 43	40 g.
Alcohol	100 ml.
Water	600 ml.

* Trade-mark product of Monsanto Chemical Co., 1700 S. Second St., St. Louis, Mo.

Directions: Heat the waxes and Santomerse slowly until melted (about 167°F-75°C). When cooling to 140°F (60°C) has occurred, add the alcohol and stir until product is uniform. Then add the water slowly and with stirring. The graphite and lampblack are stirred in last. For a brighter-black product, dissolve 10 g. of spirit-soluble nigrosine in the alcohol.

Stove Polish §6

Black—Paste Form

Sodium Hydroxide	15 g.
Coconut Oil	65 ml.
Rosin	30 g.
Paraffin Wax	65 g.
Sodium Silicate	50 g.
Graphite	150 g.
Lampblack	50 g.
Water	500 ml.

Directions: Dissolve the sodium hydroxide and sodium silicate in the water. Mix the coconut oil, rosin and paraffin, and heat until melted; then add the water solution to them while it is still warm, slowly and with stirring. Continue stirring and heat to 167°F (75°C). Allow to cool to 140°F (60°C) and stir in graphite and lampblack.

Precautions: Sodium hydroxide is corrosive, and very injurious to skin and tissues.

Stove Polish §7
Black—Paste Form

*Sodium Alkyl-Aryl Sulfonate (75%) . . .	100 g.
Glycerin	35 g.
Mineral Oil	35 ml.
Graphite	180 g.
Lampblack	75 g.
Water	550 ml.

* Any water-soluble petroleum sulfonate, or soap itself, may be used here.

Directions: Add the water to the sulfonate and stir until dissolved. Add the glycerin. Warm this solution and the oil to 140°F (60°C) and stir the solution slowly into the oil. Then stir the graphite and carbon black into the mixture.

Dry Cleaning Fluid §1

Stoddard Solvent	980 ml.
Ethyl Acetate	8 ml.
Tertiary Butyl Alcohol	8 ml.
Water	4 ml.

Directions: This product is cheaper than the Cleaning Fluid §4 but has the disadvantage that its vapors are inflammable as well as toxic. To prepare, mix the last three ingredients first, and add the Stoddard Solvent (defined in following formula) to this mixture with stirring. The water is used to impart cleaning action for dirt that is insoluble in the organic solvents; although in the concentration used, this effect is not very great. The water may cause the product to be cloudy, which will not impair its cleaning effectiveness.

Precautions: Work with this product out-of-doors, because of its inflammability hazard.

Dry Cleaning Fluid §2

Glyceryl Trioleate	20 ml.
Stoddard Solvent	380 ml.
Carbon Tetrachloride	600 ml.

Directions: Dissolve the glyceryl trioleate in the carbon tetrachloride and add the Stoddard Solvent, which is a water-white petroleum distillate defined for dry-cleaning purposes by U.S. Bureau of Standards Specifications.

Precautions: Mix this fluid out-of-doors or with thorough ventilation, because of the inflammability hazard; and because carbon tetrachloride vapor is poisonous on inhalation, and its liquid to skin and tissues.

Dry Cleaning Fluid §3

*Tergitol Anionic 7	440 g.
*Tergitol Nonionic NPX	220 g.
Oleic Acid	35 g.
Monoethanolamine	18 g.
Sodium Nitrite	8 g.
Naphtha	350 ml.

*Trade-mark product of Union Carbide Corp., 30 East 42 St., New York 17, N.Y.

Directions: Mix the first two ingredients and add the next three in order, stirring until completely dissolved. Then add the naphtha, stirring until clear; if a cloudy product results, correct with additional oleic acid.

Precautions: Naphtha is a petroleum fraction, and all flames and burning materials (e.g. cigars and cigarettes) should be avoided.

Dry Cleaning Fluid §4
Spotting Soap

Oleic Acid	530 g.
*Butyl Cellosolve	135 g.
Naphtha	150 ml.
Triethanolamine	105 ml.
Potassium Hydroxide	41 g.
Water	65 ml.

*Trade-mark product of Union Carbide Corp., 30 East 42 St., New York 17, N.Y.

Directions: Warm the mixture of the first three ingredients with steam or hot water (no flames) to 140°F (45°C). Dissolve the potassium hydroxide thoroughly in the water, and add the triethanolamine. Then add this solution to the first mixture slowly, holding at 140°F and stirring for at least one hour.

Precautions: Potassium hydroxide destroys skin and tissues, so handle with care. Naphtha is a petroleum fraction, and all flames and burning materials (e.g. cigars and cigarettes) should be avoided.

Glove Cleaner

Stoddard Solvent	400 ml.
Carbon Tetrachloride	600 ml.

Directions: Mix the liquids.

Precautions: Stoddard Solvent is a petroleum distillate, and hence a fire hazard. It is used here primarily to reduce cost of product, although it does enhance the cleaning action somewhat, and is reasonably safe when mixed in above proportions. Carbon tetrachloride is poisonous to skin and tissues, and its vapor is poisonous on inhalation.

Stain Removal

The important considerations in removing stains are the kind of material and the relation to it of the stain. The stains most easily removable are, in general, those in which the foreign substances have not penetrated into the fibers or combined with them chemically or physically. For example, grease stains can usually be removed completely because the grease does not combine with the fibers and because it can be dissolved by a solution that does not discolor the fabric or partly modify its dye. Moreover, the same solution can be used for removing grease stains from most fabrics. On the other hand, most ink stains are complex, if not quite impossible, chemical problems. Many writing inks contain both dyes and iron salts. The dyes react differently with vegetable fibers (cotton, linen, etc.), animal fibers (silk, wool, etc.), and the various types of synthetic fibers. They can be removed by sufficiently powerful chemical agents, but often not without removing the dye from the fabric as well. Then, when the dye in the inkstain has been removed from the fabric, the iron salts remain (or the compound produced by their interaction with the fibers), and this requires a different chemical treatment. Thus, to aid in the use of stain-removing solutions, various special directions are required, and these will be given in the formulas and directions which follow. Wherever possible, test a scrap or inside edge of the material with the remover before proceeding.

Stains are removed by dipping the entire garment in solution, or treating only the stained area (a process called "spotting"). The first method avoids "rings," but requires the use of much solution, and hazards the entire garment. The second has certain required steps. When spotting, always put an absorbing substance (cloth or paper) under the area to be treated. Always apply the solution from the center of the spot toward the edges. These two rules go far toward assuring the best results possible. Where there is a choice of methods, remember that in general organic solvents are least likely to discolor fabrics or to change their dyes, water and solutions of salts in water are more likely to be injurious, acids come next, and bleaches and other oxidizing agents are most harmful. Unfortunately, some stains yield only to the last group of solutions.

Stain Remover §1

Antiseptic Dye Stains on Vegetable and Synthetic Fibers

Solution A

Potassium Permanganate	15 g.
Water	1000 ml.

Solution B

Oxalic Acid	15 g.
Water	1000 ml.

Directions: Both solutions are prepared by dissolving the salt or acid in the water. Heat solution A to 50°C (122°F), and rub onto stain gently for 5 minutes, then heat solution B also to 50°C (122°F) and rub until brown coloration left by Solution A has disappeared. Rinse thoroughly with water. Solution A stains the fingers and Solution B is poisonous, so use rubber gloves. (Vegetable fibers are cotton, linen, etc.)

Precautions: Oxalic acid is poisonous. Potassium permanganate crystals should not be stored in any quality because of fire hazard.

Stain Remover §2

Antiseptic Dye Stains on Animal Fibers

Alcohol	600 ml.
Acetic Acid (28%)	400 ml.

Directions: Mix the liquids and soak the stain for five minutes. Wash thoroughly with water. Repeat operation until stain has lightened to desired extent. Total removal of such stains from animal fibers (wool, silk, etc.) is not feasible.

Precautions: Strongly acid solution.

Stain Remover §3

Nail Polish, Lipstick, Etc.

Acetone	400 ml.
Amyl Acetate	600 ml.

Directions: Mix the liquids and apply to stain, blotting up the solution as the stain dissolves. Repeated applications will usually effect complete removal. Some synthetic fibers are dissolved (i.e. destroyed) by this solution, so test the material before using if in doubt.

Stain Remover §3A

Lipstick

*Tergitol Nonionic NPX	12 g.
*Butyl Carbitol	175 ml.
Isopropyl Alcohol	130 ml.
Carbon Tetrachloride	300 ml.
Naphtha	400 ml.

* Trade-mark product of Union Carbide Corp., 30 East 42 St., New York 17, N.Y.

Directions: Mix the first three ingredients, add the last two and stir until a clear product results.

Precautions: Naphtha is a gasoline fraction, and all flames and burning materials (e.g. cigars and cigarettes) should be avoided. Carbon tetrachloride is poisonous to skin and tissues, and its vapor is poisonous on inhalation.

Stain Remover §4

Mud

*Detanol	30 g.
Water	1000 ml.

* Trade-mark product of the Commonwealth Color and Chemical Co., 3240 Grace Ave., Brooklyn, N.Y.

Directions: Wash spot thoroughly with solution, then rinse with water. If this solution is not available, use pure (Castile) soap and water. If the mud stain leaves an iron stain remaining, use Stain Remover §1 Solution B followed by thorough washing.

Stain Remover §5

Oil and Grease

Alcohol	120 ml.
Butyl Acetate	360 ml.
Toluene	220 ml.
Carbon Tetrachloride	300 ml.

Directions: Mix the liquids. Wet spot with solution, rub with absorbent material away from center of spot. Repeat process until all grease has disappeared.

Stain Remover §6

Mildew

Solution A

Concentrated Hydrochloric Acid	40 ml.
Water	960 ml.

Solution B

Hyrogen Peroxide (30%)	300 ml.
Water	700 ml.

Directions: Prepare the solutions by diluting the reagents with water in the above proportions. Apply Solution A to stained fabric, using gently, rinse once with water, then apply Solution B. Wash thoroughly with water. Repeat until spot is removed. As noted in general discussion at beginning of this Section, this treatment removes, or partly removes, dye used to color textiles.

Precautions: Hydrogen peroxide, 30%, is an unstable product that should not be stored, or exposed to light, heat, or shaking. Hydrochloric acid is a strong acid, injurious to skin and to many textiles. Wash thoroughly after application.

Stain Remover §7

Blood

Chloroform	800 ml.
Alcohol	200 ml.

Directions: Mix liquids and rub on stain with absorbent cloth. If cloth becomes colored, continue use of solution until stain has been removed. If no color is seen, then Remover §8 or §9 must be used, but §7 is preferred because it does not discolor dyed fabrics.

Stain Remover §8

Blood from Vegetable Fibers and Synthetic Fibers

Bleaching Powder	25 g.
Sodium Carbonate, Anhydrous (Soda Ash) .	20 g.
Water	1000 ml.

Directions: Dissolve the bleaching powder in half of the water, and the soda ash in the remainder. Mix the solutions and allow to stand for one hour. Filter off and reject the sediment (or pour off the clear liquid). Dip article containing stain, allow to stand two minutes, then wash thoroughly with water. As noted in the general discussion at the beginning of this Section, this treatment removes, or partly removes, dye used to color textiles.

Stain Remover §9

Blood From Animal Fibers and Colored Fibers

Solution A

Acetic Acid (28%)	100 ml.
Sodium Chloride	20 g.
Water	900 ml.

Directions: Dissolve the salt in the water and mix the acid with this solution.

Solution B

Concentrated Ammonium Hydroxide . . .	40 ml.
Water	970 ml.

Directions: Mix the ammonium hydroxide with the water. Soak the stained fabric in Solution A, wash with water, apply Solution B to neutralize any solution A remaining, then repeat washing with water.

Stain Remover §10

Oil Paint

Turpentine	800 ml.
Alcohol	200 ml.

Directions: Mix the solvents, apply to the stain; if the latter is dry and hard, allow to soak until partly softened. Rub away from the center of the spot with an absorbent cloth, continuing until the stain is removed. To remove residual turpentine (its odor is particularly persistent) rinse with alcohol and, if necessary, with carbon tetrachloride.

Stain Remover §11

Lacquer and Lacquer Paint

Amyl Acetate	400 ml.
Acetone	600 ml.

Directions: Mix the solvents and apply to the stain; allow to soak until partly softened; then rub away from center of spot. Finally, remove solvent with alcohol.

This solvent is intended for the lacquers and lacquer paints, that is, products formulated with cellulose esters or other esters, with or without colored pigments. While obviously the nature of the paint cannot be determined simply from the stain, one can always make the best guess, and, if that fails, try again.

Stain Remover §12

Varnish and Clear Lacquer

Methanol	450 ml.
Alcohol (95%)	350 ml.
Acetone	200 ml.

Directions: Mix the solvents and apply to the stain; allow to soak until partly softened; then rub away from center of spot. Finally, remove solvent with alcohol.

Stain Remover §13

Prespiration

Hydrogen Peroxide (30%)	400 ml.
Water	600 ml.

Directions: Mix the liquids and apply to stain. After one minute, wash thoroughly with water. Repeat if necessary, limiting treatment to minimize action upon dyes used to color fabric.

Precautions: Hydrogen peroxide 30% is an unstable product that should not be stored, or exposed to light, heat, or shaking.

Stain Remover §14

Iodine

Sodium Thiosulfate	120 g.
Water	1000 ml.

Directions: Dissolve salt in water and apply to stain; when stain disappears, wash with water.

Stain Remover §15

Coffee, Chocolate, and Cocoa

Glycerin	800 ml.
Alcohol (95%)	200 ml.

Directions: Mix the glycerin and alcohol and heat the mixture to 60°C (140°F). Apply to spot by saturating with the hot solution, and rubbing away from center of stain with an absorbent cloth. When stain is removed, wash out the solution with alcohol or water. If the stains do not respond to this solution, then it is necessary to use Stain Remover §13.

Stain Remover §16
Scorch Stains

Hydrogen Peroxide (6%)	100 ml.
Acetic Acid (3%)	7 ml.
Water	900 ml.

Directions: Mix the peroxide and water, and add the acid. Rub the scorch mark with this solution, using an absorbent cloth. If the spot does not lighten appreciably, try exposing it, while wet with the solution, to sunlight. If the material is too badly burned to yield to this treatment, it is probably beyond salvage.

Stain Remover §17
Tea, Tobacco, Various Non-Alcoholic Beverages

Solution A

Pyridine	60 ml.
Benzene	40 ml.

Solution B

Sodium Hydrosulfide	60 g.
Water	1000 ml.

Directions: Mix the pyridine and the benzene, dissolve the sodium hydrosulfide in the water; and heat both solutions to 65°C (149°F). Dip the garment in Solution A, or moisten the spot with that solution; then transfer to or apply Solution B. Repeat this process four or five times before concluding that the treatment is ineffective. Very old stains of this nature (the substance tannin is the actual staining agent) cannot be removed.

Stain Remover §18
Grass Stains

Alcohol (95%)	940 ml.
Acetic Acid (3%)	60 ml.

Directions: Mix the liquids and soak the stain in them, or rub the stain away from the center with an absorbent cloth. Then wash out solution with alcohol. If the material can be washed with soap and water without discoloration, that treatment will often suffice to remove grass stains.

Stain Remover §19
Fruit Stains

Hydrogen Peroxide (30%)	60 ml.
Ammonium Hydroxide	10 ml.
Water	930 ml.

Directions: Wash the fabric in soap and water, and then, if stain is not removed, treat with a 2% sodium hypochlorite solution. If that treatment does not remove the stain, or if that treatment cannot be used without danger of removing the dye from the fabric (as with many silks, wools, etc.) then try the above solution, being careful to dip the stain in water first, then apply the solution, then rinse with water. If this does not succeed, the only recourse is to Stain Remover §1, with great danger of affecting the color of the fabric.

Precautions: Hydrogen peroxide (30%) should not be stored, heated, or exposed to light unnecessarily. It has marked bleaching action on skin.

Stain Remover §20
Iron Ink* and Rust

Solution A

Ammonium Sulfide	3.7 g.
Water	1000 ml.

Solution B

Oxalic Acid	4.9 g.
Water	1000 ml.

* Note that many inks contain dyes, which this treatment will not remove. (See Introduction to this section).

Directions: Prepare both solutions by dissolving the salt and acid in water. Immerse in Solution A the portion of the cloth containing the spot; then apply Solution B. Repeat if necessary until spot disappears. Wash thoroughly with water after last application. Note that this method is applicable only to textile fabrics which are not discolored by water.

Precautions: Oxalic acid is highly poisonous.

Ink Eradicator

Solution A

Citric Acid	20 g.
Tartaric Acid	20 g.
Boric Acid	20 g.
Water	1000 ml.

Directions: Dissolve acids in water.

Solution B

Bleaching Powder	50 g.
Borax	15 g.
Water	1000 ml.

Directions: Dissolve the solids in separate portions of the water and mix. To use, apply successively Solutions A and B, blotting off excess each time, and applying water and blotting when ink is eradicated.

Paint Cleaner

Household Type

Isopropanol	40 g.
*Tergitol Anionic 7	32 g.
**Nacconol NRSF	32 g.
Tetrasodium Pyrophosphate	10 g.
Water	900 ml.

* Trade-mark product of Union Carbide Corp., 30 E. 42 St., New York 17, N.Y.
** Trade-mark product of National Aniline Division, Allied Chemical and Dye Corp., 40 Rector St., New York 6, N.Y.

Directions: Dissolve the Nacconol in the water, and stir in the Tergitol. Then add the isopropanol, followed by the tetrasodium pyrophosphate, continuing stirring until a clear product has been obtained. Used to clean painted surfaces.

Wall Paper Cleaner

Calcium Carbonate (fine-ground)	650 g.
Magnesium Oxide (calcined)	140 g.
Fuller's Earth	140 g.
Pumice (fine-powder)	50 g.
Lemongrass Oil	20 ml.

Directions: Sift the powdered ingredients together until thoroughly mixed.

then add the oil to them dropwise, with continued mixing. Be sure that all four of the powdered ingredients are very finely-divided, because this product is a rubbing powder, formulated to remove stains by abrasion and solution in the oil film that coats the solid particles. If lemongrass oil is not available, any oil of vegetable origin will do.

Wall Paper Remover

*Tergitol Nonionic NPX	125 g.
Water	875 ml.

* Trade-mark product of Union Carbide Corp., 30 East 42 St., New York 17, N.Y.

Directions: Add the Tergitol to the water and stir until fully dissolved. In use, this product should be diluted with 5-6 times its volume of water, and applied to wall paper prior to removal.

Straw Hat Cleaner

Solution A

Sodium Thiosulfate	100 g.
Alcohol	100 ml.
Glycerin	50 ml.
Water	750 ml.

Solution B

Citric Acid	20 g.
Alcohol	80 ml.
Water	900 ml.

Directions: Prepare Solution A by dissolving the sodium thiosulfate in water, and adding the alcohol and glycerin. Prepare Solution B by dissolving the citric acid in the water and adding the alcohol. In use apply Solution A with a sponge; then after 24 hours, apply Solution B. If the hat dries out of shape, as some grades will do, hot pressing is necessary.

Rug Cleaner §1

Oleic Acid	140 ml.
Triethanolamine	80 ml.
Isopropyl Alcohol	70 ml.
Ethylene Dichloride	65 ml.
*Butyl Cellosolve	25 ml.
Water	620 ml.

* Trade-mark product of Union Carbide Corp., 30 E. 42 St., New York 17, N.Y.

Directions: Mix the oleic acid, ethylene dichloride, and Butyl Cellosolve, and then add slowly and with stirring, a mixture of the triethanolamine, isopropanol, and water. The product is used for "shampooing" the rug until the desired degree of cleaning has been obtained.

Precautions: The vapors are very toxic to breathe, and the liquid is toxic to the skin, so the work should be done out-of-doors, with rubber gloves.

Rug Cleaner §2

Step *a*—Dry concentrate

*Tergitol Nonionic NPX	625 g.
Perchlorethylene	250 g.
Oleic Acid	100 g.
Monoethanolamine	25 g.

Step *b*

Concentrate (Step *a* above)	20 g.
Perchlorethylene	100 g.
Water	100 ml.
Wood Flour	1000 g.

* Trade-mark product of Union Carbide Corp., 30 E. 42 St., New York 17, N.Y.

Directions: Prepare the concentrate by mixing the four ingredients in Step *a* in the given order. Then prepare final product by dissolving the 20 g. of concentrate in 100 g. of perchlorethylene. Stir the water into the wood flour until well mixed, and then blend in the solution.

Precautions: Avoid breathing vapors of perchlorethylene.

Air Freshening Spray

Perfume	60 ml.
Isopropyl Alcohol	300 ml.
Propylene Glycol	640 ml.

Directions: Mix the isopropyl alcohol and propylene glycol, and add the perfume. This mixture is intended for use in Aerosol sprays, by addition of 5 to 8 times its volume of propellant (Freons or Genetrons). (See Chapter 1).

Sanitizing Product §1 *
Emulsion

Pine Oil	10 ml.
**Tween 20	80 g.
Water	910 ml.

* Sanitizing products are used for odor masking and disinfectant purposes, with no specific claims for anti-bacterial action.
** Trade-mark product of Atlas Powder Co., Wilmington 99, Delaware.

Directions: Mix oil and emulsifier, and stir in water slowly until inversion occurs, then add remaining water.

Sanitizing Product §2
Concentrate

Orthodichlorobenzene	760 g.
Pine Oil	25 ml.
Isopropyl Alcohol	65 ml.
*Atlas G-1020	150 ml.

* Trade-mark product of Atlas Powder Co., Wilmington 99, Delaware.

Directions: Mix oil and Atlas G-1020, and stir in other ingredients at room temperature. This is a concentrated product; add a few ounces of it to each gallon of water for use as deodorizer or antiseptic.

Sanitizing Product §3
Space Deodorant

Dipentene	50 g.
Pine Oil	10 ml.
*Tween 40	140 g.
Isopropyl Alcohol	120 ml.
Water	680 ml.

* Trade-mark product of Atlas Powder Co., Wilmington 99, Delaware.

Directions: Dissolve Tween in pine oil and dipentene. Add water and isopropyl alcohol slowly to the solution with stirring. If cloudiness develops, stir until clear before continuing addition of water.

Disinfectant §1

Cresol Type for Toilets

Rosin Soap	200 g.
Glycerin	40 ml.
Creosote Oil	300 ml.
Water	650 ml.

Directions: Mix the rosin soap and glycerin, and heat to 158°F (70°C). Then heat water to that temperature, and stir into soap mixture until uniform.* Let cool to 104°F (40°C), and stir in creosote oil.

> *If emulsification does not occur readily add 10 g. of Duponol C (trade-mark product of E. I. du Pont de Nemours Co., Wilmington 98, Delaware).

Disinfectant §2

Sodium Hydroxide	30 g.
Rosin	250 g.
Oil of Eucalyptus	300 ml.
Alcohol	50 ml.
Water	375 ml.

Directions: Dissolve the sodium hydroxide in 150 ml. of the water. Add the rosin in small pieces, heat to 167°F (75°C) stirring until uniform solution has been formed. Let cool to 122°F (50°C), and stir in the oil, followed by the remainder of the water. The alcohol is stirred in last, when the solution is cool.

Precautions: Sodium hydroxide and its solutions destroy skin and tissues.

Glue §1

Liquid-Ammonium-Casein Type

Casein	150 g.
Sodium Hydroxide	12 g.
Ammonium Chloride	16 g.
Water	900 ml.

Directions: Add 700 ml. of the water to the casein, stir thoroughly and let stand until no further swelling occurs. Dissolve sodium hydroxide in 100 ml. of water, and ammonium chloride in remainder of water, and stir in order into the casein solution.

Precautions: Sodium hydroxide destroys human tissues.

Glue §2

Liquid Sodium Hydroxide-Casein Type

Casein	150 g.
Sodium Hydroxide	6 g.
Water	900 ml.

Directions: Add 700 ml. of water to casein, stir thoroughly, and let stand until no further swelling occurs. Dissolve sodium hydroxide in remainder of water, add to casein mixture, and stir until solution is complete.

Precautions: Sodium hydroxide destroys human tissues.

Glue §3

Dry Type

Casein	750 g.
Calcium Hydroxide	55 g.
Sodium Citrate	165 g.

Directions: Mix dry powders and package in closed container. Mix with water for use as required.

Glue §4

For Porcelain and Glass

Fish Glue	550 g.
Water	1000 ml.
Gum Mastic	65 g.
Alcohol	110 ml.

Directions: Soak the glue in the water 12-24 hours. Pour off excess water and heat glue slowly until it liquefies. Remove from heat and add slowly, with stirring, the alcohol in which the gum mastic has been dissolved. By decreasing the proportions of glue and water to $\frac{1}{10}$ of above figures, this formula yields a more strongly alcoholic product useful for setting gems and other operations with jewelry.

Paste

General Household *

Dextrin	350 g.
Glycerin	20 ml.
Cane Sugar	20 g.
Alum	10 g.
Water	600 ml.

* For Paperhangers' Paste, see Chapter 3.

Directions: Add the dextrin to 550 ml. of the water. Heat to 140°F (60°C) and stir until dissolved. Dissolve the sugar, glycerin and alum in the remainder of the water, add to the dextrin solution, and heat at 176°F (80°C) until clear.

Rubber Cement

Rubber	100 g.
Ethylene Dichloride	200 ml.
Benzene	800 ml.

Directions: Cut the rubber into small pieces and allow to stand in the mixed solvents for several days, stirring occasionally. Either natural or synthetic rubber may be used.

Precautions: These ingredients are poisonous to skin and tissues, and their vapors are poisonous on inhalation. Have good ventilation during manufacture.

Pet Product §1
Animal Dandruff Treatment

Salicylic Acid	15 g.
Glycerin	45 ml.
Alcohol	950 ml.

Directions: Dissolve the salicylic acid in the alcohol and add the glycerin. Rub this product into the hair and onto the skin after shampooing.

Precautions: Salicylic acid tends to dissolve hair and tissue, so use sparingly and avoid excessive contact with hands.

Pet Product §2
Dog Shampoo

Hexachlorophene	2 g.
Pine Oil	10 ml.
Coconut Oil Soap	200 g.
Alcohol	30 ml.
Water	950 ml.

Directions: Warm the soap in the water until it dissolves and mix until uniform. Dissolve the hexachlorophene and pine oil in the alcohol, and add to the water mixture.

Pet Product §3
Flea Treatment

Stearic Acid	90 g.
Triethanolamine	30 g.
*Duponol OS	15 g.
Light Mineral Oil	300 ml.
Water	675 ml.

* Trade-mark product of E. I. du Pont de Nemours & Co.,
Wilmington 99, Del.

Directions: Add the triethanolamine and Duponol to the water and warm
to 158°F (70°C). Melt the stearic acid, add to it the mineral oil, and heat to
158°F. Stir the water solution into it slowly. This product is to be diluted
with thirty times its volume of water before application and rinsed off the
animal afterwards.

Pet Product §4
Germicidal "Dry Cleaning" Powder

Hexachlorophene	2 g.
DDT	3 g.
Sodium Carbonate	50 g.
Starch	475 g.
Kaolin	475 g.

Directions: In 100 g. of the kaolin, mix thoroughly the hexachlorophene,
DDT and sodium carbonate, in that order. Then mix this powder with the
starch and remainder of the kaolin.

Precautions: Thorough mixing is essential. This product should not be
used on cats, because they are extraordinarily sensitive to DDT.

Insecticide Spray §1
General

Pyrethrum (20% solution)	20 ml.
DDT	30 g.
Cyclohexanone	50 ml.
Petroleum Oil	50 ml.
Dispersing Medium	850 ml.

Directions: The petroleum oil should be a water-white product, having a
viscosity of S.A.E. 30 (a rating established by the Society of Automotive
Engineers for lubricating oils). Dissolve the pyrethrum and DDT in the
cyclohexanone, add the petroleum oil and dispersing medium. This product

is formulated for an Aerosol type package and dispersing medium (see Chapter 1.)

Insecticide Spray §2
Bedbug Exterminator

Pyrethrum Solution (20%)	300 ml.
Mineral Oil	300 ml.
Carbon Tetrachloride	400 ml.

Directions: Add the first two ingredients to the carbon tetrachloride, with stirring.

Precautions: Carbon tetrachloride is poisonous to skin and tissues, and its vapor is poisonous on inhalation.

Insecticide Powder §1
DDT Powder for Insects

DDT	100 g.
Talc	900 g.

Directions: Mix the DDT and the talc thoroughly by sifting. Be careful not to inhale this dust. Its toxicity, while often slight, is highly variable, both to man and animals. It is effective against a wide variety of insects.

Insecticide Powder §2
General Insecticide Powder

Naphthalene	360 g.
Calcium Carbonate	220 g.
Talc	180 g.
Calcium Hydroxide	150 g.
Iron Oxide	75 g.
Bentonite	10 g.
Toluic Acid	3 g.
Creosote Oil	12 ml.

Directions: Dissolve the toluic acid in the creosote oil and then stir this liquid slowly into the bentonite. Continue the stirring until absorbed. Mix the calcium carbonate, calcium hydroxide, and iron oxide thoroughly by stirring or sifting. Then stir into them the bentonite preparation, and finally stir in the naphthalene. This preparation is a dry, general-purpose household insecticide. It is especially effective against moths, although it is also useful against insects.

Insecticide Powder §3
Roach Powder

Pyrethrum . . . . 250 g.
Sodium Fluoride . . . . 225 g.
Talc . . . . 500 g.
Nile Blue . . . . 25 g.

Directions: Mix the pyrethrum and the talc thoroughly by stirring or sifting, and then add the sodium fluoride, which should be in the form of very fine crystals so that it will mix readily with the other ingredients.

Precautions: This product is poisonous to man and animals, and the dye is added so it can be seen and distinguished from white powdered substances.

Insecticide Powder §4
Roach Powder

Sodium Fluoride . . . . 225 g.
Borax . . . . 250 g.
Cane Sugar . . . . 150 g.
Flour . . . . 350 g.
Nile Blue . . . . 25 g.

Directions: Obtain all ingredients in powder or fine-crystalline form to insure stability of mixture in shaking. Mix thoroughly in above order.

Precautions: This product is poisonous to man and animals, and the dye is added so it can be seen and distinguished from white powdered substances.

Insecticide Powder §5
Roach Powder

Trisodium Phosphate . . . . 50 g.
Salicylic Acid . . . . 50 g.
Borax . . . . 300 g.
Cane Sugar . . . . 200 g.
Flour . . . . 400 g.

Directions: The same as Insecticide Powder §4.

Insect Repellent

Diethyl Toluamide . . . . 100 ml.
*Carbitol . . . . 250 ml.
*Carbitol Acetate . . . . 250 ml.
Alcohol . . . . 400 ml.

* Trade-mark product of Union Carbide Corp., 30 East 42 St., New York 17, N.Y.

Directions: Add the first three ingredients to the alcohol, with stirring.

Moth Spray §1

Paradichlorobenzene	40 g.
Butyl Acetate	100 ml.
Naphtha	300 ml.
Carbon Tetrachloride	600 ml.

Directions: Dissolve the paradichlorobenzene in the carbon tetrachloride and add the other ingredients. The naphtha is used only to reduce cost of product and may be omitted.

Precautions: Naphtha is an inflammable gasoline fraction; carbon tetrachloride is poisonous to skin and tissues, and its vapor is poisonous on inhalation.

Moth Spray §2

Naphthalene	20 g.
Camphor	10 g.
Ethyl Acetate	100 ml.
Naphtha	300 ml.
Ethylene Dichloride	300 ml.
Carbon Tetrachloride	300 ml.

Directions: Dissolve the naphthalene and camphor in the ethylene dichloride and add the other ingredients. The naphtha is used only to reduce cost of product and may be omitted.

Precautions: Naphtha is an inflammable gasoline fraction; carbon tetrachloride is poisonous to skin and tissues, and its vapor is poisonous on inhalation. Ethylene dichloride is also toxic.

Moth Spray §3

Mothproofing Clothing, Furniture, etc.

Sodium Aluminum Fluosilicate	5 g.
Water	1000 ml.

Directions: Dissolve salt in water. Do not use on materials injured by water. Especially effective on woolen goods.

Termite Treatment

For Wood

Sodium Fluoride	20 g.
Water	1000 ml.

Directions: Dissolve salt in water and apply to uncoated (i.e. without paint or varnish) wooden surfaces.

Precautions: This preparation is poisonous to man and animals.

Rodenticide §1
Warfarin in Solid Mixture

Warfarin Concentrate (½%) . . . . . 50 ml.
Mixed Animal Feed . . . . 950 g.

Directions: Mix the Warfarin concentrate thoroughly with the bait, i.e. animal feed, by spreading the latter on a wooden surface and sprinkling the liquid onto it, stirring the mass with a stick to assure fairly uniform distribution of the poison. In use, remember that several doses are required to kill (a safety feature for livestock) and therefore the material must be left where rodents have constant access to a substantial quantity of it.

Precautions: Toxic to man and animals.

Rodenticide §2
Warfarin in Water

Warfarin Sodium Salt (½% solution) . . . 100 ml.
Water . . . . 900 ml.

Directions: Pour solution in pan and leave where rodents have constant access to it. This application in water is particularly desirable where water supplies are more limited than food, as in flour mills and grain bins.

Precautions: Toxic to man and animals.

Rodenticide §3

Flour . . . . 300 g.
Cheese . . . . 300 g.
Tallow . . . . 200 g.
Powdered Red Squill . . . . 200 g.

Directions: Mix the red squill with the flour. Melt the cheese and tallow together and pour over the mixed powder. When cool, break into pieces for use.

Fire Extinguishing Powder

Ammonium Sulfate . . . . 740 g.
Silex . . . . 180 g.
Sodium Bicarbonate . . . . 70 g.
Ammonium Phosphate . . . . . . 10 g.

Directions: Mix dry powders by sifting. This product evolves incombustible gases when heated and also yields some fused solids in hot fire, both of which retard access of atmospheric oxygen to the material burning.

Fireproofing Solution §1
For Heavy Cloth

Ammonium Chloride	375 g.
Ammonium Phosphate	200 g.
Water	1000 ml.

Directions: Dissolve the salts in the water, dip the cloth until saturated, wring out excess solution, and hang up to dry. The material will not burn, although very hot fires will fuse the salts and char the material. This limitation applies to all such fireproofing agents, as does also the restriction that washing or continued exposure to rain will dissolve them, and require repetition of the treatment.

Fireproofing Solution §2
For Light Cloth

Borax	75 g.
Boric Acid	75 g.
Water	1000 ml.

Directions: The same as for Fireproofing Solution §1.

Fireproofing Solution §3
For Paperboard and Paper

Ammonium Sulfate	100 g.
Boric Acid	40 g.
Borax	30 g.
Water	1000 ml.

Directions: The same as for Fireproofing Solution §1.

Waterproofing Solution §1
For Heavy Cloth (Canvas)

Beeswax	100 g.
White Lead, Ground in Oil	120 g.
Rosin	90 g.
Raw Linseed Oil	1000 ml.

Directions: Heat the beeswax and rosin until they melt, remove from heat and allow to cool briefly, add the linseed oil with stirring, then the white lead. Apply while hot to the upper surface of the canvas, which has previously been moistened with water on its underside.

Waterproofing Solution §2

For Light Cloth (Wearing Apparel)

Paraffin	2 g.
Gum Dammar	10 g.
Para Rubber	10 g.
Benzene	100 ml.
Carbon Tetrachloride	900 ml.

Directions: Dissolve the rubber in the benzene, then add the carbon tetrachloride, then dissolve the paraffin and the gum in the mixture. The solution formed will waterproof fabrics on dipping, wringing and allowing to dry. It is extremely combustible and poisonous to breathe, so wear rubber gloves and work out-of-doors.

Precautions: Carbon tetrachloride is poisonous to skin and tissues, and its vapor is poisonous on inhalation.

Waterproofing Solution §3

For Paper

Paraffin Wax	220 g.
Glycerin	10 g.
Stearic Acid	25 ml.
Water	750 ml.

Directions: Heat the glycerin to about 125°C. Add the stearic acid slowly and with stirring. Remove from heat, melt the paraffin wax on a water bath. Then add the glycerin-stearic acid product to the paraffin. Heat the water nearly to boiling and add the wax mixture to it with stirring, continuing stirring until nearly cold. Coat the paper on the outside with this product.

Chapter 7

PHOTOGRAPHIC FORMULAS

Developers

The most important ingredients in a developing solution consist of one or more developing agents, an antioxidant such as sodium (or potassium) sulfite or bisulfite, an alkali substance such as sodium (or potassium) carbonate or hydroxide, and an antifogging agent, such as a bromide. There is also, of course, the solvent, usually water, in which these ingredients are dissolved. As a developer solution is used, it tends to become less effective, partly by depletion and partly by contamination with products of the development. Therefore, while the addition of replenishers can be used to some extent to maintain developing solutions in continued use, it cannot be continued indefinitely, and a regular practice of periodic discarding of solutions should be followed, or of replenishment with solutions formulated for that purpose by the photographic manufacturers.

This statement applies, of course, to solutions in continued use. For batch development, new developer solution should be used each time. For small-scale batch work, the most practical course is usually to purchase the packaged product of a manufacturer, such as Eastman or Ansco, and simply follow the directions on the label.

Developer §1

*Kodak Developer D-11
(Process tank or tray developer)

*Elon	1 g.
Anhydrous Sodium Sulfite	75 g.
Hydroquinone	9 g.
Sodium Carbonate Monohydrate	30 g.
Potassium Bromide	5 g.
Water to make	1000 ml.

* Trade-mark of Eastman Kodak Co., Rochester, N.Y.

Directions: Warm 500 ml. of water to 125°F (51°C) and dissolve in order the above ingredients. When solution is complete, adjust volume to 1000 ml. by adding water. This solution is formulated for use as is in process photography; but should be diluted with an equal volume of water for development of continuous tone subjects.

Time of Development: 4 minutes (tray) or 5 minutes (tank) at 68°F (20°C).

Developer §2
*Kodak Developer D-61A
(Process tank or tray developer)

*Elon	3 g.
Anhydrous Sodium Sulfate	90 g.
Sodium Bisulfite	2 g.
Hydroquinone	6 g.
Sodium Carbonate Monohydrate	14 g.
Potassium Bromide	2 g.
Water to make	1000 ml.

* Trade-mark of Eastman Kodak Co., Rochester, N.Y.

Directions: Heat 500 ml. of water to 125°F (51°C) and dissolve in order the above ingredients. When solution is complete, adjust volume to 1000 ml. by adding water. For tray use, or continuous agitation tank use, use 1 part solution to 1 part water, but for intermittently-agitated tank use, use 1 part solution to three parts water.

Time of Development: Constant agitation, 6 minutes at 68°F (20°C.) Intermittent agitation 12 minutes at 68°F.

Developer §3
*Ansco §103
(Universal film and paper developer)

Metol	3½ g.
Anhydrous Sodium Sulfite	57 g.
Hydroquinone	11½ g.
Sodium Carbonate Monohydrate	78 g.
Potassium Bromide	1.2 g.
Water to make	1000 ml.

* Trade-mark of Ansco Division, General Aniline & Film Corp., Binghamton, N.Y.

Directions: Dissolve above solids in order in 750 ml. of the water warmed to 125°F (51°C), then add additional water to make 1000 ml. For films and the faster contact and bromide papers, use 1 part of above solution to 2 parts water. For the slower contact and bromide papers, use 1 part solution to 3-4 parts water.

Time of Development: Film and fast paper development, 5 minutes at 68°F (20°C). Slower paper development 1 to 1½ minutes at 70°F (21°C).

Developer §4

*Kodak Developer DK-20
(Fine grain developer for films and plates)

*Elon	5 g.
Anhydrous Sodium Sulfite	100 g.
*Kodalk	2 g.
Potassium Thiocyanate	1 g.
Potassium Bromide	½ g.
Water to make	1000 ml.

* Trade-mark of Eastman Kodak Co., Rochester, N.Y.

Directions: Warm 750 ml. of the water to 125°F (51°C) and dissolve solids in order, then add additional water to make volume 1000 ml.

Time of Development: For various materials, the average is 15 minutes at 68°F (20°C) (Tank). This time should be increased as developer becomes depleted, unless replenishment is effected.

Developer §5

*Ansco §15
(Fine grain tray developer)

Metol	8 g.
Anhydrous Sodium Sulfite	125 g.
Anhydrous Sodium Carbonate	12 g.
Potassium Bromide	1½ g.
Water to make	1000 ml.

* Trade-mark of Ansco Division, General Aniline & Film Corp., Binghamton, N.Y.

Directions: Warm 750 ml. of the water to 125°F (51°C) and dissolve solids in order. Add additional water to make volume 1000 ml.

Time of Development: 4-5 minutes at 68°F (20°C). For greater contrast, allow longer time of development.

Developer §6

*Kodak Developer DK-23
(Roll Developer)

*Elon	7.5 g.
Anhydrous Sodium Sulfite	100 g.
Water to make	1000 ml.

* Trade-mark of Eastman Kodak Co., Rochester, N.Y.

Directions: Warm 750 ml. water to 125°F (51°C) an⌐ dissolve solids in order. Add additional water to make volume 1000 ml.

Time of Development: In tray, about 10 minutes, in tank, about 12 minutes at 68°F (20°C). Discard or replenish developer after 2000 sq. in. of film have been developed with above quantity.

Developer §7

*Kodak Developer D-76
(Pictorial views and panchromatic film)

*Elon	2 g.
Anhydrous Sodium Sulfite	100 g.
Hydroquinone	5 g.
Granular Borax	2 g.
Water to make	1000 ml.

* Trade-mark of Eastman Kodak Co., Rochester, N.Y.

Directions: Warm 750 ml. of water to 125°F (51°C) and dissolve solids in order. Add additional water to make volume 1000 ml.

Time of Development: In tray, about 12 minutes at 68°F (20°C). In tank, for roll films, about 16 minutes at same temperature.

Developer §8

*Kodak Developer D-72
(For fast and panchromatic film, for fast
plates, and for papers)

*Elon	3 g.
Anhydrous Sodium Sulfite	45 g.
Hydroquinone	12 g.
Sodium Carbonate Monohydrate	80 g.
Potassium Bromide	2 g.
Water to make	1000 ml.

* Trade-mark of Eastman Kodak Co., Rochester, N.Y.

Directions: Warm 750 ml. of the water to 125°F (51°C) and dissolve solids in order. Add additional water to make volume 1000 ml. While most commonly used by dilution of one part developer with one part water, for less contrast, proportions of 1:2 may be taken, and for greater contrast, the developer may be used without dilution. For developing papers, the dilution and time of development should be adapted to the needs of the particular paper. Thus bromide papers should be developed about 1½ minutes at 68°-70°F (20-21°C) at a 1:4 dilution (four parts water to one part developer) while for chloride papers, a shorter time (45 seconds) with a stronger solution (1:12) at the same temperature, is preferable.

Time of Development (For Films): At 1:1 dilution, in tray 2½ to 4 minutes, in tank 3 to 5 minutes, both at 68°F (20°C).

Developer §9

*Ansco Developer 17
(Fine grain developer, soft-working type, various types of films, including motion picture film)

Metol	1½ g.
Anhydrous Sodium Sulfite	80 g.
Hydroquinone	3 g.
Granular Borax	3 g.
Potassium Bromide	½ g.
Water to make	1000 ml.

* Trade-mark of Ansco Division, General Aniline & Film Corp., Binghamton, New York.

Directions: Warm 750 ml. of the water to 125°F (51°C) and dissolve solids in order. Add additional water to make volume 1000 ml.

Time of Development: For fine grain films 12-15 minutes; for direct copy and portrait films 12-20 minutes.

Developer §10

*Kodak Developer D-25
(Roll films, for minimum graininess)

*Elon	7½ g.
Anhydrous Sodium Sulfite	100 g.
Sodium Bisulfite	15 g.
Water to make	1000 ml.

* Trade-mark of Eastman Kodak Co., Rochester, N.Y.

Directions: Warm 750 ml. of the water to 125°F (51°C) and dissolve solids in order. Add additional water to make volume 1000 ml.

Time of Development: In tank, average time 20 minutes at 68°F (20°C) and 11 minutes at 77°F (25°C).

Developer §11

*Kodak Developer D-52
(For portrait paper)

*Elon	1½ g.
Anhydrous Sodium Sulfite	22½ g.
Hydroquinone	6 g.
Sodium Carbonate, Monohydrate	17 g.
Potassium Bromide	1½ g.
Water to make	1000 ml.

* Trade-mark of Eastman Kodak Co., Rochester, N.Y.

Directions: Warm 750 ml. of the water to 125°F (51°C) and dissolve solids in order. Add additional water to make volume 1000 ml. This developer should be diluted 1:1 with water for use on most professional contact papers, however, for enlarging and bromide papers, it should be used without dilution. In either case it should be strengthened before use by addition of 1½ g. potassium bromide dissolved in a few ml. of water.

Time of Development: 1½ minutes at 68°F (20°C).

Developer §12

*Ansco 110 Developer
(Brown-black tones on projection
and contact papers)

Hydroquinone	22½ g.
Anhydrous Sodium Sulfite	57 g.
Sodium Carbonate Monohydrate	75 g.
Potassium Bromide	2-¾ g.
Water to make	1000 ml.

* Trade-mark of Ansco Division, General Aniline & Film Corp., Binghamton, New York.

Directions: Warm 750 ml. of the water to 125°F (51°C) and dissolve solids in order. Add additional water to make volume 1000 ml. To use, dilute one part developer with 5 parts water.

Time of Development: Prints must receive relatively long exposure (3-4 times as much as normal) and then be developed in diluted developer for at least 5 minutes at 68°F (20°C).

Developer §13

*Kodak Developer DK-93
(For films, plates and papers)

*Kodelon	5 g.
Anhydrous Sodium Sulfite	30 g.
Hydroquinone	2½ g.
*Kodalk	20 g.
Potassium Bromide	½ g.
Water to make	1000 ml.

*Trade-mark of Eastman Kodak Co., Rochester, N.Y.

Directions: Warm 750 ml. of the water to 125°F (51°C) and dissolve solids in order. Add additional water to make volume 1000 ml.

Time of Development: For films and plates, about 6 minutes at 68°F (20°C) giving greater or less time as more or less contrast is desired. For papers, if warm tones are desired, develop for 2 minutes; for colder tones, add 20 g. more Kodalk and develop 1-2 minutes; all development at 68°F (20°C).

Developer §14

*Kodak Developer D-74
(Olive-brown tone on professional
contact papers)

*Elon	1½ g.
Anhydrous Sodium Sulfite	48 g.
Hydroquinone	9 g.
*Athenon	13 g.
Anhydrous Sodium Carbonate	24 g.
Potassium Bromide	4½ g.
Water to make	1000 ml.

*Trade-mark of Eastman Kodak Co., Rochester, N.Y.

Directions: Warm 750 ml. of the water to 125°F (51°C) and dissolve the solids in order. Add additional water to make volume 1000 ml. To use, dilute developer with equal parts of water.

Time of Development: 1½ minutes at 68°F (20°C). Rinse immediately (See Stop Bath §1) before fixing.

Stop Baths

The term "stop bath" is applied to acid baths which are used after development and before fixing in order to arrest quickly the development reaction. In addition to this primary purpose, these baths also assist in preventing developer stain, and in preserving the strength of the acid hardening and fixing bath.

In using stop baths containing chrome alum, be sure to keep the film in motion while it is in the bath. Otherwise the alkali in the developer, which is still on the film, will precipitate chromic hydroxide on the film surface.

Note that hardening stop baths (such as Stop Bath §3) are used when working at temperatures of 75°F (24°C) and above to harden the gelatin more quickly than is possible with the usual hardening and fixing baths.

Stop Bath §1
*Kodak Stop Bath SB 1

Glacial Acetic Acid	13 ml.
Water to make	1000 ml.

*Trade-mark of Eastman Kodak Co., Rochester, N.Y.

Directions: Add the acid to the water, taking care to avoid contact with the skin. Instead of the glacial acetic acid, 48 ml. of 28% acetic acid may be used. For developing, immerse film or print for 5-10 seconds, keeping it in motion while in the bath. Since the developer is alkaline, this stop bath becomes exhausted quite quickly (about 1500 sq. in. of print). Therefore, for highly alkaline developers, a stop bath containing 2-3 times as much acetic acid is preferable.

Stop Bath §2
(For Films and Plates)

Potassium Chrome Alum	30 g.
Water to make	1000 ml.

Directions: Dissolve the alum in the water. The film may remain in this bath up to 3 minutes, provided it is agitated for at least the first 30 seconds. The bath should be replaced frequently.

Stop Bath §3
*Kodak Hardening Bath SB 4

Potassium Chrome Alum	30 g.
Anhydrous Sodium Sulfate	60 g.
Water to make	1000 ml.

*Trade-mark of Eastman Kodak Co., Rochester, N.Y.

Directions: Dissolve the two salts in the water. The negatives should remain in the bath at least 3 minutes, with agitation for the first 30 seconds. The bath should be replaced frequently.

Stop Bath §4
*Kodak Stop Bath SB 5

Anhydrous Sodium Sulfate	45 g.
Glacial Acetic Acid	9 ml.
Water to make	1000 ml.

*Trade-mark of Eastman Kodak Co., Rochester, N.Y.

Directions: Add the acid to the water, taking care to avoid contact with the skin. Instead of the glacial acetic acid, 32 ml. of 28% acetic acid may be used. Then dissolve the sodium sulfate in the acid solution. To use, immerse film or plate after developments, for 30 seconds, with agitation. This bath should be replaced frequently.

Hardener §1
*Kodak Hardener SH-1

Formaldehyde Solution (37%)	10 ml.
Sodium Carbonate Monohydrate	6 g.
Water	1000 ml.

*Trade-mark of Eastman Kodak Co., Rochester, N.Y.

Directions: Dissolve the sodium carbonate in the water and add the formaldehyde. This formula is used primarily for the hardening of negatives which would be softened in the process of intensification or reduction, or of cleaning. Immerse in this bath for about 3 minutes rinse, fix and then wash before undertaking the operations mentioned above.

Hardener §2
*Kodax Hardener F-5a

Anhydrous Sodium Sulfite	75 g.
Glacial Acetic Acid	83 ml.
Crystalline Boric Acid	37½ g.
Potassium Alum	75 g.
Water	1000 ml.

*Trade-mark of Eastman Kodak Co., Rochester, N.Y.

Directions: Warm 600 ml. of water to 125°F (51°C) and dissolve ingredients in above order. Be careful to avoid contact of skin with glacial acetic acid. If it is not available, use 235 ml. of 28% acetic acid instead. This hardener is frequently used as a fixing bath by adding 1 part of above to 4 parts of a solution in water containing 300 g. sodium thiosulfate per liter.

Fixing Baths

The operation of fixing is the conversion of the silver halide (and, to some extent, the other halide ions present) into water-soluble compounds which can be removed by washing. The most widely used fixing agent is the thiosulfate radical, which is generally used in the form of its sodium salt ("hypo"). However, ammonium or potassium thiosulfate have been used, and various other fixing agents are known. Fixing baths are usually formulated with other substances than the fixing agent, because unless a stop bath is used, the developing solution remaining in the emulsion layer will be oxidized to form products which stain the gelatin. Therefore, fixing baths are usually formulated to contain stopping and hardening agents.

Fixing Bath §1

*Kodak Fixing Bath §5
(For films, plates and papers)

Sodium Thiosulfate	240 g.
Anhydrous Sodium Sulfite	15 g.
Glacial Acetic Acid	13 ml.
Boric Acid	7½ g.
Potassium Alum	15 g.
Water to make	1000 ml.

* Trade-mark of Eastman Kodak Co., Rochester, N.Y.

Directions: Add the ingredients to 700 ml. of the water (warmed to 125°F-51°C) in above order, stirring until dissolved after each addition; then additional water to make 1000 ml. Be careful to avoid contact of skin with glacial acid; or use 48 ml. of 28% acetic acid instead. This is a hardening fixing bath, which should take 5 to 10 minutes for fixing.

Fixing Bath §2

*Kodak Rapid Fixing Bath F-7
(For films, plates and papers)

Sodium Thiosulfate	360 g.
Ammonium Chloride	50 g.
Anhydrous Sodium Sulfite	15 g.
Glacial Acetic Acid	13 ml.
Boric Acid	7½ g.
Potassium Alum	15 g.

* Trade-mark of Eastman Kodak Co., Rochester, N.Y.

Directions: The same as Fixing Bath §1, except that this bath is more rapid, and over-fixing should be avoided.

Fixing Bath §3

*Kodak Fixing Bath F-24
(For films, plates and papers—non-hardening)

Sodium Thiosulfate	240 g.
Anhydrous Sodium Sulfite	10 g.
Sodium Bisulfite	25 g.
Water	1000 ml.

* Trade-mark of Eastman Kodak Co., Rochester, N.Y.

Directions: Dissolve the salts in 600 ml. of the water at 125°F (51°C). Then add water to bring volume of solution to 1000 ml. Use at 68°F (20°C).

Fixing Bath §4

*Kodak Fixing Bath F-16
(For films and plates)

A

Sodium Thiosulfate	320 g.
Anhydrous Sodium Sulfite	20 g.
Water	1000 ml.

B

Potassium Chrome Alum	60 g.
Concentrated Sulfuric Acid	8 ml.
Water	1000 ml.

* Trade-mark of Eastman Kodak Co., Rochester, N.Y.

Directions: Prepare the two solutions separately, by adding the ingredients to 600 ml. of the water warmed to 125°F (51°C) in order and stirring until each is dissolved. Then bring volume to 1000 ml. with water. Be careful to avoid contact of sulfuric acid with skin. To prepare fixing bath, use 1 part B to 3 parts A. Fixing time 5-10 minutes. This is a hardening fixing bath.

Fixing Bath §5

*Ansco Fixing Bath 201

A

Sodium Thiosulfate	240 g.
Water	500 ml.

B

Glacial Acetic Acid	12 ml.
Potassium Alum	15 g.
Anhydrous Sodium Sulfite	15 g.
Water	150 ml.

* Trade-mark of Ansco Division, General Aniline and Film Corp., Binghamton, N.Y.

Directions: Prepare A and B separately by warming water to 125°F (51°C) and adding ingredients in order, stirring until each is dissolved. Be careful to avoid contact of skin with glacial acetic acid. If it is not available, use 45 ml. 28% acetic acid instead. When the solutions have cooled to room temperature, add B to A with rapid stirring. Fixing time 5-10 minutes at 68°F (20°C). This is a hardening fixing bath.

Fixing Bath §6

*Kodak Fixing Bath F-1
(For papers)

A

Sodium Thiosulfate	240 g.
Water	1000 ml.

B

Glacial Acetic Acid	13 ml.
Potassium Alum	15 g.
Anhydrous Sodium Sulfite	15 g.
Water	80 ml.

* Trade-mark of Eastman Kodak Co., Rochester, N.Y.

Directions: For A, warm 600 ml. of water to 125°F (51°C), dissolve the sodium thiosulfate in it, and add additional water to bring volume to 1000 ml. For B, warm water to 125°F (51°C) add 13 ml. glacial acetic acid (or 48 ml. 28% acetic acid), then add the alum, stirring until dissolved; then the sodium sulfite, also stirring until dissolved. Be careful to avoid contact of glacial acetic acid with skin. When both solutions have cooled to room temperature, add B to A with stirring. Fixing time 5-10 minutes.

Hypo Eliminator

*Kodak Hypo Eliminator HE-1

Hydrogen Peroxide 3%	125 ml.
Dilute Ammonia	100 ml.
Water to make	1000 ml.

* Trade-mark of Eastman Kodak Co., Rochester, N.Y.

Directions: Add the hydrogen peroxide to 600 ml. of the water. Then prepare the dilute ammonia (10 ml. concentrated ammonium hydroxide and 90 ml. water) and add it with slow stirring. Then add more water to bring volume to 1000 ml. This hypo eliminator is intended for use after fixed prints have been washed in running water for about 30 minutes. Leave them in eliminator for 6 minutes, then wash again for 10 minutes.

Intensification and Reduction Baths

Intensification and reduction are processes for modification of the contrast values in a negative to produce corresponding variations in the finished print. While the considerable range of choice now available in contrast of contact printing papers has somewhat decreased the need for intensification and reduction of negatives, enlarging or projection papers do not provide so many grades of contrast. Moreover, intensification is often useful in preparing film slides. Therefore, intensification and reduction baths are still used on negatives, and intensification is also applied to positives that are to be projected.

Intensifier §1

*Kodak Intensifier In-4

Potassium Dichromate	90 g.
Concentrated Hydrochloric Acid	64 ml.
Water to make	1000 ml.

* Trade-mark of Eastman Kodak Company, Rochester, N.Y.

Directions: Dissolve the salt in the water, and add the acid with stirring. Avoid contact of acid with skin, and do not breathe its fumes. To use this intensifier, add 1 quart (by volume) of it to 9 quarts of water. Immerse negative in it at 68°F (20°C) until thoroughly bleached, then redevelop fully in a suitable developer (such as 1 part of Developer §8 to 3 parts water, used at 68°F for five minutes).

Intensifier §2

*Kodak Intensifier In-5
(For Positive and Negative Film)

Silver Nitrate	10 g.
Anhydrous Sodium Sulfite	12½ g.
Sodium Thiosulfate	17½ g.
*Elon	4 g.
Water to make	1000 ml.

* Trade-mark of Eastman Kodak Co., Rochester, N.Y.

Directions: Prepare four solutions: (A) 10 g. of silver nitrate in 150 ml of water; (B) 10 g. of the sodium sulfite in 150 ml. of water; (C) the 17½ g. of sodium thiosulfate in 150 ml. of water, and (D) the remaining 2½ g. of sodium sulfite and the *Elon in 550 ml. of water. Add (B) to (A), then add (C), and finally, add (D). Stir throughout and work quickly.

This intensifier is stable only for about ½ hour. Its effect depends upon duration of immersion, which should not be greater than 25 minutes. Follow it with 2 minutes treatment in a 30% sodium thiosulfate solution, and wash.

Intensifier §3

*Kodak Intensifier In-6
(Strong action with high-speed negatives)

A

Concentrated Sulfuric Acid	30 ml.
Potassium Dichromate	22½ g.
Water to make	1000 ml.

B

Sodium Bisulfite	3.8 g.
Hydroquinone	15 g.
*Photo-Flo Solution	3.8 ml.
Water to make	1000 ml.

C

Sodium Thiosulfate	22½ g.
Water	1000 ml.

* Trade-mark of Eastman Kodak Co., Rochester, N.Y.

Directions: Prepare the three solutions by dissolving ingredients in order in 750 ml. water, then making up to 1000 ml. (Avoid contact of skin with sulfuric acid. Add it slowly with stirring.) Stir while adding all ingredients. To use, add to 1 part A, 2 parts B followed by 2 parts C, and finally add 1 part A, all with stirring. The prepared solution is stable for 2-3 hours; it should be used only once. First wash negatives, treat them with Hardening Bath §1, then wash again. After this preparation, immerse them in this Intensifier for 10 minutes, or less as desired, at 68°F (20°C) followed by washing and drying.

Reducer §1

*Kodak Reducer R-2
(For over-exposed negatives)

A

Potassium Permanganate	52½ g.
Water to make	1000 ml.

B

Concentrated Sulfuric Acid	32 ml.
Water to make	1000 ml.

* Trade-mark of Eastman Kodak Co., Rochester, N.Y.

Directions: Prepare A by dissolving permanganate in water, and B by adding sulfuric acid to water slowly and with stirring. (Avoid skin contact or spattering of acid.) To use add 1 part A and 2 parts B to 64 parts water. Reduce negative as desired. This bath may develop yellow stain, which requires hypo treatment (Fixing Bath §2) before washing.

Reducer §2

*Kodak Reducer §1
(Over-developed high-contrast negatives)

Ammonium Persulfate	60 g.
Concentrated Sulfuric Acid	3 ml.
Water	1000 ml.

* Trade-mark of Eastman Kodak Co., Rochester, N.Y.

Directions: Dissolve persulfate in water, and add sulfuric acid with stirring (avoid contact with skin, or spattering). In use, dilute 1 part of solution with 2 parts (by volume) of water. Reduce negative as desired, and treat with hypo (Fixing Bath §2) before washing.

Reducer §3

*Kodak Reducer R-4a
(Farmer's Reducer, for overexposed negatives)

A

Potassium Ferricyanide	75 g.
Water to make	1000 ml.

B

Sodium Thiosulfate	240 g.
Water to make	1000 ml.

* Trade-mark of Eastman Kodak Co., Rochester, N.Y.

Directions: Prepare A and B separately by dissolving the salt in most of the water, and then adding water to make volume 1000 ml. To use, add 30 ml. of A to 120 ml. of B, then add water to make 1000 ml. Pour at once over the negative, and as soon as desired degree of reduction is obtained, remove and wash thoroughly. Solution A is active reducing agent, and must be diluted as directed to slow its action.

Reducer §4

*Kodak Reducer R-4b
(Farmer's Reducer—general
purpose—proportional)

A

Potassium Ferricyanide	7½ g.
Water to make	1000 ml.

B

Sodium Thiosulfate	200 g.
Water to make	1000 ml.

* Trade-mark of Eastman Kodak Co., Rochester, N.Y.

Directions: Prepare A and B separately by dissolving the salt in most of the water, and then adding water to make volume 1000 ml. To use, treat negatives with A at about 68°F (20°C) until desired reduction is obtained (1-4 minutes). Then place in B for five minutes, and wash. This two-solution treatment reduces overdeveloped negatives, as well as being useful in other cases where reduction is desired.

Reducer §5

*Kodak Reducer R-8
(For over-exposed and over-developed negatives)

Ferric Chloride	25 g.
Potassium Citrate	75 g.
Anhydrous Sodium Sulfite	30 g.
Citric Acid	20 g.
Sodium Thiosulfate	200 g.
Water to make	1000 ml.

* Trade-mark of Eastman Kodak Co., Rochester, N.Y.

Directions: Dissolve the ingredients in above order in 750 ml. of the water which has been warmed to 125°F (51°C). Add additional water to make volume 1000 ml. Treat negatives with reducer at about 68°F (20°C) until desired reduction is obtained (1-10 minutes). Dilute solution if it is too active.

Reducer §6

*Kodak Reducer R-8a

Citric Acid	22½ g.
Iron Alum (Ferric Ammonium Sulfate) . .	45 g.
Potassium Citrate	75 g.
Anhydrous Sodium Sulfite	30 g.
Sodium Thiosulfate	200 g.
Water to make	1000 ml.

*Trade-mark of Eastman Kodak Co., Rochester, N.Y.

Directions: The same as Reducer §5.

Toning

The process of toning depends upon the fact that the photographic image is composed of metallic silver, which is capable of undergoing various chemical and physical processes that modify its color. The silver may merely be converted into a silver compound; it may be replaced by another metal; or it may be dyed, usually by first converting it into a compound that unites with (acts as a mordant for) the dye. It is apparent, therefore, that toning processes are capable of almost limitless variation, yielding a very wide range of colors and effects. However, they are not equally applicable under all conditions.

The most important limitation upon the selection and effectiveness of toning processes is the degree of dispersion of the silver particles of the photographic image. The smaller they are, the greater is the range of effects possible, especially with the sulfide and metallic toners. Therefore, prints or transparencies to be toned should be developed for fineness of grain, as far as is possible with the particular emulsion. Since the character of the emulsion is so important, the information available from the manufacturer about the applicability of a particular toner to a particular paper is especially pertinent. As a general rule, glossy papers do not produce such enhanced toning effects as do the matte or semi-matte papers, but this observation should be supplemented by specific information about toning characteristics of a particular paper, and where the toner is purchased ready-to-use, upon the papers for which it is recommended by the manufacturer.

A necessary preliminary step to the use of most toning processes is thorough fixing and complete elimination of the fixing agent. For this purpose, you should use one of the fixing baths given earlier in this chapter which are stated to have hardening properties. Then the last traces of this fixing bath should be removed by thorough washing, preferably supplemented by the use of one of the hypo eliminators, whose formulas are also given in this chapter.

Toner §1

*Kodak Iron Toner T-12
(Single Solution—Blue Tones on All Types of Papers)

Ferric Ammonium Citrate	4 g.
Oxalic Acid	4 g.
Potassium Ferricyanide	4 g.
Water to make	1000 ml.

* Trade-mark of Eastman Kodak Co., Rochester, N.Y.

Directions: Dissolve each ingredient separately in 100 ml. of water, mix, and add water to bring volume to 1000 ml. The print may remain in this toner until the desired color results (10-15 minutes), and should then be thoroughly washed. Its color is affected by certain occasional atmospheric gases (chiefly hydrogen sulfide), which may be prevented by a coating of lacquer.

Toner §2

*Kodak Polysulfide Toner T-8
(Single Solution—Sepia Tones)

Potassium Sulfide	7½ g.
Sodium Carbonate Monohydrate	2½ g.
Water	1000 ml.

* Trade-mark of Eastman Kodak Co., Rochester, N.Y.

Directions: Dissolve the ingredients in 500 ml. water, and add additional water to make volume 1000 ml. The print should be agitated during its immersion in this bath. The time should be 15-20 minutes at 68°F (20°C) or 3-4 minutes at 100°F (38°C). Then apply the following treatment:

1. Wash for 10 seconds in running water.
2. Immerse in hardening bath (2 parts Hardener §2 to 16 parts water) for 2 minutes.
3. Wash thoroughly.

Toner §3

*Ansco Sepia Toner
(2-Solution Process—Yields Warm Brown Tones)

A

Potassium Ferricyanide	50 g.
Sodium Carbonate Monohydrate	23 g.
Potassium Bromide	10 g.
Water to make	1000 ml.

B

Sodium Sulfide	90 g.
Water	1000 ml.

* Trade-mark Ansco Division, General Aniline & Film Corp., Binghamton, New York.

Directions: Prepare A by dissolving each ingredient in 300 ml. water, mixing, and adjusting volume to 1000 ml. with water. Prepare B by dissolving the sodium sulfide in 700 ml. water, and adjusting volume to 1000 ml. To use, wash print well and agitate in A until print is light brown in color. Then wash print well—10-15 minutes, and immerse in a solution of 1 part B in 3-8 parts water until desired shade is obtained (about 1 minute).

Toner §4

*Kodak Sulfide Sepia Toner T-7a

A

Potassium Ferricyanide	37½ g.
Potassium Bromide	37½ g.
Potassium Oxalate	97½ g.
Glacial Acetic Acid	5½ ml.
Water to make	1000 ml.

B

Sodium Sulfide	90 g.
Water to make	1000 ml.

* Trade-mark of Eastman Kodak Co., Rochester, N.Y.

Directions: Prepare A by dissolving ingredients in 750 ml. water, in above order, and making up to 1000 ml. Avoid skin-contact with glacial acetic acid. If it is not available, use 20 ml. 28% acetic acid instead. Prepare B in same manner. To use dilute A with water in 1:1 ratio; and dilute B with water in 1:8 ratio. Immerse print in first solution until black of shadows has disappeared (about 1 minute). Rinse thoroughly in running water. Immerse in second solution until detail is restored (about ½ minute). Rinse thoroughly, and immerse print in a solution made by diluting Hardener §2 (given earlier in chapter) with water in 1:8 ratio. Wash ½ hour.

Chapter 8

COSMETICS, HAND CLEANERS
AND RELATED PRODUCTS

In this chapter have been grouped the formulas for products prepared for use on the human body. As might be expected, their requirements are more exacting, both in the kind of ingredients which may be used, and the manner of preparation. Thus, where the process involves the interaction of one or more chemically active ingredients, as for example, the emulsification of a fat or other ester by an alkali carbonate, care must be taken to be sure the reaction is complete before the product is packaged or used. The hazard to be faced throughout this chapter is not merely that of producing a poor product, but also that of causing human injury.

Before presenting the various specific types of products, there are certain ingredients which occur so often, and which are so exacting in their requirements, that they deserve special consideration. They are color, perfume and preservatives.

In certain cosmetic products, color is a major factor, if not the major factor in the sales appeal and market success. Instances that immediately suggest themselves are nail enamels and lipsticks, because the merchandising history of those products is marked by well-known instances in which the development of great new businesses has resulted from the introduction of a new and appealing range of colors. Therefore, if you wish to prepare cosmetics of this kind, or of any kind that requires the addition of color, you should work out your colors with a qualified color manufacturer or cosmetic material supply house (see list in Appendix for suggestions). There are good reasons why you should not mix your own colors.

In the first place, the use of colors in products prepared for human consumption or application is strictly regulated by most of the leading governments. In the United States, there are three groups of authorized colors. The FD&C (Food, Drug and Cosmetic) colors are permissible for use in products, such as foods and drugs, prepared for internal consumption. They are also permissible for use in cosmetics. Those in Group 2 (the D&C colors) are restricted to use in drugs and cosmetics, while the third group, the Ext. D&C colors may not be used in cosmetics that come into contact with mucous membranes (e.g. lips). *None of the colors in any* of these groups may be used in preparations for the orbital cavity (eyes), which are limited to certain earth colors.

For your information, the three groups of colors are listed in the appendix. While the second one (the D&C colors) might seem long enough for many purposes, it is subject to a further limitation: The color you use must be soluble in the product. Since few, if any, colors are equally soluble in water, alcohol, oil, lacquer solvents, and all the other media that may characterize the product, or its disperse medium, this question of solubility is a further limitation on your choice. Therefore, color manufacturers have worked out combinations of permissible colors to meet the solubility and permanence requirements of the various products. Since the color is so small a part of the volume, and the cost, of most cosmetics, you will usually find it profitable to concentrate your attention on other phases of production or marketing.

The same statement applies, with almost equal force, to the perfuming of cosmetics. While here you are not confronted by legal regulations, you certainly face questions of cost. These are evident from the perfume formulas given at the end of this chapter, which show the relatively large number of ingredients that enter into the composition of a perfume, many of them in quantities so small that perfume production to be profitable is necessarily a primary activity, and it is not practical to make your own perfume merely to obtain the relatively small quantities needed to impart odor to cosmetic products.

In view of the foregoing considerations, the formulas for the cosmetics in this chapter will not give specific dyes or perfumes, but will read merely "color and perfume." They will also carry the words, where necessary, "Preservative 10 ml," or whatever quantity of preservative may be needed. The preservative indicated is made by dissolving 1 g. of methyl *para*-hydroxybenzoate in 10 ml. of ethyl alcohol. This is a general purpose preservative, suitable for use in the wide variety of media encountered in cosmetic work. Wherever possible, the preservative should be formulated for the particular product by a preservative manufacturer, just as has already been recommended for colors and perfumes.

Hand Cleaner §1

Detergent, Without Trade Name Products

Pumice (powdered)	380 g.
Soap Powder	270 g.
Borax	70 g.
Sodium Carbonate, Anhydrous (soda ash) . .	35 g.
Glycerin	30 ml.
Water	700 ml.

Directions: Dissolve the glycerin, borax and soda ash in 175 ml. of the water; dissolve the soap in the remainder of the water. Stir the solutions together, then add the pumice with stirring as the mixture thickens.

Hand Cleaner §2

Detergent, Without Trade Name Products

Liquid Soap	200 ml.
Ammonium Oleate	200 ml.
Glycerin	100 ml.
Alcohol	75 ml.
Turpentine	25 ml.
Fine Sand	900 g.
Powdered Pumice	180 g.

Directions: Mix the soap and ammonium oleate, stir in the glycerin, alcohol and turpentine; and continue stirring until mixture is uniform. Then stir in the sand and pumice.

Hand Cleaner §3

*Carbowax	200 g.
**Ultrawet	806 ml.
***Carboxymethocel A	60 g.
Lanolin	50 g.
Glycerin	50 ml.
Dioxane	200 ml.
Sodium Pyrophosphate	40 g.
Water	320 ml.

* Trade-mark product of Union Carbide Corp., 30 East 42 St., New York 17, N.Y.
** Trade-mark product of Atlantic Refining Co., 260 S. Broad St., Philadelphia 1, Pa.
*** Trade-mark product of Dow Chemical Co., Midland, Mich.

Directions: Dissolve the sodium pyrophosphate in the water, then add the ingredients in order, with high-speed stirring.

Hand Cleaner §4

Heavy Duty Cleaner

*Renex 25 Detergent	320 g.
Lanolin	50 g.
Mineral Oil 65/75	30 g.
Bentonite	100 g.
Cornmeal	500 g.

* Trade-mark product of Atlas Powder Co., Wilmington 99, Del.

Directions: Mix lanolin and mineral oil with gentle heating. Mix separately the other three ingredients and add the first mix to them.

Hand Cleaner §5

"Waterless" Type

*Renex 20 Detergent	62.5 g.
*Arlacel 83	12.5 g.
**Sodium CMC	25 g.
Water	900 g.
Preservative (See Introduction to this chapter)	10 ml.

* Trade-mark product of Atlas Powder Co., Wilmington 99, Del.
** Trade-mark product of Hercules Powder Co., 900 Market St., Wilmington, Del.

Directions: Dissolve Sodium CMC in water with heating. Add the other ingredients.

Hand Cleaner §6

"Waterless" Type

Deodorized Kerosene	300-450 g.
Lanolin	30 g.
*Arlacel 40	25 g.
*Tween 40	75 g.
Water	420-570 ml.
Preservative (See Introduction to this chapter)	10 ml.

* Trade-mark product of Atlas Powder Co., Wilmington 99, Delaware.

Directions: Mix first four ingredients and heat to 140°F (60°C). Add preservative to water, heat to 144°F (62°C), and add to first mixture with stirring, continuing stirring until cool.

Hand Cleaner §7

Liquid Hand Soap

*Coconut Oil Soap	200 g.
Glycerin	50 ml.
Water	980 ml.
**Atlas G-1441 Lanolin Derivative	20 g.
Preservative (See Introduction to this chapter)	10 ml.
Perfume and color (See Introduction to this chapter)	

* If coconut oil soap is unobtainable, it and the glycerin may be prepared by heating about 140 g. of coconut oil to 176°F (80°C) and adding enough strong potassium carbonate solution to saponify it. However, this product must be checked by titration with acid to make sure there is no excess of potassium carbonate. Therefore, it is preferable to purchase the soap.

** Product of Atlas Powder Co., Wilmington 99, Del.

Directions: Dissolve the soap in the water, add glycerin, and heat solution to 152°F (67°C). Heat Atlas G-1441 to 149°F (65°C) and stir soap solution into it. Cool; then add preservative, color and perfume with continued stirring.

Hand Cleaner §8

Liquid Soap

Antiseptic for Sensitive Skin

Castor Oil Soap	65 g.
Chlorxylenol	15 g.
Terpineol	15 g.
*Terpinoline	15 g.
Alcohol	10 ml.
Water	880 ml.

* Trade-mark product of Hercules Powder Co., 900 Market St., Wilmington, Delware.

Directions: Dissolve the terpineol, Terpinoline, and chlorxylenol in the alcohol. Dissolve the soap in the water. Continue stirring, and add the alcoholic solution to the water solution.

Hand Lotion §1

Emulsion with Lanolin

*Tegin	50 g.
Oleic Acid	30 g.
Mineral Oil	15 ml.
Lanolin	10 g.
Triethanolamine	12 g.
**Duponol C	10 g.
Preservative (See Introduction to this chapter)	10 ml.
Water	980 ml.
Color and perfume (See Introduction to this chapter)	

* Trade-mark product of Goldschmidt Chemical Corp., 153 Waverly Pl., New York 14, N.Y.
** Trade-mark product of E. I. du Pont de Nemours Co., Wilmington 98, Del.

Directions: Dissolve Duponol and preservative in water and heat to 194°F (90°C). Heat mixture of first four ingredients to same temperature and add them slowly to 400 ml. water, with stirring. Add triethanolamine to remainder of water, heat to 194°F (90°C), and stir into other mixture. Then stir in color and perfume.

Hand Lotion §2

Emulsion with Lanolin

Stearic Acid	70 g.
Lanolin	5 g.
*Arlacel 80	5 g.
*Tween 60	25 g.
*Sorbo	50 g.
Preservative (See Introduction to this chapter)	10 ml.
Water	845 ml.
Perfume	

* Trade-mark product of Atlas Powder Co., Wilmington 99, Del.

Directions: Add Sorbo and preservative to water and heat to 203°F (95°C). Heat mixture of first four ingredients to 194°F (90°C) and pour them into water solution, with vigorous stirring. Continue stirring to 86°F (30°C) adding perfume at 122°F (50°C).

Hand Lotion §3

Emulsion with Almond Oil and Lanolin

*Tegin	50 g.
Oleic Acid	35 g.
Lanolin	25 g.
Almond Oil	35 ml.
**Duponol C	10 g.
Triethanolamine	12 g.
Preservative (See Introduction to this chapter)	10 ml.
Water	960 ml.
Color and perfume (almond odor)	

* Trade-mark product of Goldschmidt Chemical Corp.,
153 Waverly Pl., New York 14, N.Y.
** Trade-mark product of E. I. du Pont de Nemours Co.,
Wilmington 98, Del.

Directions: The same as Hand Lotion §1.

Hand Cream §1

With Lanolin

*Polyethylene Glycol 400 Monostearate . . .	40 g.
*Polyethylene Glycol Stearate	50 g.
Lanolin (anhydrous)	10 g.
Terpineol	2 ml.
*Polyethylene Glycol	20 g.
Preservative (See Introduction to this chapter)	10 ml.
Water	910 ml.
Perfume and Color	

* Trade-mark product of Union Carbide Corp., 30 East 42
St., New York 17, N.Y.

Directions: Heat first three ingredients together until melted, add the terpineol, and continue heating to 140°F (60°C). Heat water to same temperature and add it rapidly, with vigorous stirring. Then add the Polyethylene glycol with slow stirring. When mixture has cooled to 104°F (40°C), add preservative and perfume. Continue stirring until product has cooled to room temperature.

Hand Cream §2

With Silicone Product

Stearic Acid	200 g.
*Arlacel 60	15 g.
*Tween 60	35 g.
**Silicone Fluid-Velvasil 1000	100 g.
*Sorbo	200 g.
Preservative (See Introduction to this chapter)	10 ml.
Water	450 ml.
Perfume	

* Trade-mark product of Atlas Powder Co., Wilmington 99, Delaware.
** Trade-mark product of General Electric Co., Schenectady, N.Y.

Directions: Mix the first four ingredients and heat to 158°F (70°C). Mix the Sorbo, water, and preservative and heat to 162°F (72°C), and add it to the previous mixture with stirring. Continue stirring during cooling to 113°F (45°C), adding perfume.

Hand Cream §3

Oil-in-Water Type

Stearic Acid	100 g.
*Arlacel 60	52 g.
*Arlacel 80	10 g.
*Tween 60	28 g.
Preservative (See Introduction to this chapter)	10 ml.
Water	810 ml.
Perfume	

* Trade-mark product of Atlas Powder Co., Wilmington 99, Del.

Directions: Mix first four ingredients and heat to 176°F (80°C). Then add them to water-preservative mixture, which has been heated to 185°F (85°C), with rapid stirring. Stir until product has cooled to 122°F (50°C), adding perfume.

Shampoo §1

Soap Type Liquid (Without trade name product)

Coconut Oil	200 g.
Olive Oil	50 g.
Potassium Hydroxide	55 g.
Alcohol	100 g.
Water	600 ml.
Perfume (See Introduction to this Chapter)	

Directions: Dissolve the potassium hydroxide in 150 ml. of the water thoroughly. Heat the mixed oils to 158°F. (70°C) and add the potassium hydroxide solution slowly, with constant stirring. Hold at this temperature for 1 hour, after addition is completed, with continued stirring, then heat the remainder of the water to the same temperature, and add with stirring. When cool, add the alcohol and perfume.

Precautions: Potassium hydroxide destroys skin and tissues. Be careful in handling it, and be sure emulsification is complete.

Shampoo §2
Soapless Type Liquid

Sulfonated Castor Oil (100% basis) . . .	125 g.
Sulfonated Olive Oil (100% basis)	125 g.
Sulfonated Coconut Oil (100% basis) . . .	125 g.
*Polyethylene Glycol	10 ml.
**Amino-methyl-propanediol	10 ml.
Water	600 ml.
Perfume	

 * Trade-mark product of Union Carbide Corp., 30 East 42 St., New York 17, N.Y.
 ** Trade-mark product of Commercial Solvents Co., 260 Madison Ave., New York 16, N.Y.

Directions: Mix first three ingredients, heat to 104°F (40°C) and stir in the amino-methyl-propanediol and the polyethylene glycol; followed by the water. Add perfume when cool.

Shampoo §3
Soapless Type Liquid

*Onyx-ol 336	100 g.
*Maprofix TLS-50	50 g.
Water	850 ml.
Preservative (See Introduction to this chapter)	10 ml.

 * Trade-mark product of Onyx Oil and Chemical Co., Jersey City 2, N.J.

Directions: Mix the two active ingredients, and add the water and preservative with stirring.

Shampoo §4
Non-Foaming Liquid

*Renex 20 . . . . 100 ml.
Water . . . . 900 ml.
Preservative (See Introduction to this chapter) 10 ml.

* Trade-mark product of Atlas Powder Co., Wilmington 99, Del.

Directions: Mix Renex, water, and preservative with stirring.

Shampoo §5
Liquid Cream Lotion

*Duponol WAQ . . . . 400 g.
Magnesium Stearate . . . . 10 g.
**Ninol 979 . . . . 40 g.
***Polyethylene Glycol 400 Distearate . . . 10 g.
Sodium Chloride . . . . 5 g.
Water . . . . 535 ml.
Perfume

* Trade-mark product of E. I. du Pont de Nemours Co., Wilmington 98, Del.
** Trade-mark product of Ninol Laboratories, 1719 Clinton St., Chicago 16, Ill.
*** Trade-mark product of Kessler Chemical Co., State Rd. & Cottman St., Philadelphia, Pa.

Directions: Heat 100 g. of the Duponol to 100°F (38°C). Stir in the magnesium stearate. When uniform, stir in remaining Duponol at 100°F. Add remaining ingredients in order, dissolving the sodium chloride in 30 ml. of the water. Stir until uniform, heat slowly to 180°F (82°C), then cool to 120°F (49°C), adding perfume. Continue stirring throughout entire operation.

Shampoo §6

Liquid Cream Lotion

*Duponol WAQ	300 g.
Magnesium Stearate	10 g.
**Ninol 979	40 g.
**Ninol CB-60	10 g.
***Polyethylene glycol 400 Distearate . . .	10 g.
****Emcol MAS	5 g.
Sodium Chloride	3 g.
Water	622 ml.
Perfume	

* Trade-mark product of E. I. du Pont de Nemours Co., Wilmington 98, Del.
** Trade-mark product of Ninol Laboratories, 1719 Clinton St., Chicago 16, Ill.
*** Trade-mark product of Kessler Chemical Co., State Rd. & Cottman St., Philadelphia, Pa.
**** Trade-mark product of Emulsol Corp., 59 E. Madison St., Chicago 3, Ill.

Directions: Same as shampoo §5.

Shampoo §7

Clear Liquid

*Duponol EP	400 g.
**Ninol 979	60 g.
***Polyethylene Glycol 600 Distearate . . .	10 g.
Sodium Chloride	10 g.
Water	520 ml.
Perfume	

* Trade-mark product of E. I. du Pont de Nemours Co., Wilmington 98, Del.
** Trade-mark product of Ninol Laboratories, 1719 Clinton St., Chicago 16, Ill.
*** Trade-mark product of Kessler Chemical Co., State Rd. & Cottman St., Philadelphia, Pa.

Directions: Dissolve sodium chloride in water, add other ingredients. Heat to 167°F (75°C) and stir until uniform. When nearly cool stir in perfume.

Precaution: Test perfume to avoid clouding.

Hair Rinse Solution §1

Citric Acid	160 g.
Boric Acid	30 g.
Tartaric Acid	100 g.
Water	800 ml.
Alcohol	100 ml.

Perfume and Color (See Introduction to this chapter)

Directions: Dissolve the acids in water and add the alcohol, perfume and color.

Hair Rinse Solution §2

Cream Type

*Ammonyx 4	125 g.
**Tegacid	30 g.
Water	845 ml.

Perfume and Color

* Trade-mark product of Onyx Oil & Chemical Co., Jersey City 2, N.J.
** Trade-mark product of Goldschmidt Chemical Co., 153 Waverly Pl., New York 14, N.Y.

Directions: Dissolve the Tegacid in water, heating to 194°F (90°C) with stirring, and cool. When the temperature has dropped to 113°-122°F (45°-50°C), add Ammonyx 4 and stir until the mixture cools to room temperature. Add perfume and color, if desired.

Hair Rinse Solution §3

Henna Rinse

Infusion of Henna Leaves	550 ml.
Alcohol	440 ml.
Preservative	10 ml.

Perfume

Directions: To prepare infusion add 200 g. henna leaves to 550 ml. boiling water and boil for 5 minutes. Set solution aside for about 3 hours and filter. Then add alcohol, preservative and perfume.

Color Rinse Solutions

The color rinses are acid solutions in water of various acid, water-soluble, permissible dyes. (See list of D&C colors in Appendix.) They are combined to produce the shades desired and dissolved in water which has been strongly acidified (30-40%) with tartaric acid. Some are perfumed, thus lemon rinse is a weak solution of a D&C yellow dye, which is perfumed with oil of lemon. An important feature of modern color rinses is the use of a leveling agent, to produce uniformity of coloring. Unfortunately, the newer leveling agents are patented, and are not available for use except by license.

Sometimes these rinses are used after treatment of the hair with hair bleach, which assures more even coloring by discharging the coloring matter previously in the hair. An example of the formulation of these color rinses is given in the following formula.

Hair Color Rinse Concentrate

Color—Ext. D&C Black #1	1 g.
Methyl Cellulose	8 g.
Sodium Tartrate	10 g.
Tartaric Acid	32 g.
Isopropyl Alcohol	400 ml.
Water	600 ml.

Directions: Dissolve the methyl cellulose in the isopropyl alcohol, then add 550 ml. of the water. Dissolve the sodium tartrate and tartaric acid in the remainder of the water, and add to the other solution. Finally add the color, and stir until uniform. Mark this product "To use, add 1 ounce of this liquid to 1 quart of water." For other colors than black use other D&C colors or Ext. D&C colors (Appendix E) or combinations of them.

Hair Bleach

Concentrated Ammonium Hydroxide	30 ml.
Hydrogen Peroxide (17 volumes)	250 ml.
Water	720 ml.

Directions: Add the ammonium hydroxide to the water, then add the hydrogen peroxide. This is not a stable product.

Precautions: 17 volume peroxide is not the common form, but a much more concentrated solution. It should not be heated, exposed to light (use dark glass bottles), or shaken.

Hair Dressing §1
Clear-Lanolin Type

*Atlas G-1441 Lanolin Derivative	150 g.
Water	840 ml.
Preservative (See Introduction to this chapter)	10 ml.
Perfume and Color (See Introduction to this chapter)	

* Product of Atlas Powder Co., Wilmington 99, Del.

Directions: Heat G-1441 to 158°F (70°C). Heat water and preservative to 162°F (72°C) and add to G-1441.

Hair Dressing §2
Oil-in-Water Type

Mineral Oil	375 g.
Petrolatum	75 g.
Beeswax	20 g.
*Arlacel 83	20 g.
**Atlas G-1425 Lanolin derivative	45 g.
Preservative	10 ml.
Water	465 ml.
Perfume	

* Trade-mark product of Atlas Powder Co., Wilmington 99, Del.
** Product of Atlas Powder Co., Wilmington 99, Del.

Directions: Heat first five ingredients to 158°F (70°C) with stirring. Heat water and preservative to 162°F (72°C), and add to other mixture with stirring. Continue stirring until mixture cools to 113°F (45°C), then add perfume.

Hair Dressing §3
Oil-in-Water Type with Lanolin

Lanolin	200 g.
Mineral Oil	100 g.
Petrolatum	150 g.
Beeswax	120 g.
*Arlacel 60	50 g.
*Tween 60	50 g.
Borax	10 g.
Preservative	10 ml.
Water	320 ml.
Perfume	

* Trade-mark product of Atlas Powder Co., Wilmington 99, Del.

Directions: Heat first six ingredients to 158°F (70°C) with stirring. Heat water, borax, and preservative to 162°F (72°C) and add to other mixture with stirring. Continue stirring until mixture cools to 113°F (45°C) then add perfume.

Hair Dressing §4
Water-in-Oil Type with Lanolin

Mineral Oil	375 g.
Petrolatum	75 g.
Lanolin	30 g.
*Arlacel 83	30 g.
Beeswax	20 g.
Zinc Stearate	10 g.
Borax	5 g.
Preservative (See Introduction to this chapter)	10 ml.
Water	455 ml.
Perfume	

* Trade-mark product of Atlas Powder Co., Wilmington 99, Del.

Directions: Heat first six ingredients to 167°F (75°C). Add borax and preservative to water, and add to other mixture with stirring. Continue stirring until product has cooled to 113°F (45°C), adding perfume.

Hair Lotion §1
Quinine Hair "Tonic"

Tincture Cinchona	40 ml.
Eau de Cologne	120 ml.
*Carbitol	80 ml.
Ethyl Alcohol	640 ml.
Orange Flower Water	120 ml.
Color	

* Trade-mark product of Union Carbide Corp., 30 East 42 St., New York 17, N.Y.

Directions: Mix in above order. Note that perfume is included in formula, since it is a major component.

Hair Lotion §2

Benzoin Hair "Tonic"

Tincture of Benzoin	15 ml.
Eau de Cologne	120 ml.
Ethyl Alcohol	800 ml.
*Carbitol	30 ml.
Glycol	30 ml.

* Trade-mark product of Union Carbide Corp., 30 East 42 St., New York 17, N.Y.

Directions: Same as Hair Lotion §2.

Hair Lotion §3

Cholesterol Hair "Tonic"

Lecithin	2 g.
Cholesterol	8 g.
Glycol	60 ml.
Eau de Cologne	120 ml.
Ethyl Alcohol	800 ml.
Color (See Introduction to this chapter)	

Directions: Dissolve solids in glycol; add Eau de Cologne and alcohol.

Hair Wave-Set §1

Karaya Gum	10 g.
Isopropyl Alcohol	200 ml.
Preservative (See Introduction to this chapter)	10 ml.
Water	800 ml.
Propylene Glycol	25 ml.
Potassium Carbonate	3 g.
Perfume and color (See Introduction to this chapter)	

Directions: Dissolve the gum in the alcohol, add the preservative, add 650 ml. of the water, heat to 140°F (60°C), let stand for several hours, then filter. Dissolve the potassium carbonate in the remaining water and add to solution. Then add remaining ingredients.

Hair Wave-Set §2

Acacia	170 g.
Isopropyl Alcohol	200 ml.
Preservative (See Introduction to this chapter)	10 ml.
Water	750 ml.
Perfume and Color	

Directions: Add water, heated to 140°F (60°C) to acacia. Let stand for several hours. Filter, then add other ingredients in above order.

Hair Wave-Set §3

Gelatin	10 g.
Water	800 ml.
*Duponol C	109 g.
Ethyl Alcohol	90 ml.
Propylene Glycol	20 ml.
Preservative	10 ml.
Perfume and color	

* Trade-mark product of E. I. du Pont de Nemours Co., Wilmington 98, Del.

Directions: Add 500 ml. of the water, heated to 140°F (60°C) to the gelatin and soak until uniform solution is produced. Dissolve the Duponol C in the remaining water and add to gelatin solution. Mix the other ingredients separately and add to above solution.

Hair Wave-Set §4

Hair Lacquer

Polyvinylpyrrolidone	150 g.
*Silicone Fluid 555	50 ml.
Lanolin	10 g.
Dimethyl Phthalate	10 g.
Ethyl Alcohol	1000 ml.
Perfume and Color	

* Trade-mark product of Dow Chemical Corp., Midland, Mich.

Directions: Dissolve the first four ingredients in the alcohol in the order listed above. Then add the perfume and color. The above is a spraying lacquer, which should be finely divided for best results, as by pressure-spraying container (see Chapter I).

Permanent Wave Solution §1

Potassium Hydroxide	10 g.
Sodium Sulfite	20 g.
Monoethanolamine	50 ml.
Sulfonated Castor Oil	15 ml.
Water	900 ml.

Directions: Add the potassium hydroxide to 100 ml. of the water, and stir until *completely* dissolved. Then dissolve the sodium sulfite in another 100 ml. of the water. Mix the sulfonated castor oil and monoethanolamine. Then mix the three solutions and add the remaining water.

Precautions: This is a strong solution. Be sure ingredients are dissolved, and instruct user to wash off carefully after hair is waved, and preferably use a dilute solution of one of the neutralizers given for the following Wave Solution.

Permanent Wave Solution §2

Thioglycollic Acid (75%)	50 g.
Concentrated Ammonium Hydroxide . . .	50 ml.
*Nopco 1408	25 g.
Water	900 ml.

* Trade-mark product of Nopco Chemical Co., Harrison, N.J.

Directions: Mix the thioglycollic acid thoroughly with 200 ml. of the water, then stir in the ammonium hydroxide and the Nopco and add the remaining water.

Precaution: Supply above Permanent Wave Solution always with the following Neutralizing Solution, which must follow its use.

Neutralizing Solution for Permanent Wave Solution §2

Hydrogen Peroxide (17 vol.)	160 ml.
Citric Acid	200 g.
Water	840 ml.

Directions: Dissolve the citric acid in 500 ml. of the water; add the remainder of the water to the peroxide; then mix the solutions.

Precautions: Hydrogen Peroxide (17 vol.) is unstable, should not be stored, and must be protected from heat, light, and agitation. The above product does not keep well, and should be prepared fresh, because the Permanent Waving Solution §2 will damage the hair if not neutralized. Since the principle of such solutions is that they modify hair structure, thus causing it to take new shape, their proper length of time of application before neutralization varies with the individual type of hair.

Neutralizing Powder for Permanent Wave Solution §2

Sodium Perborate	95 g.
Citric Acid	890 g.
*Duponol C	15 g.

* Trade-mark product of E. I. de Pont de Nemours & Co., Wilmington 98, Del.

Directions: Mix solids rapidly, and package quickly.

Precautions: This product is hydroscopic and should be kept in tightly-closing container, or individual small packages. The above batch makes 70-80 individual treatments.

Shaving Cream §1

Lather-forming

Coconut Oil Soap	450 g.
Stearic Acid	50 g.
*Duponol C	25 ml.
Glycerin	180 ml.
Water	600 ml.
Perfume (See Introduction to this chapter)	

* Trade-mark product of E. I. du Pont de Nemours & Co., Wilmington 98, Del.

Directions: Add Duponol to water, and heat to 158°F (70°C). Add soap and glycerin slowly, with stirring. Melt stearic acid separately, and stir into mixture, continuing stirring until thoroughly mixed. Then add perfume.

Note: The customary method of preparation of soap products is to emulsify the oil and stearic acid mixture with sodium or potassium hydroxide solutions. To do this, however, requires chemical control of completeness of process.

Shaving Cream §2

Lather-forming, with Lanolin

Coconut Oil Soap	450 g.
Stearic Acid	50 g.
*Duponol C	25 g.
**Tegin	25 g.
Lanolin	15 g.
Glycerin	170 ml.
Water	600 ml.

* Trade-mark product of E. I. du Pont de Nemours & Co., Wilmington 98, Del.
** Trade-mark product of Goldschmidt Chemical Co., 153 Waverly Pl., New York 14. N.Y.

Directions: The same as Shaving Cream §1, except that the Tegin and lanolin are stirred into the soap before it is mixed with the water.

Shaving Cream §3

Lather-forming, With Menthol

Coconut Oil Soap	450 g.
Stearic Acid	50 g.
*Duponol C	25 g.
Menthol	2.5 g.
Alcohol	10 ml.
Triethanolamine	10 ml.
Glycerin	170 ml.
Water	600 ml.

* Trade-mark product of E. I. du Pont de Nemours & Co., Wilmington 98, Del.

Directions: The same as Shaving Cream §1, except that the menthol is dissolved in the alcohol, and added with the triethanolamine, before the glycerin and perfume.

Shaving Cream §4

Brushless

Stearic Acid	150 g.
Propylene Glycol Monostearate	35 g.
Mineral Oil	30 g.
Glycerin	50 ml.
Triethanolamine	15 ml.
Water	900 ml.

Directions: Heat the first three ingredients to 176°F (80°C). Dissolve the triethanolamine and glycerin in the water, and heat to the same temperature, and add this solution to the first mixture, slowly and with stirring.

Shaving Cream §5

Brushless, with Emulsifier

Stearic Acid	180 g.
Mineral Oil	50 g.
*Tween 60	50 g.
*Sorbo	50 g.
Borax	20 g.
Triethanolamine	10 g.
Preservative (See Introduction to this chapter)	10 ml.
Water	640 ml.
Perfume (See Introduction to this chapter)	

* Trade-mark product of Atlas Powder Co., Wilmington 99, Delaware.

Directions: Heat first three ingredients to 194°F (90°C). Mix water, Sorbo, borax, triethanolamine, and preservative solution, and heat to 203°F (95°C). Add water solution to first mixture, with stirring. Continue stirring until it has cooled to set point and stir occasionally until product has cooled to room temperature, then add perfume.

Precautions: Have exhaust fan or good ventilation for ammonia fumes.

Shaving Soap, Liquid

Coconut Oil Soap	150 g.
*Tegin	10 g.
Stearic Acid	50 g.
**Duponol C	15 g.
Glycerin	80 ml.
Alcohol	50 ml.
Water	850 ml.
Perfume	

* Trade-mark product of Goldschmidt Chemical Corp., 153 Waverly Pl., New York 14, N.Y.
** Trade-mark product of E. I. du Pont de Nemours Co., Wilmington 98, Del.

Directions: Mix water and alcohol. Then dissolve the Duponol and glycerin in this solution. Heat together the first three ingredients to 176°F (80°C) and stir this mixture into the first solution. After cooling, stir in the perfume.

Note: This product should be clear and suitable for spray application.

Shaving Lotion §1

Astringent

Boric Acid	12 g.
Alcohol	400 ml.
Water	600 ml.

Directions: Dissolve the boric acid in the water and add the alcohol.

Shaving Lotion §2

Antiseptic (For Use Before Shaving)

Hexachlorophene	1½ g.
Alcohol	400 ml.
Propylene Glycol	50 ml.
Water	550 ml.
Perfume	

Directions: Dissolve the hexachlorophene in 20 ml. of the alcohol, then add the remainder of the alcohol. Add propylene glycol to the water and stir into the alcoholic solution.

Vanishing Cream §1

Stearic Acid	250 g.
Glycerin	110 ml.
Potassium Carbonate	12 g.
Preservative (See Introduction to this chapter)	10 ml.
Water	650 ml.
Perfume (See Introduction to this chapter)	

Directions: Melt the stearic acid and heat it to 176°F (80°C). Dissolve potassium carbonate and glycerin in water, and heat to same temperature. Add water solution to stearic acid slowly, with vigorous stirring. Then add preservative. Continue heat and stirring until evolution of gas ceases. Cool to 104°F (40°C) and add perfume with stirring.

Vanishing Cream §2

(With Lanolin)

Stearic Acid	190 g.
Glycerin	25 ml.
Lanolin	20 g.
Triethanolamine	10 g.
Water	800 ml.
Preservative (See Introduction to this chapter)	10 ml.
Perfume	

Directions: Melt together the stearic acid and lanolin and heat to 176°F (80°C). Add the triethanolamine and glycerin to the water, heat to 176°F, and pour into the first mixture with constant stirring for 1 hour. When cooling to 140°F (60°C) has occurred, add preservative and when cooling to 104°F (40°C) has occurred, stir in perfume.

Vanishing Cream §3

Stearic Acid . . . . 140 g.
*Lorol   . . . . 30 g.
Trithanolamine . . . . 7 g.
*Duponol C . . . . 5 g.
Glycerin . . . . 50 g.
Water   . . . . 770 ml.
Preservative (See Introduction to this chapter)   10 ml.
Perfume

*Trade-mark product of E. I. du Pont de Nemours Co., Wilmington 98, Del.

Directions: Mix the first three ingredients and heat to 180°F (82°C). Add the Duponol and the glycerin to the water and heat to same temperature and add to previous mixture with stirring. Continue stirring to 140°F (60°C), adding preservative and perfume.

Cold Cream §1

Mineral Oil . . . . 520 ml.
Beeswax . . . . 160 g.
Paraffin Wax   . . . . 60 g.
Borax   . . . . 10 g.
Water   . . . . 330 ml.
Preservative (See Introduction to this chapter)   10 ml.
Perfume   "   "

Directions: Dissolve borax in water, heat, and hold at 167°F (75°C). Melt wax and oil together and heat to 158°F (70°C). Add with vigorous stirring to water solution, continuing stirring until mixture cools to 122°F (50°C) when perfume and preservative is added.

Cold Cream §2

Mineral Oil . . . . 550 ml.
Beeswax . . . . 100 g.
Paraffin Wax   . . . . 50 g.
Spermaceti . . . . 55 g.
Borax   . . . . 8 g.
Water   . . . . 300 ml.
Preservative (See Introduction to this chapter)   10 ml.
Perfume   "   "

Directions: The same as Cold Cream §1.

Cold Cream §3
With Lanolin

Mineral Oil	570 ml.
Beeswax	25 g.
Lanolin	60 g.
Stearic Acid	65 g.
Triethanolamine	10 g.
Glycerin	10 ml.
Borax	10 g.
Water	400 ml.
Preservative (See Introduction to this chapter)	10 ml.
Perfume	

Directions: Mix first four ingredients and heat to 167°F (75°C). Dissolve in water the glycerin, borax, and triethanolamine, with heating to same temperature; then add to first mixture with stirring. After cooling to 122°F (50°C), stir in perfume and preservative.

Cold Cream §4

Mineral Oil	420 g.
Beeswax	65 g.
*Lorol	45 g.
*Duponol C	5 g.
Borax	3¼ g.
Water	460 ml.
Perfume	

    * Trade-mark product of E. I. du Pont de Nemours Co., Wilmington 98, Del.

Directions: Mix the first three ingredients and heat to 180°F (82°C). Add the Duponol and borax to the water, heat to same temperature and add to previous mixture with stirring. Continue stirring to 140°F (60°C) adding perfume.

Cleansing Cream

Stearic Acid	100 g.
Mineral Oil	500 g.
Lanolin	70 g.
Terpineol	1 g.
Triethanolamine	12.5 g.
Propylene Glycol	50 g.
Water	250 ml.
Preservative (See Introduction to this chapter)	10 ml.
Perfume	

Directions: Heat water to 158°F (70°C), adding triethanolamine. Heat first four ingredients and glycol at same temperature until melted, and stir water solution into them. Continue stirring until mixture cools to 122°F (50°C), then stir in preservative and perfume.

Cleansing Lotion §1

Mineral Oil	125 g.
*Polyethylene Glycol 400 Monostearate . .	110 g.
Beeswax	100 g.
Lanolin	50 g.
Propylene Glycol	50 g.
Triethanolamine	10 g.
Water	540 ml.
Preservative (See Introduction to this chapter)	10 ml.
Perfume (See Introduction to this chapter)	

* Trade-mark product of Union Carbide Corp., 30 E. 42 St., New York 17, N.Y.

Directions: Heat first five ingredients together to 167°F (75°C) until uniform. Add triethanolamine to water, heat to same temperature, and add to first mixture with vigorous stirring. When cooling to 104°F (40°C) has occurred, add preservative and perfume.

Cleansing Lotion §2

Mineral Oil	150 g.
*Diglycol Laurate	90 g.
**Ceramol Wax	25 g.
Lanolin	10 g.
Water	715 ml.
Preservative	10 ml.
Perfume	

* Trade-mark product of Glyco Products Co., 26 Court St., Brooklyn, N.Y.
** Trade-mark product of Aceto Chemical Co., 40-40 Lawrence St., Flushing, L.I., N.Y.

Directions: Heat first four ingredients at 167°F (75°C) until uniform, with stirring. Heat water to same temperature, and add it with stirring. When uniform, discontinue heating. After cooling to 104°F (40°C) has occurred, stir in preservative and perfume.

Night Cream

Mineral Oil	280 ml.
Olive Oil	45 ml.
Lanolin	125 g.
Stearic Acid	40 g.
Spermaceti	65 g.
Cetyl Alcohol	125 g.
Triethanolamine	109 g.
Water	400 ml.
Preservative (See Introduction to this chapter)	10 ml.
Perfume	

Directions: Heat water to 158°F (70°C) adding triethanolamine. Heat first six ingredients together to same temperature, and stir water solution into them. Continue stirring until mixture cools to 122°F (50°C), then stir in preservative and perfume.

Foundation Cream

*Tegin	35 g.
Stearic Acid	240 g.
Lanolin	15 g.
Isopropyl Myristate	40 g.
Triethanolamine	10 g.
Water	800 ml.
Aluminum Hydroxide	25 g.
Propylene Glycol	25 ml.

*Trade-mark product of Goldschmidt Chemical Corp., 153 Waverly Pl., New York 14, N.Y.

Directions: Heat the water and triethanolamine to 176°F (80°C). Heat the first four ingredients to the same temperature, and add the water solution to them with stirring. Continue stirring until temperature has fallen to 149°F (65°C); then add a mixture of the glycol and aluminum hydroxide.

Emollient Cream §1

Oil-in-Water Type

Mineral Oil	350 g.
Beeswax	170 g.
Lanolin	100 g.
*Arlacel 60	20 g.
*Tween 60	30 g.
Water	330 ml.
Preservative (See Introduction to this chapter)	10 ml.
Perfume	

*Trade-mark product of Atlas Powder Co., Wilmington 99, Delaware.

Directions: Mix first five ingredients and heat to 158°F (70°C). Add preservative to water and heat to 162°F (72°C). Add water slowly to first mixture with continued stirring. When product has cooled to 122°F (50°C) add perfume. Pack just before setting occurs.

Emollient Cream §2
Water in Oil Type

Petrolatum	350 g.
Mineral Oil	150 g.
Paraffin Wax	50 g.
Ceresin Wax	50 g.
Lanolin	10 g.
*Arlacel 83	20 g.
**Atlas G-1425 Lanolin derivative	20 g.
*Sorbo	25 g.
Magnesium Sulfate	2 g.
Water	300 ml.
Preservative	10 ml.
Perfume	

* Trade-mark product of Atlas Powder Co., Wilmington 99, Del.
** Product of Atlas Powder Co., Wilmington 99, Delaware.

Directions: Heat first seven ingredients to 167°F (75°C). Dissolve Sorbo, magnesium sulfate, and preservative solution in water and heat to 167°F, then adding it slowly to first mixture with stirring. Continue stirring until product has cooled to 131°F (55°C), then add perfume.

All Purpose Cream §1

*Lorol	110 g.
Beeswax	80 g.
Paraffin	70 g.
Mineral Oil	260 g.
*Duponol C	10 g.
Triethanolamine	4 g.
Water	465 ml.
Preservative (See Introduction to this chapter)	10 ml.
Perfume	

* Trade-mark product of E. I. du Pont de Nemours Co., Wilmington 98, Del.

Directions: Heat first four ingredients to 180°F (82°C). Add Duponol, preservative, and triethanolamine to water and heat to same temperature, adding to first mixture slowly with stirring. Continue stirring until mixture has cooled to 140°F (60°C), adding perfume.

All-Purpose Cream §2

Oil-in-Water Type

Stearic Acid	150 g.
Lanolin	40 g.
Beeswax	20 g.
Mineral Oil	230 g.
*Tween 85	10 g.
*Arlacel 85	10 g.
*Sorbo	122 g.
Water	418 ml.
Preservative (See Introduction to this chapter)	10 ml.
Perfume	

* Trade-mark product of Atlas Powder Co., Wilmington 99, Delaware.

Directions: Mix first six ingredients and heat slowly to 158°F (70°C). Add Sorbo and preservative to water and heat to 162°F (72°C). Add water solution slowly to first mixture with continued stirring. When product cools to 113°F (45°C), add perfume, and continue stirring until setting occurs.

All-Purpose Cream §3

Oil-in-Water Type

Stearic Acid	150 g.
Lanolin	20 g.
Beeswax	20 g.
Mineral Oil	240 g.
*Myrj 52	50 g.
*Sorbo	100 g.
Water	420 ml.
Preservative (See Introduction to this chapter)	10 ml.
Perfume	

* Trade-mark product of Atlas Powder Co., Wilmington 99, Delaware.

Directions: Mix first five ingredients and heat slowly to 158°F (70°C). Add Sorbo and preservative to water; heat to 162°F (72°C), and add slowly to first mixture with moderate stirring. Stir until product cools to 72°F (20°C) and add perfume.

Skin Freshening Lotion

Glycerin	80 ml.
Boric Acid	35 g.
Oil of Lemon	3 g.
Citrol	2 g.
Hexachlorophene	1 g.
Alcohol	200 ml.
Water	720 ml.

Directions: Dissolve the glycerin and boric acid in the water, and the other ingredients in the alcohol, and add the alcohol solution to the water solution with stirring.

Bubble Bath §1

*Maprofix TLS-500	150 g.
*Super-Amide L 9	75 g.
Water	775 ml.
Perfume and Color (See Introduction to this chapter)	

* Trade-mark product of Onyx Oil & Chemical Co., Jersey City 2, N.J.

Directions: Dissolve the Maprofix in the water, add the Super-Amide, and warm gently with stirring until a clear solution results. Then stir in perfume and color.

Bubble Bath §2

*Maprofix TLS-50	50 g.
*Onyxol 336	100 g.
Water	850 ml.
Perfume and Color (See Introduction to this chapter)	

* Trade-mark product of Onyx Oil & Chemical Co., Jersey City 2, N.J.

Directions: Mix the two active ingredients and add the water with stirring. Then add perfume and color.

Eye Shadow §1

Zinc Oxide	300 g.
Ceresin	200 g.
Beeswax	300 g.
Petrolatum	500 g.
*Color	50-150 g.

* Colors for eye shadow should be purchased from a cosmetic supply house or color dealer because no coal-tar dyes, and only a few earth colors, may be used.

Directions: Mix all ingredients except the color and heat together with stirring until they form a uniform mixture. Then add the color, stirring until uniformly distributed.

Eye Shadow §2

(With Lanolin)

Lanolin	100 g.
Spermaceti	150 g.
Petrolatum	550 g.
Zinc Oxide	350 g.
*Color	50-150 g.

* See note on Eye Shadow §1.

Directions: Same as Eye Shadow §1.

Cream Mascara

Stearic Acid	75 g.
Beeswax	85 g.
Carnauba Wax	20 g.
Triisopropylamine	33 g.
*Color	100 g.
Water	650 ml.

* Colors for mascara should be purchased from a cosmetic supply house or color dealer because no coal-tar dyes, and only a few earth colors, may be used.

Directions: Mix the first three ingredients. Stir gently, adding the color and heat to 185°F (85°C). Mix the triisopropylamine and the water, heat to 185°F (85°C) and add to first mixture slowly with stirring. Continue stirring and hold at 185°F (85°C) until uniform. Set aside for several days before packaging.

Eyebrow Pencil

Beeswax	320 g.
Paraffin	240 g.
Mineral Oil	220 g.
**Cetal	120 g.
Lanolin	100 g.
*Color	

* Color for eye products is subject to stringent regulations, and should be purchased for the specific purpose from a cosmetic or color supply house.
** Trade-mark product of Robinson, Wagner Co., 110 East 42 St., New York 17, N.Y.

Directions: Mix the color with the Cetal by warming and stirring. Then add the other ingredients and warm until melted. Stir to uniform liquid, cool slightly, and cast.

Lipstick §1

Beeswax	330 g.
Castor Oil	330 g.
*Tegin	120 g.
Lanolin	50 g.
Isopropyl Palmitate	50 g.
Tetrabromofluorescein	20 g.
Antioxidant and Color	100 g.

* Trade-mark product of Goldschmidt Chemical Co., 137 Waverly Place, New York, N.Y.

Directions: Melt together the beeswax, Tegin, lanolin, and isopropyl palmitate; then stir in the castor oil. When cooling to 122°F (50°C) has occurred, stir in color, tetrabromofluorescein and antioxidant. The latter should be formulated for the product along with the color by the color supplier. This material is kept heated until ready for casting.

Lipstick §2

Beeswax	200 g.
Ceresin	200 g.
Lard (cosmetic quality)	250 g.
Lanolin	80 g.
Mineral Oil	15 g.
*Tetrabromofluorescein	20 g.
*Color	80-120 g.

* The color and tetrabromofluorescein should be obtained from a cosmetic or color supply house.

Directions: Mix the first two ingredients and heat until melted. Proceed in the same way, but separately, with the lanolin and the lard, adding to them the tetrabromofluorescein and color, followed by the mineral oil. Finally, add this mixture, when uniform, to the melted beeswax-ceresin mixture.

Toothpaste

*Sorbo	300 g.
Irish Moss	7 to 9 g.
Saccharin	5 g.
Methyl Parahydroxybenzoate	1.2 g.
Propyl Parahydroxybenzoate	0.2 g.
Mineral Oil	10 g.
Water	164.6 to 166.6 ml.
Sodium Lauryl Sulfate	20 g.
Dicalcium Phosphate (Dihydrate)	480 g.
Peppermint Oil or other Flavor Oil	10 g.

* Trade-mark product of Atlas Powder Co., Wilmington, Delaware.

Directions: Sprinkle the Irish moss on the surface of the Sorbo while agitating and continue agitation until gum is well dispersed. Add the saccharin, methyl and propyl parahydroxybenzoates, and mineral oil, continuing agitation until dispersion is complete. Add the water. Heat the mixture to 65°C. Add the sodium lauryl sulfate and agitate for 15 minutes while maintaining the heat. Remove from heat and add the dicalcium phosphate. Cool to room temperature and add the flavor oil. Mill twice. De-aerate under vacuum. (Note that for making tooth paste, a small mill and vacuum pump are almost essential, even for small scale production.) Pack into tubes.

Tooth Powder §1
Foaming

Soap Powder	100 g.
Kaolin	300 g.
Calcium Carbonate	300 g.
Magnesium Carbonate	300 g.
Flavor	

Directions: Mix powders and stir in flavor.

Tooth Powder §2

Calcium Carbonate	475 g.
Tricalcium Phosphate	470 g.
Powdered Acacia	20 g.
*Seakem	20 g.
**Duponol C	10 g.
Citric Acid	5 g.
Flavor	

* Trade-mark product of Seaplant Chemical Co., 63 David St., New Bedford, Mass.
** Trade-mark product of E. I. du Pont de Nemours Co., Wilmington 98, Del.

Directions: Mix dry powders in above order, then stir in flavor.

Tooth Powder §3
Antiseptic

Calcium Carbonate	550 g.
Dicalcium Phosphate	400 g.
*Triton X-120	35 g.
Oil of Peppermint	0.2 ml.
Oil of Cinnamon	0.2 ml.
Saccharin	4 ml.
*Hyamine 10X	3 g.

* Trade-mark product of Rohm and Haas Company, 222 West Washington Square, Philadelphia 5, Pa.

Directions: Grind together the first two ingredients (or mix in fine ground form). To small amount of the mixture, add the oils in a small mortar, and rub until thoroughly mixed. Return this material to mixed powders and add remaining ingredients, continuing stirring until thoroughly mixed.

Denture Powder

*Hyamine 10X	25 g.
*Triton X-100	25 g.
Tetrasodium Pyrophosphate	950 g.

* Trade-mark product of Rohm and Haas Company, 222 West Washington Square, Philadelphia 5, Pa.

Directions: Grind thoroughly together, or obtain in finely divided form and mix thoroughly.

Mouth Wash

Boric Acid	25 g.
Benzoic Acid	8 g.
Resorcinol	8 g.
Methyl Salicylate	5 g.
Menthol	1 g.
Thymol	1 g.
Alcohol	225 ml.
Water	775 ml.
Color	

Directions: Dissolve the first three ingredients in the water and the remainder (except the color) in the alcohol. Mix the two solutions, then add an alcoholic or aqueous solution of the color. The latter should be purchased for the purpose from a food or cosmetic supply house.

Deodorant Cream §1

*Tegin	25 g.
Sodium Lauryl Sulfate	21 g.
Aluminum Sulfate 18H$_2$O	80 g.
Aluminum Sulfocarbolate	50 g.
Titanium Dioxide	20 g.
Water	600 ml.
Perfume (See Introduction to this chapter)	

* Trade-mark product of Goldschmidt Chemical Corp., 153 Waverly Pl., New York 14, N.Y.

Directions: Mix the first two ingredients with the water and heat to 203°F (95°C), then allow to cool. Mix the other ingredients thoroughly together and stir them into the water solution.

Deodorant Cream §2

*Tegin	200 g.
Beeswax	50 g.
Glycerin	40 g.
Zinc Peroxide	50 g.
Titanium Dioxide	50 g.
Water	650 ml.
Perfume	

* Trade-mark product of Goldschmidt Chemical Corp., 153 Waverly Pl., New York 14, N.Y.

Directions: Mix the first three ingredients with the water and heat to 203°F (95°C). Then allow to cool. Mix the other ingredients thoroughly together and stir them into the water solution.

Deodorant Cream §3

Stearic Acid . . . . 190 g.
Isopropyl Myristate-Palmitate . . . . . 40 g.
*Myrj 51 . . . . 20 g.
*Tween 60 . . . . 80 g.
Hexachlorophene . . . . 5 g.
Water . . . . 665 ml.
Preservative . . . . 10 ml.
Perfume

* Trade-mark product of Atlas Powder Co., Wilmington
99, Delaware.

Directions: Mix first five ingredients and heat to 158°F (70°C). Add preservative to water, heat to 162°F (72°C) and add to first mixture with continuous stirring until setting occurs. Perfume and pack.

Anti-Perspirant Lotion

Stearic Acid . . . . 80 g.
Beeswax . . . . 20 g.
*Myrj 52 . . . . 60 g.
**Atlas G-2162 . . . . 35 g.
Preservative (See Introduction to this chapter) 10 ml.
Water . . . . 585 ml.
***Aluminum Chlorhydroxide Complex . . 220 g.
Perfume (See Introduction to this chapter)

* Trade-mark product of Atlas Powder Co., Wilmington
99, Del.
** Product of Atlas Powder Co., Wilmington 99, Del.
*** Obtainable from the Robel's Co., Berkeley Heights, U.S.

Directions: Heat first four ingredients to 176°F (80°C). Add preservative to water and heat to 185°F (85°C). Add slowly, with stirring to first mixture. Continue stirring until mixture has cooled to 95°F (35°C) and add the aluminum chlorhydroxide, continuing stirring until latter is thoroughly dissolved. Add perfume.

Deodorant Stick

Petrolatum . . . . 260 g.
Paraffin . . . . 65 g.
Spermaceti . . . . 200 g.
Beeswax . . . . 135 g.
Aluminum Sulfocarbolate . . . . 100 g.
Zinc Oxide . . . . 120 g.
Zinc Stearate . . . . 120 g.
Perfume (See Introduction to this chapter)

Directions: Melt together the first four ingredients and stir the remaining ingredients into this solution. Hold at heated temperature until ready to cast into sticks.

Anti-Perspirant Stick

Stearic Acid (70% C_{18}-low I.V.)	30 g.
Palmitic Acid (90% C_{16}-low I.V.)	20 g.
Alcohol	345 g.
*Sorbo	50 g.
Sodium Hydroxide	6.5 g.
Water	50 ml.
**Solution in Water of Sodium Aluminum Chlorhydroxy Lactate (40% by weight)	500 g.

* Trade-mark product of Atlas Powder Co., Wilmington 99, Delaware.
** Obtainable from the Robeis Co., Berkeley Heights, N.J.

Directions: Mix the first four ingredients and heat to 140°F (65°C). Dissolve the sodium hydroxide thoroughly in the water, heat to 158°F (70°C), and add to first mixture with stirring. Heat the last ingredient to 140°F (60°C) and add it to other mixture when latter has cooled to 144°F (62°C). Pour at 140°F into heated molds. Remove from mold when cool, wrap in aluminum foil, and pack in airtight containers.

Face Powder §1

Talc	750 g.
Titanium Dioxide	80 g.
Zinc Stearate	85 g.
Calcium Carbonate (precipitated chalk)	75 g.
Color (See Introduction to this Chapter	10 g.
Perfume	

Directions: Purchase the color and perfume from a supplier or dealer for this purpose. Mix them first with a small portion of the powder and then add bulk of the ingredients. Note that all powders should be ground finely and to roughly the same size (through 100 mesh).

Face Powder §2
Compact Form

Talc	500 g.
Kaolin	200 g.
Calcium Stearate	100 g.
Zinc Oxide	100 g.
Magnesium Carbonate	50 g.
Gum Acacia	10 g.
*Sodium Alginate	5 g.
Preservative (See Introduction to this chapter)	10 ml.
Alcohol	4 ml.
Water	100 ml.
Perfume and Color	

* Trade-mark product of Algin Corp. of America, 24 State St., New York 4, N.Y.

Directions: Grind the first five ingredients with the perfume and color. Heat the water to boiling, remove from heat, and add to unused ingredients. Stir this solution until uniform and add it to powder to form a plastic mass for molding into cakes.

Face Powder §3
Liquid Powder

Titanium Dioxide	100 g.
Calcium Carbonate	60 g.
Bentonite	50 g.
Talc	40 g.
Sorbitol	50 ml.
Preservative	10 ml.
Alcohol	200 ml.
Water	640 ml.

Directions: Grind solids (or obtain in *very* fine ground form, that is, through 200 or 340-mesh). Add sorbitol and preservative to water and alcohol and grind in (or stir in) solids.

Rouge
Cake Type

Talc	450 g.
Titanium Dioxide	50 g.
Magnesium Carbonate	300 g.
Calcium Stearate	140 g.
*Sodium Alginate	5 g.
*Calcium Carragheen Sulfate	5 g.
Preservative (See Introduction to this chapter)	2 ml.
Alcohol	4 ml.
Water	100 ml.
Perfume (See Introduction to this chapter)	
Color (See Introduction to this chapter)	

* Trade-mark product of Algin Corp. of America, 24 State St., New York 4, N.Y.

Directions: Grind the first four ingredients with the perfume and color. Heat the water to boiling, remove from heat, and add to unused ingredients. Stir this solution until uniform and add it to powder to form a plastic mass for shaping into cakes.

Cream Rouge

*Tegin	125 g.
Beeswax	50 g.
Mineral Oil	50 g.
**Sorbo	30 g.
Preservative (See Introduction to this chapter)	10 ml.
Water	750 ml.
Color	
Perfume	

* Trade-mark product of Goldschmidt Chemical Corp., 153 Waverly Pl., New York 14, N.Y.
** Trade-mark product of Atlas Powder Co., Wilmington 99, Del.

Directions: Melt the Tegin and beeswax together, add mineral oil and color. Heat water to 176°F (80°C) adding the Sorbo, and pour this solution into the first one, stirring until uniform. Cool and add preservative and perfume.

Body Powder

Talc	680 g.
Calcium Carbonate (precipitated chalk)	220 g.
Zinc Stearate	50 g.
Boric Acid	50 g.
Perfume	

Directions: Mix powders thoroughly, adding perfume.

Baby Powder

Talc	680 g.
Kaolin	100 g.
Boric Acid	100 g.
Calcium Carbonate (precipitated chalk) . .	70 g.
Zinc Stearate	50 g.
Perfume	

Directions: Mix powders thoroughly, adding perfume.

Nail Enamel

*Nitrocellulose (R.S. ¼ Second)	125 g.
**Cellosolve Stearate	60 g.
Tricresyl Phosphate	50 g.
**Cellosolve	400 g.
Ethyl Acetate	175 g.
Butyl Acetate	200 g.
Color (See Introduction to this chapter)	

* One manufacturer of nitrocellulose is the Hercules Powder Co., 900 Market St., Wilmington, Del. Their many varieties include the RS ¼ second (Regular Soluble, of ¼ second viscosity) specified here. For small quantity production, some of the lacquer dealers listed in the Classified Telephone Directory will sell nitrocellulose base solutions.
** Trade-mark product of Union Carbide Corp., 30 E. 42 St., New York 17, N.Y.

Directions: Dissolve the nitrocellulose, tricresyl phosphate and Cellosolve stearate in the Cellosolve and mix the color in the ethyl acetate and butyl acetate, and then add this solution slowly to the nitrocellulose solution, with stirring.

Precautions: Nitrocellulose must never be allowed to become dry or heated. Nail enamel makers often work with its solutions, but even these constitute a fire hazard.

Nail Enamel Remover §1

*Carbitol	800 ml.
Amyl Acetate	100 ml.
Glyceryl Ricinoleate	100 g.

* Trade name product of Union Carbide Corp., 30 East 42 St., New York 17, N.Y.

Directions: Mix in above order and stir until uniform.

Nail Enamel Remover §2

Butyl Acetate	650 ml
Diethyl Phthalate	200 g.
Glyceryl Ricinoleate	150 g.

Directions: Mix in above order and stir until uniform.

Nail White

Tegin	200 g.
**Carbitol	40 g.
Spermaceti	40 g.
Titanium Dioxide	250 g.
Preservative (See Introduction to this chapter)	10 ml.
Water	460 ml.
Perfume (See Introduction to this chapter)	

* Trade-mark product of Goldschmidt Chemical Corp., 153 Waverly Pl., New York 14, N.Y.
** Trade-mark product of Union Carbide Corp., 30 E. 42 St., New York 17, N.Y.

Directions: Melt the spermaceti and stir in the titanium dioxide until uniform. Then add the Tegin and Carbitol. Heat mixture to 185°F (85°C) and stir in water, which has been heated to that temperature. After cooling, stir in preservative and perfume.

Cuticle Softener

Trisodium Phosphate	40 g.
Glycerin	250 g.
Water	750 ml.

Directions: Dissolve trisodium phosphate *completely* in part of the water. Add remaining water and glycerin.

Precautions: Trisodium phosphate will injure skin if not thoroughly dissolved.

Bath Salts

Sodium Bicarbonate (Powdered)	500 g.
Citric Acid (Powdered)	390 g.
Corn Starch (Fine)	110 g.
Perfume and Color (See Introduction to this chapter)	

Directions: Mix the sodium bicarbonate and starch thoroughly. Stir in the citric acid and heat to 203°F (95°C) until softening occurs. Then screen through sieve having openings of the size desired in the product. Spray on alcoholic solution of perfume and color, and package at once.

Sun Protection Formula §1

Sun Tan Oil

Sesame Oil	465 ml.
Mineral Oil (Water-white)	465 ml.
Menthyl Salicylate	68 ml.
Hydroquinone	2 g.
Perfume (See Introduction to this chapter)	

Directions: Mix the oils, dissolve the menthyl salicylate (which is the effective sun-shielding ingredient) in them, and then dissolve the hydroquinone. Add perfume, if desired.

Sun Protection Formula §2

Sun Tan Oil

Mineral Oil (Light)	800 g.
*Modulan	120 g.
**Filtrosol A	80 g.
Perfume	

* Trade-mark product of American Cholesterol Products Inc., Milltown, N.J.
** Trade-mark product of Schimmel & Co., Inc., 601 West 26 St., New York 1, N.Y.

Directions: Mix first three ingredients and warm gently to dissolve Modulan. When cool, stir in perfume.

Sun Protection Formula §3

Sun Tan Cream

Cold Cream	430 g.
Vanishing Cream (See formulas given earlier in chapter)	430 g.
Sesame Oil	150 ml.
Menthyl Anthranilate	50 ml.
Cholesterol	20 ml.
Perfume	

Directions: Mix the last four materials together, and then mix them thoroughly with the creams by adding a little cream to them and stirring until thoroughly distributed, then continue to add the cream while stirring. Add perfume, if desired.

Sun Protection Formula §4

Sun Tan Cream

Glycerin	110 ml.
Sodium Hydroxide	4 g.
Ammonium Hydroxide (26% aqueous solution)	10 ml.
Water	640 ml.
Stearic Acid	200 g.
Cetyl Alcohol	5 g.
Menthyl Anthranilate	40 ml.
Perfume	

Directions: Dissolve the sodium hydroxide in the water, add the ammonium hydroxide and glycerin, and heat to 175°F (80°C). In a separate container, melt the stearic acid, stir into it the cetyl alcohol and menthyl anthranilate, and heat this mixture also to 175°F (80°C). Then add the first mixture to the second with constant stirring until cool. Perfume the partly-cooled mixture before solidification occurs.

Sun Protection Formula §5

Sun Tan Cream

Glyceryl Monostearate S	120 g.
Spermaceti	50 g.
Glycerin	50 g.
Mineral Oil	20 g.
Preservative	10 ml.
Water	680 ml.
*Filtrosol A	80 ml.
Perfume	

*Trade-mark product Schimmel & Co., Inc., 601 West 26 St., New York 1, N.Y.

Directions: Mix all ingredients except Filtrosol and perfume, and heat to 194°F (90°C). Stop heating, and stir until uniform. Heat Filtrosol to same temperature, and add slowly with stirring. When cool, add perfume.

Sun Protection Formula §6

Sun Tan Lotion

Alcohol	750 ml.
Glycerin	80 ml.
Menthyl Salicylate	65 ml.
Water	225 ml.
Perfume	

Directions: Mix the first three ingredients and stir until clear. Then add the water, with continued stirring. Add perfume, if desired.

Sun Protection Formula §7

Sun Tan Lotion

Menthyl Salicylate	40 ml.
*Tegin	20 ml.
Stearic Acid	15 g.
Cetyl Alcohol	5 g.
Triethanolamine	10 ml.
Benzyl Alcohol	6 ml.
Water	900 ml.
Perfume	

* Trade-mark product of Goldschmidt Chemical Corp., 153 Waverly Pl., New York 14, N.Y.

Directions: Mix all the ingredients except the water and heat to 175°F (80°C) with stirring. When the mixture is clear, heat the water to 175°F (80°C) also, and add it, continuing stirring until cold. Perfume before product solidifies.

Sun Protection Formula §8

Sun Tan Lotion

*Carboxymethocel S	100 g.
**Tween 20	5 g.
***Carbowax 1500	50 g.
Bentonite	30 g.
Magnesium Oxide	10 g.
Mineral Black	5 g.
Menthyl Salicylate	20 g.
Titanium Dioxide	130 g.
Petrolatum	20 g.
Isopropyl Alcohol	200 ml.
Water	420 ml.
Perfume	

* Trade-mark product of Dow Chemical Co., Midland, Mich.
** Trade-mark product of Atlas Powder Co., Wilmington 99, Del.
*** Trade-mark product of Union Carbide Corp., 30 East 42 St., New York 17, N.Y.

Directions: Dissolve the carboxymethocel in the water by vigorous stirring and add the other ingredients in the above order. Add perfume if desired.

Sun Protection Formula §9

Sun Tan Lotion

*Amerchol L-101	80 g.
Stearic Acid	25 g.
Petrolatum	25 g.
Triethanolamine	8 g.
Preservative (See Introduction to this chapter)	5 ml.
Water	775 ml.
**Filtrosol A	70 g.
Perfume (See Introduction to this Chapter)	

* Trade-mark product of American Cholesterol Products Inc., Milltown, N.J.
** Trade-mark product of Schimmel & Co., 601 West 26 St., New York 1, N.Y.

Directions: Mix first three ingredients and heat at 194°F (90°C) until melted. Mix water, preservative and triethanolamine, heat to same temperature and add to first mixture with stirring. Continue stirring, and when cooling to 113°F (45°C) has occurred, add Filtrosol A containing perfume. Stir until room temperature is reached.

Sun Protection Formula §10

Sun Tan Lotion for Aerosol Packaging

*Filtrosol A	80 g.
Mineral Oil	60 g.
Stearic Acid	17 g.
Propylene Glycol Monostearate (Self-emulsifying)	34 g.
Triethanolamine	8 g.
Preservative	10 ml.
Water	800 ml.
Perfume	

* Trade-mark product of Schimmel & Co., 601 W. 26 St., New York 1, N.Y.

Directions: Mix first four ingredients and heat to 194°F (90°C). Dissolve triethanolamine in 400 ml. of the water and heat to same temperature. Add it slowly to other mixture with gentle stirring. Add preservative to remainder of the water, heat to 194°F (90°C), and add to other mixture. When cooling to 104°F (40°C) has occurred, add perfume, and stir until cool.

Perfume and Related Products

The number of perfume formulas included in this book has been somewhat restricted, in spite of the fact that perfume production has always been a most interesting field. It has, however, two exacting requirements. The first is the amount of capital necessary. Perfume formulas contain many ingredients, most of which are usually costly, and available only in considerably larger quantities than are sufficient for trial production. The second requirement is the extent of variation necessary in perfume formulations to be used for scenting other products. These variations are dictated in part by the physical form and chemical composition of the product, and partly by its selling price, which obviously influences the cost of a perfume used in it. Clearly, a detailed treatment of perfumes for all products, and in varying price ranges requires an entire book. In fact, excellent books have already been written on the subject, such as *"The Production, Manufacture and Application of Perfumes of All Types"* (Sixth Edition) by William A. Poucher, which should be consulted for further information. Therefore, the treatment of perfumes in this book will be limited to a few representative formulas.

These formulas are essentially modern synthetic perfumes, and have been chosen to yield good products. To this end they contain, in most cases, a considerable proportion of natural floral oils or absolutes. There are, of course, more costly perfumes, prepared primarily from natural raw materials; there are also lower-quality perfumes prepared to meet price specifications. Such formulas may be developed, within limits, from the formulas in this section; if more radical departures are desired, or more specific purposes are to be served, the manufacturer or supplier should be consulted.

The group of formulas which follow are called Perfume Bases. They are concentrated perfumes which are entirely without alcohol or other diluents. For this reason, and also because of their content of natural oils and absolutes, and their other high quality ingredients, they are costly products. Therefore, they are used to best advantage in the preparation of alcoholic perfumes, or of toilet waters, both of which are discussed later in this chapter.

Perfume Base §1

Carnation

Benzyl Salicylate	110 ml.
Isoeugenol	200 ml.
Heliotropin	60 ml.
Neroli	35 ml.
Carnation Absolute	20 ml.
Phenylacetic Aldehyde	10 ml.
Ylang-Ylang Oil	120 ml.
Petitgrain Oil	25 ml.
Eugenol	200 ml.
Amyl Salicylate	30 ml.
Jasmin	60 ml.
Bergamot Oil	10 ml.
Bois de Rose Oil	8 ml.
Phenyl-Propyl Aldehyde	2 ml.
Benzoin R	10 g.
Ketone Musk	10 g.
Hydroxy-Citronellal	20 ml.
Isoamylphenylacetate	30 ml.
Terpineol	30 ml.

Directions: The above ingredients, when mixed in the order given, should yield a clear product. In view of the considerable variation in natural materials there is always a possibility that turbidity may develop. One way to safeguard against this is to pay the premium price for turpeneless natural oils, by specifying the turpeneless quality—for example, in the case of the ylang-ylang oil and petitgrain oil in the above formula. Another working rule is to dissolve such solids as the ketone musk and benzoin R in the above formula in the isoeugenol. If turbidity does develop it may be necessary to filter with a clarifying agent such as talc. Since this is a costly operation with an expensive product like the above, the step should be avoided by care in mixing, through observing the precautions already given.

The number of ingredients in the formula above, and the seven other perfume base formulas, are relatively large, in order to give high-quality products containing many odor notes. The cost can be reduced, at some sacrifice in quality, by using fewer ingredients. In making such eliminations, however, be careful not to eliminate fixators, i.e. ingredients whose chief function is to give the perfume its lasting quality and blending properties. In the formula above, the important fixators are benzoin R and ketone musk, while the fixators used in the seven other formulas include, in addition to these two, such other substances as civet absolute, ambrette absolute, tolu balsam, C9 aldehyde, coumarin, Peru balsam and orris root.

Perfume Base §2

Gardenia

Benzyl Acetate	190 ml.
Hydroxy Citronellal	140 ml.
Phenyl Methyl Carbinyl Acetate	40 ml.
Amyl Cinnamic Aldehyde	45 ml.
Cyclohexanyl Butyrate	70 ml.
Terpineol	40 ml.
Alpha Ionone	100 ml.
Phenyl Acetaldehyde	15 ml.
Bergamot Oil	100 ml.
Linalol	100 ml.
Benzoin R	10 g.
Musk Ketone	15 g.
Ambrette Absolute	10 ml.
Jasmin Absolute	45 ml.
Heliotropin	10 ml.
Civet Absolute	13 ml.
Mimosa Absolute	25 ml.
Tubrose Absolute	10 ml.
Tolu Balsam	20 ml.
C9 Aldehyde	2 ml.

Directions: The same as Perfume Base §1.

Perfume Base §3

Jasmin

Benzyl Acetate	300 ml.
Benzyl Formate	25 ml.
Benzyl Alcohol	100 ml.
Methyl Salicylate	20 ml.
Linalol	150 ml.
Ethyl Cinnamic Aldehyde	55 ml.
Methyl Anthranilate	40 ml.
Terpineol	20 ml.
Ylang-Ylang Oil	30 ml.
Heliotropin	10 ml.
Neroli Oil	10 ml.
Benzyl Alcohol	10 ml.
Jasmin Absolute	50 ml.
Hydroxy Citronellal	150 ml.
Benzoin R	20 g.
C9 Aldehyde	10 ml.

Directions: The same as Perfume Base §1.

Perfume Base §4
Lily-of-the-Valley

Hydroxy Citronellal	280 ml.
Bois de Rose Oil	190 ml.
Bergamot Oil	60 ml.
Terpineol	150 ml.
Linalol	80 ml.
Rhodinol	40 ml.
Heliotropin	45 ml.
Alpha Ionone	40 ml.
Benzyl Acetate	35 ml.
Jasmin Absolute	20 ml.
Ylang-Ylang Absolute	20 ml.
Geraniol	10 ml.
Cyclamen Aldehyde	5 ml.
Petitgrain Oil	5 ml.
Musk Ketone	20 g.

Directions: The same as for Perfume Base §1.

Perfume Base §5
Orchid

Isobutyl Salicylate	320 ml.
Amyl Salicylate	40 ml.
Nerol	80 ml.
Geraniol	80 ml.
Rhodinol	80 ml.
Tuberose Oil	30 ml.
Jasmin Oil	30 ml.
Phenylethyl Alcohol	80 ml.
Phenylacetic Aldehyde	50 ml.
Hydroxy Citronellol	50 ml.
Ylang-Ylang Oil	50 ml.
Benzoin R	50 g.
Coumarin	40 g.
Peru Balsam	10 ml.
C9 Aldehyde	10 ml.

Directions: The same as for Perfume Base §1.

Perfume Base §6
Rose

Rhodinol	180 ml.
Rhodinyl Acetate	100 ml.
Alpha Ionone	100 ml.
Phenylethyl Alcohol	110 ml.
Jasmin Oil	70 ml.
Geraniol	120 ml.
Citronellol	70 ml.
Bois de Rose Oil	30 ml.
Bergamot Oil	40 ml.
Rose Absolute	50 ml.
Ethyl Cinnamate	40 ml.
Geranyl Acetate	30 ml.
Musk Ketone	30 g.
Cinnamic Alcohol	20 ml.
C9 Aldehyde	5 ml.
Benzyl Isoeugenol	5 ml.

Directions: The same as for Perfume Base §1.

Perfume Base §7
Violet

Methyl Ionone	320 ml.
Alpha Ionone	100 ml.
Beta Ionone	100 ml.
Violet Absolute	50 ml.
Rose Absolute	20 ml.
Tuberose Absolute	10 ml.
Oil of Bergamot	60 ml.
Phenylethyl Acetate	20 ml.
Anisic Aldehyde	35 ml.
Ethyl Myristinate	35 ml.
Eugenol	45 ml.
Ylang-Ylang Oil	65 ml.
Heliotropin	40 ml.
Methyl Heptine Carbonate	15 ml.
Orris Concrete	30 ml.
Hydroxy Citronellal	20 ml.
Musk Ketone	15 g.
Santalwood Oil	10 ml.
C9 Aldehyde	10 ml.

Directions: The same as for Perfume Base §1.

Perfume Base §8

Chypre

Bergamot Oil	100 ml.
Sassafras Oil	100 ml.
Rose Absolute	100 ml.
Orange Flower Absolute	70 ml.
Violet Absolute	70 ml.
Cassie Absolute	70 ml.
Sage Clary Absolute	60 ml.
Tuberose Absolute	60 ml.
Orris Concrete	40 ml.
Vanillin	100 g.
Orris Root	20 g.
Patchouli Oil	20 ml.
Ambrette Seed Oil	100 ml.
Coumarin	90 g.

Directions: The same as for Perfume Base §1.

Alcoholic Perfumes

Alcoholic perfumes may be prepared from perfume bases which have already been given by blending them suitably with alcohol. In conducting this operation the best practice is to use, in addition to the perfume base and the alcohol, an additional amount of a fixator which is soluble in alcohol and, for high quality products, some additional perfume oil having the dominant note of the product in question.

To illustrate this operation, excellent alcoholic perfumes may be prepared from any of the foregoing perfume bases by adding 800-900 ml. of alcohol to 160-60 ml. of the perfume base, with the difference of some 40-50 ml. made up largely of an alcoholic extract of civet, musk or other fixators which may be partly replaced by 10 g. of benzoin R. A desirable additional ingredient would be 10-20 ml. of the floral absolute; that is, of carnation absolute in the case of a carnation perfume, of violet absolute in the case of a violet perfume, or a jasmin and an orange blossom absolute in the case or an orchid perfume.

Toilet Waters

Toilet waters are perfumed alcohol-water mixtures, differing from the alcohol perfumes in that they contain a considerable proportion of water. These products have a long history, some of the more famous of them, such as Eau de Cologne, having been manufactured for hundreds of years.

The older processes of manufacture included distillation of the product, which avoided the need for high-purity alcohol. Today, toilet waters have in general become lower cost products which are not distilled. Therefore, they must be made from alcohol of perfumer's quality.

Toilet Water §1

Eau de Cologne

Lemon Oil	7 ml.
Origanum Oil (2 lb. per gal.)	1 ml.
Rosemary Oil	1 ml.
Neroli Oil	5 ml.
Bergamot Oil	11 ml.
Tincture Benzoin	3 ml.
Orange Flower Water	60 ml.
Alcohol (95%)	822 ml.
Water	90 ml.

Directions: Dissolve the oils in the alcohol. Allow to stand for several days. Add the tincture Benzoin, and let stand for 1 week. Add the water and orange flower water over a period of 4 days. (Filter with talc or other clarifying agent.)

Toilet Water §2

Lavender Water

Lavender Oil	23 ml.
Bergamot Oil	5 ml.
Rose Oil	5 ml.
Lemon Oil	2 ml.
Tincture of Musk (4 oz. per gal.)	10 ml.
Alcohol (95%)	805 ml.
Orange Flower Water	60 ml.
Water	90 ml.

Directions: The same as for Toilet Water §1.

Toilet Water §3
Florida Water

Lime Oil	2 ml.
Cinnamon Oil	1 ml.
Clove Oil	2 ml.
Cinnamic Aldehyde	3 ml.
Rose Oil	6 ml.
Neroli Oil	9 ml.
Lavender Oil	10 ml.
Bergamot Oil	28 ml.
Tincture of Musk (4 oz. per gal.)	2 ml.
Orange Flower Water	100 ml.
Alcohol (95%)	787 ml.
Water	50 ml.

Directions: The same as for Toilet Water §1.

Perfume Stick

Stearic Acid	65 g.
Glycerin	65 g.
Sodium Hydroxide	9 g.
Perfume	20 ml.
Water	30 ml.
Alcohol	850 ml.
Color (See Introduction to this chapter)	

Directions: Mix the stearic acid, glycerin and 600 ml. of the alcohol, and heat on water bath at 149°F (65°C) until dissolved. Dissolve the sodium hydroxide in the water, and add to other mixture with stirring. Keep warm for 20 minutes, and determine pH. If it is over 10. (thus giving distinct pink color to phenolphthalein indicator) add more stearic acid to adjust. Dissolve the perfume and color in remainder of the alcohol, and add to solution. Mold while still warm.

Chapter 9

FOOD PRODUCTS

The manufactured food products fall generally into the class of the quantity production formulations, which must be prepared at low unit cost and with a considerable degree of mechanization to meet present-day competition. The importance of this factor of cost is shown clearly by the modern baking industry, whose products differ from cookbook recipes not so much in the nature of their ingredients as in the form in which they are used in order to permit economies in handling. There is, for example, widespread use of powdered egg products, powdered milk, and other natural materials in powdered form, in which form they are easier to handle, to store, to measure and, above all, to standardize. In view of this fundamental similarity of the ingredients, and the large-scale nature of the operations, the staple-product food industries do not fall within the scope of this book, as defined in Chapter 1. Therefore, in general, they are not discussed at length in this chapter.

Exceptions to this policy has been made in a few instances, such as those of the Sausage Formulas and Soup Formulas, which are given early in this chapter. They illustrate clearly the problems of food-product manufacture on an intermediate-quantity scale. Sausage obviously cannot be produced in 1000 g. batches. Therefore, the quantities given in sausage formulas are for the production of 100 pound batches or somewhat more. Moreover, in practical processing many combinations of meat are used, depending upon cost and availability. Therefore, each sausage formula gives several alternative meat combinations.

Moreover, for sausage manufacture, certain mechanical equipment is necessary. This includes the so-called "cutters," which are vessels equipped with high-speed cutting machinery that reduces the meat to the small particle size necessary in most of these types of sausage. This high-speed cutting operation produces heat and ice must be added to prevent the temperature of the meat from being increased by this heat. Besides the cutter, you need for sausage production a grinder, a mixer, a smokehouse, a cooker and a refrigerator. Equipment for mechanical stuffing is usually desirable. Before starting commercial work, you should also familiarize yourself with the necessary skills in using this equipment.

Another characteristic of quantity-production processing of food products is in the additives used. In fact, many of the great advances in food technology have been due to the scientific development of additive products to extend the life and stability of food products, to improve their appearance and flavor, and to confer other desirable properties upon them. At the present time, these additives have been developed by their manufacturers to the point where, if used as directed, they are never even remotely injurious to the consumer, and in many instances are distinctly beneficial, as in the case of the vitamins, and other dietary-supplement additives.

The production of these additives, which also include the anti-staling, anti-drying, and anti-rancidity ingredients for baked goods, as well as the colors and flavors, should be left in the hands of the specialized additive, color, and flavor manufacturers. Therefore, this chapter has been written upon the assumption that you will follow this course. By so doing, you will undoubtedly save money, because the cost of the additives is usually too small a portion of the product cost to permit the intermediate-scale processer to make his own profitably. Moreover, you will gain the benefit of specialized advice in choosing additives for your particular products.

An exception to this policy has been made in the case of the Synthetic Flavors. A few simple formulations of these products have been included to show you their general nature. However, it is obvious that a flavor manufacturer has means, both in the greater number of ingredients and in cross-blending, to produce better synthetic flavors. Moreover, he can advise you upon their compatibility with your product, and upon the extent to which you should consider the use of flavoring that is partly or entirely composed of products of natural origin, which represents an increasing present-day trend.

Coloring, like flavoring, is a specialty product that should be purchased from a supplier specifically for the product. The colors usable in foods are strictly limited by government regulations, which in the U.S. limit them to a small list of dyes (the FD&C colors) and a few simple natural colors like the vegetable colors and caramel (essentially burnt sugar). The label must state that artificial coloring has been added. Moreover, color may never be used to simulate the color of the natural product (e.g. red color must not be used in meat products or yellow in baked goods).

Fruit Flavors

Fruit flavors are now manufactured in many types. For example, syrup manufacturers supply bottlers with 100% natural fruit flavors, with partly synthetic flavors or with entirely synthetic (imitation) flavors. Therefore, if you plan to produce synthetic flavors by using the following formulas, be sure to check into the possible improvement to be obtained by purchasing from a flavor manufacturer some of the natural products and combining them with your material.

Synthetic Flavor §1
Cherry

Benzaldehyde	750 ml.
Ethyl Acetate	180 ml.
Vanillin	100 g.
Color (See Introduction to this chapter)	

Directions: Dissolve the vanillin in the benzaldehyde and add the ethyl acetate.

This flavor is very strong and should be used in limited concentration. As is true of practically all imitation flavors, its use in many products requires the addition of some natural flavor to produce the best results. If this synthetic is used alone in preparing the syrup, the following formula will yield good results.

Synthetic Syrup §1A
Cherry

Sugar	225 g.
Tartaric Acid	140 g.
Synthetic Flavor §1 (Cherry) (see above)	15 ml.
Water	1000 ml.
Color	

Directions: Dissolve the sugar and then the tartaric acid in the water by stirring and warming. Continue heating to 115°C (221°F). Allow to cool. Dissolve the color in the flavor and mix thoroughly with the syrup.

Synthetic Flavor §2
Raspberry

Ethyl Acetate	300 ml.
Ethyl Butyrate	225 ml.
Amyl Acetate	150 ml.
Ethyl Formate	75 ml.
Amyl Butyrate	75 ml.
Benzyl Butyrate	65 ml.
Vanillin	65 g.
Color	

Directions: The same as for Synthetic Flavor §1.

Synthetic Syrup §2A

Raspberry

Sugar	225 g.
Tartaric Acid	140 g.
Synthetic Flavor §2 (Raspberry) (see above)	15 ml.
Water	1000 ml.
Color	

Directions: The same as for Synthetic Syrup §1A.

Synthetic Flavor §3

Grape

Methyl Anthranilate	650 ml.
Ethyl Acetate	100 ml.
Ethyl Butyrate	100 ml.
Methyl Salicylate	45 ml.
Color	

Directions: The same as for Synthetic Flavor §1.

Synthetic Syrup §3A

Grape

Sugar	225 g.
Tartaric Acid	140 g.
Synthetic Flavor §3 (Grape) (See above)	15 ml.
Water	1000 ml.
Color	

Directions: The same as for Synthetic Syrup §1A.

Synthetic Flavor §4

Strawberry

Ethyl Acetate	300 ml.
Amyl Acetate	270 ml.
Ethyl Butyrate	225 ml.
Ethyl Formate	75 ml.
Vanillin	65 g.
Color	

Directions: The same as for Synthetic Flavor §1.

Synthetic Syrup §4A

Strawberry

Sugar	225 g.
Tartaric Acid	140 g.
Synthetic Flavor §4 (Strawberry) (see above)	15 ml.
Water	1000 ml.
Color	

Directions: The same as for Synthetic Syrup §1A.

Sausage Products

For equipment requirements for sausage products, see first two pages of this chapter.

Sausage Formula §1

Skinless Frankfurters-Grade I

Materials (Select one of the four combinations given)

42 lbs. straight cow meat or boneless veal—fine plate
33 lbs. pork trimmings—fine plate
75 lbs.

30 lbs. cow meat ⎫
15 lbs. beef trimmings ⎬ fine plate
15 lbs. pork cheeks ⎭
15 lbs. back fat—³⁄₁₆ plate
75 lbs.

38 lbs. boneless veal ⎫ fine plate
22 lbs. beef trimmings ⎭
15 lbs. skinned jowls—³⁄₁₆ plate
75 lbs.

45 lbs. bull meat or boneless chuck—fine plate
30 lbs. skinned jowls—³⁄₁₆ plate
75 lbs.

Seasoning

4½ oz. Prague powder*
5½ oz. sugar
4½ oz. pepper
1½ oz. coriander
½ teaspoon cardamom
2 lbs. salt
5 lbs. dry milk (or binder flour)
1½ oz. onion powder

Use 15-20 pounds ice—depending on binding quality of meats used

*Trade-mark product of Griffith Laboratories, Inc., 1415 W. 37 St., Chicago, Ill.

Directions: To start the chopping operation for frankfurters place beef in the silent cutter, add spices, and chop to emulsion, adding two-thirds of the ice gradually. When the proper fineness is reached, add the balance of ice and pork. Chop for another 2 to 3 minutes before adding dry milk.

Continue to chop until a temperature of 58°F is reached which will take anywhere from 12 to 18 minutes depending on how cold the raw material was to start with.

Chopping procedures are about the same for cheaper qualities of frankfurters with the exception that all meats are in the silent cutter at the same time—only the fat pork is to be held back and added with the last part of the ice, followed with the binder flour the same way as using dry milk in better grades of frankfurters.

After stuffing, bring frankfurters to smokehouse and start smoking at 115° to 120°F, raising temperature gradually to as high as 170°F. This may take 1½ hours or more. When the proper outside color is reached, cook at 160°F from 8 to 12 minutes according to the size of the product. Hang on trees or trucks, wash off with a very short hot shower, then chill with cold water for about 10 minutes. Before the product goes in the cooler it should be drained well and kept away from heavy drafts as this will cause wrinkling. After frankfurters are properly chilled, pack and ship.

Sausage Formula §2

Bologna—Grade I

Materials (Select one of the four combinations given)

42 lbs. straight cow meat or boneless veal—fine plate
33 lbs. pork trimmings—fine plate
75 lbs.

30 lbs. cow meat ⎫
15 lbs. beef trimmings ⎬ fine plate
15 lbs. pork cheeks ⎭
15 lbs. back fat—3/16 plate
75 lbs.

38 lbs. boneless veal ⎫
22 lbs. beef trimmings ⎬ fine plate
15 lbs. skinned jowls—3/16 plate
75 lbs.

45 lbs. bull meat or boneless chuck—fine plate
30 lbs. skinned jowls 3/16 plate
75 lbs.

Seasoning

4½ oz. Prague powder*
5   oz. sugar
4½ oz. pepper
2   oz. coriander
1   oz. nutmeg
1   teaspoon garlic
5   lbs. dry milk
2   lbs. salt

Use 10-15 lbs. ice—depending on binding quality of the material used.

* Trade-mark product (See Sausage Formula §1).

Directions: Bologna is chopped the same as frankfurters unless it is preferred to show little fat cubes in the finished product as in Leona sausage. In this case, hold back 5 pounds of the fat pork for each 100-pound batch—add to batch before emptying the machine, allowing 3 to 5 turns according to size of cubes wanted. Fat pork for cubing should be firm and cold, otherwise it will mash in the machine and not result in nice cubes. The stuffing and smoking directions are the same as those in Sausage Formula §3.

Sausage Formula §3

Large and Ring Bologna—Grade II

Materials (Select one of the five combinations given)

35 lbs. bull meat or chucks
15 lbs. beef or pork hearts
12 lbs. pork stomachs or beef tripe
13 lbs. skinned jowls
‾‾
75 lbs.

25 lbs. cow meat or boneless veal
20 lbs. beef cheeks
12 lbs. beef tripe
18 lbs. skinned jowls
‾‾
75 lbs.

34 lbs. bull meat or chucks
15 lbs. beef trimmings
15 lbs. tripe or stomachs
 3 lbs. beef or pork spleens
 8 lbs. skinned jowls
‾‾
75 lbs.

20 lbs. cow meat or veal
10 lbs. beef trimmings
15 lbs. cheeks No. 1
 5 lbs. beef hearts
10 lbs. tripe or stomachs
15 lbs. skinned jowls
—————
75 lbs.

43 lbs. bull meat or chucks
17 lbs. tripe or stomachs
15 lbs. skinned jowls
—————
75 lbs.

Seasoning

5   oz. Prague powder*
6   oz. sugar
5   oz. pepper
2   oz. coriander
1   oz. paprika
2½ oz. onion powder
1   teaspoon garlic
5   lbs. dry milk
2¼ lbs. salt
5   lbs. bull meat flour

Use 10-15 lbs. ice—depending on binding quality of raw material used.

If permissible by State laws the amount of milk, cereal, and ice can be increased considerably.

For cheaper grades of bolognas increase garlic to 1 ounce per 10 pounds or even more.

* Trade-mark product (See Sausage Formula §1).

Directions: Pack tight in stuffer and stuff very carefully to avoid air pockets as much as possible. Punch bung bologna with sharp ice pick after stuffing to give air in the casing a chance to escape.

It is preferable to hold large bolognas in a 38° to 42°F temperature overnight to give it time to set. If this is done it should be kept outside in room temperature for a considerable time before bringing into the smokehouse. Shower for 1 minute before putting in smokehouse.

Start smoking at a temperature of 120° to 140°F, raising it within 2 hours to 160°F. Hold for about 3 hours at 160° to 165°F, then step up the temperature to as high as 180°F, until an internal temperature of 148° to 150°F is reached. Then bring it under the shower, wash for 1 minute or so with hot water, following with cold shower for 15 to 25 minutes depending on the size of the product. Remove, hold in room temperature until dry. Transfer to cooler, hold overnight before shipping.

Ring bologna should be stuffed, smoked and cooked the same day. It is smoked the same as frankfurters. It takes from 1 to 2 hours longer to get the color and cure desired.

Cook at 160°F for about 25 to 35 minutes according to size until the internal temperature of 148° to 150°F is reached. Chill in the same manner as frankfurters. After chilling, throw hot water over it. This will bring out a brighter appearance and will also make it dry much faster. Keep in cooler overnight before shipping.

The formula for ring bologna is the same as for large bologna. Ring bologna, however, is stuffed in beef rounds.

Sausage Formula §4
Minced Lunch Meat—Grade I

Materials (Select one of the three combinations given)

```
 50 lbs. cow meat or veal—chop
 20 lbs. pork cheeks   ⎫  ³⁄₁₆ plate
 15 lbs. pork hearts   ⎭
 15 lbs. regular pork trimmings
100 lbs.
```

```
 30 lbs. bull meat—chop
 20 lbs. beef trimmings ⎫ fine plate
 15 lbs. beef hearts    ⎭
 15 lbs. pork cheeks    ⎫ ³⁄₁₆ plate
 20 lbs. skinned jowls  ⎭
100 lbs.
```

```
 30 lbs. bull meat—chop
 20 lbs. beef cheeks—fine plate
 25 lbs. pork or veal hearts ⎫ ³⁄₁₆ plate
 25 lbs. skinned jowls       ⎭
100 lbs.
```

Seasoning

```
6     oz. Prague powder*
7     oz. sugar
2½ lbs. salt
8     oz. ham bologna seasoning
5   lbs. dry milk
```

Use 20-25 pounds ice

* Trade-mark product (See Sausage Formula §1).

Directions: Chop cow meat, bull meat, or veal adding ice gradually until it is emulsified. The spices and cure should be mixed by hand and only about half of it added by the start of the chopping—the balance to go in before the dry milk is added. After this is chopped, place it in the mixer, adding the balance of the meat which has been ground through a three-sixteenth-inch plate and mix for about 3 minutes, chopping finer. Chop pork hearts and beef cheeks approximately 2 minutes.

If pimentos are wanted in the product, chop two 8½-ounce cans of red pimentos with knife by hand on a cutting board—drain off all juices before adding it in mixer. Do not use fresh pimentos or peppers as they will very easily cause the product to go sour in the smokehouse.

Smoke and cook the same way as large bolognas.

Be sure to cook bladders used for minced lunch meat either in lukewarm water overnight or in warm water at least 2 to 3 hours before stuffing, turning the same occasionally as they will not expand uniformly and may burst when stuffing, if this has not been done.

Stuffing and smoking rules for minced lunch meat are the same as for large bologna.

Wire screens are not to be removed from minced lunch meat until product is completely chilled. Any meat on the outside caused by punching with ice pick should be scraped off as soon as it is taken out of the screen.

Sausage Formula §5

Minced Lunch Meat—Grade II

Materials (*Select one of the two combinations given*)

```
 25 lbs. cow meat or veal      ⎫
 25 lbs. beef or pork cheeks   ⎬ chop
 15 lbs. pork or veal hearts   ⎭
 20 lbs. skinned jowls—3/16 plate
 15 lbs. pork stomachs or beef tripe—fine plate
100 lbs.
```

```
 40 lbs. bull meat—chop
 20 lbs. beef hearts—fine plate
 25 lbs. skinned jowls—3/16 plate
 15 lbs. tripe or stomachs—fine plate
100 lbs.
```

Seasoning

Same as for Sausage Formula §4

Directions: Same as Sausage Formula §4.

Sausage Formula §6

Braunschweiger—Formula I

Materials

50 lbs. hog livers, trimmed, washed and chilled
10 lbs. cured veal
40 lbs. regular fresh pork trimmings
―――
100 lbs.

Seasoning

5 oz. Prague powder*
2 lbs. 1 oz. salt
5 oz. dextrose
6½ oz. white pepper
2½ oz. coriander
1½ oz. mace
1 oz. ground celery
¾ oz. ground cinnamon
¾ oz. cardamom
10 oz. onion juice or 1¾ oz. onion powder or 2 lbs. raw
    onions
3½ lbs. dry milk
Do not add any ice to this mixture. Have livers well drained.

* Trade-mark product (See Sausage Formula §1).

Directions: Grind veal through fine plate and chop with livers. Veal should be free from all sinews but not cooked. When this is chopped until it begins to bubble it is nearly done. It should be chopped as long as possible without getting it warm. Cured raw veal is used to help prevent discoloration in finished product. Then add salt, seasoning, and dry milk and eggs, if they are used.

Chop onions, onion powder, or onion juice with liver and veal. Then add hog brains. Be sure fresh pork trimmings are cold. Continue chopping until mass is smooth, but do not allow it to get too warm in chopper.

Stuff in medium or large bungs or artificial casings. Cook at 165°F to an inside temperature of at least 148°F. Cool gradually, but not through, so there will be some heat left in center. Remove from hot water tank and immerse in ice water about 12 minutes. Then hang on a truck.

If cold water is turned into the cooker and water is allowed to run and cool the sausage, gradually take it out of the cooker while still warm and before it is chilled through. Then rinse off with hot water and place immediately in the smokehouse. If handled in this way there will be no ring as so often seen in Braunschweiger.

Many sausage operators have difficulty in producing a Braunschweiger sausage that has a consistently good flavor, good color, and is free from greening and ring. Some have better results from one formula than others. For that reason alternative formulas have been included in this section.

Sausage Formula §7

Braunschweiger—Formula II

Materials (Select one of the three combinations given)

```
 50 lbs.  pork livers
 45 lbs.  skinned jowls
  5 lbs.  beef suet
100 lbs.
```

```
 50 lbs.  pork livers
 15 lbs.  pork cheeks
 35 lbs.  regular pork trimmings
100 lbs.
```

```
 50 lbs.  pork livers
 35 lbs.  back fat
 15 lbs.  boneless veal or lean pork trimmings
100 lbs.
```

Seasoning

```
 2 lbs. salt
10 oz.  pepper
 3 oz.  coriander
 2 oz.  marjoram
 2 oz.  ginger
 4 oz.  onion powder
 5 oz.  Prague powder*
 6 oz.  sugar
```

No dry milk with natural casings. 2-4 pounds with artificial casings.

* Trade-mark product (See Sausage Formula §1).

Directions: Never use old pork livers for Braunschweiger. They must be fresh and chilled good or fresh frozen. Cut out arteries before grinding.

Grind all meats through the three-sixteenth-inch plate mixing all meats together with a few handfuls of ice while grinding so meats will go in the silent cutter as cold as possible. This will not be necessary if frozen livers are used. The silent cutter should be chilled with ice water which is to be drained off before loading with meats. The reason for this is to gain as much as possible on chopping time.

Place all meats in silent cutter, add spices and another couple of handfuls of ice and chop until the material is getting fluffy and starts bubbling—should not be over 50°F when taken out of machine.

Spices should be mixed with the salt and sugar and Prague powder before adding to meats in the cutter.

Stuff in sewed hog bungs—export prime hog bungs or artificial casings. Stuff very carefully, avoiding air pockets. When all of the batch is stuffed, place in truck with fairly hot water for a few minutes before transferring to cooking tank.

The water in the tank should be about 160°F when sausages are placed in it and should be kept at that temperature, never over until an internal temperature of about 148° is reached, which will take from 1 to 2 hours depending on the size of the casings.

When finished it should be chilled rapidly in a truck with ice water, then hung on sticks and placed on tree. Leave hanging until reasonably dry before placing in cooler. If smoking is required, place in smokehouse the following day. Smoke at 90-100°F until the suitable color is reached. This will take anywhere from 4 to 6 hours. Chill again overnight before shipping.

The sausages should be handled very carefully at all times as they will break very easily. It is also advisable to use cartons for shipping.

Sausage Formula §8
Cooked Salami

Materials (Select one of the three combinations given)

40 lbs. bull meat—fine plate
20 lbs. pork cheeks—$\frac{3}{16}$ plate
20 lbs. pork hearts—fine plate
20 lbs. regular pork trimmings—$\frac{3}{16}$ plate
100 lbs.

40 lbs. cow meat—fine plate
20 lbs. boneless veal—$\frac{3}{16}$ plate
20 lbs. beef cheeks—fine plate
20 lbs. skinned jowls—$\frac{3}{16}$ plate
100 lbs.

40 lbs. veal—fine plate
20 lbs. beef cheeks—fine plate
15 lbs. pork hearts—fine plate
25 lbs. trimmed jowls—$\frac{3}{16}$ plate
100 lbs.

Seasoning

3 lbs. salt
6 oz. Prague powder*
7 oz. sugar
8 oz. cracked black pepper
1 oz. cardamom
4 lbs. dry milk
1 teaspoon garlic

   * Trade-mark product (See Sausage Formula §1).

Directions: Mix all seasoning well by hand before putting in mixer. Place all meats except fat pork in mixer, add spices and one gallon of ice cold water gradually. Mix until spices and water are absorbed, then add fat pork and mix for another 2 to 3 minutes.

Stuff light, hang on trees and place in a 38° to 40°F cooler overnight. The next day put sausage in room temperature for an hour or more before putting in smokehouse of 100° to 110°F without smoke, or very little smoke. Raise the temperature 10°F every half-hour going up to as high as 180° if possible and finish that high or not less than 140° internal temperature.

Shower with hot water and then with cold for about 10 minutes. Let hang in room until dry, then transfer to cooler. It is ready to ship the day after. A rather large horn should be used in stuffing to bring out a uniform looking product.

Sausage Formula §9

Pork Sausage "Country Style"

Materials (*Select one of the three combinations given*)

15 lbs. fresh ham fat or good shoulder fat
<u>85</u> lbs. extra lean pork trimmings
100 lbs.

55 lbs. lean skinned bellies
<u>45</u> lbs. lean pork trimmings
100 lbs.

65 lbs. straight ham and shoulder meat
<u>35</u> lbs. skinned jowls
100 lbs.

Seasoning

2   lbs. salt
7   oz. dextrose
6   oz. ground white pepper
2   oz. ginger
1½ oz. rubbed dalmatian sage

OR

2½ lbs. salt
6   oz. dextrose
1   oz. crushed chili pepper
2½ oz. ground black pepper
2–4 oz. rubbed dalmatian sage

Precaution: Straight boned and skinned corn fed hogs, omit or add some jowls, shoulder fat or ham fat to get proper proportion of lean and fat in the finished product. In most cases the straight hog will be about right. Fry some of it frequently to check yield.

Directions

If meats have been boned shortly before manufacturing, trimmings should be returned to cooler for several hours, and then spread out in shallow trucks or other suitable containers. Near freezing temperature is preferable and will speed up the conditioning process. This is one of the most important procedures to get a good firm product with the proper appearance and keeping quality. Do not use frozen pork unless trimmings have been packed in airtight containers. If necessary to use these, mix if possible with at least 50 percent fresh trimmings. Grinder, mixer, trucks, or other containers and stuffer should have been sterilized with steam or extreme hot water and chilled with ice or ice water before using.

Extreme care must be taken to use sharp knives and plates for pork sausage so there will be no possibility for mashing or beating the meat. The best way is to keep certain sets of knives and plates for use on pork sausage only. Improper grinding will reduce the keeping quality of pork sausage considerably and cause it to look much fatter and not show the bright pinkish color desired from the dealer and consumer.

Grind meats through the largest plate available—preferably 3 or 4 hole. Put in mixer and mix for approximately 2 minutes, adding the spices, which have been previously mixed by hand in a pan. Return to grinder and grind as follows: For 1 pound cellophane roll or 1 pound cloth bag, parchment lined and casing, through the fine plate. For hog casing or bulk sausage, grind through three-sixteenth-inch plate. Feed grinder fast enough but make sure that meat will not back up on the worm, especially if meat is not firm. Stuff immediately after grinding and return as fast as possible to cooler. The most suitable temperature to keep pork sausage is about 34°F. When shipping long distances it is well to put the sausage in the freezer for several hours prior to loading out.

Make pork sausage every day as needed. This is the top secret of pork sausage business. Never rework or over-age pork sausage as this is a sure killer. Use returned product in place of pork trimmings in limited quantities on cheaper grades of bolognas and frankfurters. It cannot be used for anything if sour or moldy.

Sheep casing or hog casing should be hung on sticks after linking, given a very short cold shower before returning to cooler for packing. Be sure the product is perfectly dry before packing. A fan is very helpful in drying if the product is to be shipped the day it is made.

Sausage Formula §10

Fresh Liver Sausage

Materials (Select one of four combinations given)

40 lbs.	pork livers
30 lbs.	hog faces, including cheeks, no ears
20 lbs.	pork stomachs or beef tripe
10 lbs.	fresh pork skins
100 lbs.	

40 lbs.	pork livers
40 lbs.	pork snouts and lips
20 lbs.	jowls, skin on
100 lbs.	

40 lbs.	pork livers
20 lbs.	beef tripe
10 lbs.	fresh skins
30 lbs.	jowls—skin on
100 lbs.	

40 lbs.	pork livers
20 lbs.	boneless veal
20 lbs.	pork snouts or lips
20 lbs.	back fat—skin on
100 lbs.	

Seasoning

2½ lbs.	salt
6 oz.	white pepper
1½ oz.	marjoram
1 oz.	nutmeg or mace
7 oz.	onion powder
4 lbs.	dry milk

Directions: Cook all meats except livers until you can easily punch with fingers. Slash livers at about 1-inch spaces. Scald with very hot water in tub until no more of the pinkish color shows. Keep the livers well stirred while in the scalding process. Overcooking will cause them to shrink too much and will also leave an undesirable bitter taste.

Grind through fine plate. Chop, adding all spices and about 1 gallon of the broth in which the meats were cooked. When the desired fineness is reached, add dry milk and chop just long enough to mix well.

All meats must be hot when going in the chopper. Do not chop until all arrangements for immediate stuffing have been made. Stuff in hog bungs, beef rounds or beef middles, whichever is preferred by the trade.

Cook at 165° to 170°F for 45 to 70 minutes depending on size of casings used. Chill in truck with ice water until firm. Hang on trucks, wash with cold water, and transfer to cold cooler at once. Pack and ship the following day. This product is highly perishable and should not be kept too long in stock.

Sausage Formula §11

Smoked Links—Grade II

Materials (Select one of the five combinations given)

25 lbs. bull meat
15 lbs. beef or pork hearts
15 lbs. pork stomachs
15 lbs. beef tripe trimmings
15 lbs. pork snouts—if possible frozen
15 lbs. pork or beef skirts
_____
100 lbs.

30 lbs. cow meat or veal
15 lbs. beef trimmings
20 lbs. beef tripe
20 lbs. beef stomachs
5 lbs. beef or pork melts
10 lbs. skinned jowls
_____
100 lbs.

35 lbs. bull meat
30 lbs. beef tripe
30 lbs. pork snouts—if possible frozen
5 lbs. pork or beef melts
_____
100 lbs.

25 lbs. cow meat or veal
30 lbs. beef cheeks
30 lbs. stomachs
10 lbs. skinned jowls
5 lbs. melts
_____
100 lbs.

```
 20 lbs. bull meat
 15 lbs. beef cheeks
 40 lbs. pork snouts—frozen
 25 lbs. beef tripe
100 lbs.
```

Seasoning

```
2½ lbs. salt
7    oz. sugar
6    oz. Prague powder*
5    oz. pepper
1½ oz. paprika
2    oz. ginger
1    oz. sage
4    lbs. bull meat flour
```

Use ten pounds ice

*Trade-mark product (See Sausage Formula §1).

Directions: Pork snouts should be frozen before grinding and should be ground through the 1-inch plate first. Grind all meat through fine plate, except fat pork, if formula calls for any. This should go through three-sixteenths-inch plate and be added in chopper just for the last few turns. Any pork stomachs or beef tripe called for should go through fine plate and be mixed in with mixer but not chopped.

Chop all beef or veal adding about one-half of spices and 5 pounds of fine chipped ice. Do not run over 50°F. Add ice, meats, and spices. When temperature reaches 45°F add bull meat flour for another few turns.

Load all chopped meats in mixer, add pork stomachs or tripe which have been ground through fine plate. Mix for about 2 minutes. Stuff in medium wide hog casing links 6 or 8 inches long.

Smoke the same day starting at 120° to 130°F, raising 10° every 30 minutes until temperature registers 160° to 165° or until perfect cure shows in the center. Cook approximately 25 to 30 minutes until internal temperature of 146° is reached, shower with cold water for about 10 minutes, then wash with very hot water. This will bring out a brighter appearance and will help the product to dry much faster. Keep hanging in room temperature. When sausages are dry transfer to cooler, pack, and ship the next day.

Veal Loaf

Materials (Select one of the three combinations given)

```
60 lbs. boneless veal—Straight carcass
40 lbs. regular pork trimmings
100 lbs.
```

40 lbs. boneless veal
30 lbs. pork cheeks
30 lbs. skinned jowls
100 lbs.

40 lbs. cow meat
40 lbs. beef trimmings
20 lbs. back fat
100 lbs.

Seasoning

3 lbs. salt
3 oz. sugar
6 oz. pepper
3 oz. ginger
3 oz. onion powder
5 oz. Prague powder*
10 lbs. dry milk

Use 25-30 pounds ice, depending on quality of meats used.

*Trade-mark product (See Sausage Formula §1).

Directions: Chop veal or beef, adding spices, cure with half of the ice for a few minutes, than add balance of ice, pork trimmings, jowls, and dry milk. Chop to 50°F if held overnight before baking; to 55° if baked on same day. Stuff and bake same as pickle and pimento loaf.

This loaf should have a rather pale pink appearance when cut, to identify veal. If this color is not desired use as much as 8 ounces of sugar and 6 ounces of Prague powder.

Corned Beef Loaf

300 pounds boneless chucks or lean straight cow meat.

Directions: Cut up by knife into 2- to 3-pound size pieces. Load in steam jacketed kettle, add enough water to cover meat. Dissolve 30 ounces of Prague powder in 1 gallon of warm water, add to meat in kettle, mixing it well together.

Put 6 ounces of whole bay leaves in strong ham stockinette, knotted at the top, and cook with the meat. Care must be taken not to tear the bag while stirring the meats. Do not use bay leaves for anything else but to cook out the flavor.

Bring the batch to a very slow boil, giving the Prague powder the proper chance to work a good cure. Cook until very tender, adding a little water at times if needed. It is very important to stir the meat every few minutes.

Add 1 gallon grated fresh horse-radish about 5 minutes before removing. When well done grind through 2-inch plate into meat truck.

Mix the following by hand:

6 lbs. powdered gelatin
6 lbs. salt
3 lbs. sugar

Add to meat in truck, mixing the whole with shovel until all gelatin is completely dissolved.

Fill by hand in 6-pound tins, let stand in cooler overnight for shipping meat next day.

If stuffing in viskings is preferred, they should be left on stuffing table until they begin to firm up, turning them occasionally so fat and broth will not separate before hanging on trees.

Chili Con Carne

Materials

50 lbs. beef kidney suet
50 lbs. beef chucks
50 lbs. beef hearts

Seasoning

$\frac{3}{4}$ lb. salt
$\frac{1}{2}$ gal. can tomatoes
2 lbs. ground onions or 3 oz. onion powder or 10 oz.
onion juice
2 oz. fresh ground garlic or $\frac{1}{2}$ oz. garlic powder or 1 oz.
garlic juice
5 lbs. chili pepper
8 oz. Spanish paprika
12 oz. cominos seed
4 oz. oregano
6 oz. black pepper

Directions: Grind kidney suet through one-quarter-inch plate and cook in jacketed kettle until melted. Add salt, onions, tomatoes, and garlic and mix well. Grind beef chucks through one-quarter- or three-eighth-inch plate and add to seasoning and fat. Cook ingredients until tender, or about 1$\frac{1}{2}$ hours.

Not long before cooking is completed add remainder of seasoning. Finish cooking chili mixture and allow it to cool off, stirring occasionally to keep the meat from settling. Let the temperature of mixture drop to about 120° and fill in artificial casings or in molds. If artificial casings are used the ends should be tied off and the cased product dipped in hot water to rinse off grease. After this rinsing the product may be held at room temperature for a short time and then placed in the cooler to set as rapidly as possible. If the chili does not set without separation of the fat, temperature of the product should be higher when it is stuffed. It is then chilled rapidly in cold water.

The following formulas are for sausage items which can be processed without using a silent cutter or mixer.

Beef Bung—Beef Middle or Ring Bologna Sausage

Materials

60 lbs. lean beef, preferably boneless chucks
40 lbs. regular pork trimmings
100 lbs.

Seasoning

3 lbs. salt
8 oz. sugar
7 oz. white pepper
2 oz. nutmeg
⅓ oz. garlic powder (optional)
6 oz. Prague powder*
3½ to 5 lbs. bull meat flour, depending on State laws
10 lbs. ice for all meat product, or
15 to 20 lbs. ice if cereal is used.

* Trade-mark product (See Sausage Formula §1).

Directions: Grind beef through plate of not less than three-fourths of an inch. Mix with salt and Prague powder. Place meat in cooler overnight. Tightly pack down in tub or other suitable container. Chill sausage material overnight or as much as 2 or 3 days if production is to be staggered.

Grind beef again through one-eighth-inch plate. Add pork trimmings in small cut pieces, spices, flour and ice. Mix well by hand. Grind again twice through one-eighth-inch plate. Mix well once more by hand. Pack tightly in stuffer to avoid air pockets and stuff in previously prepared casings.

Frankfurters in Hog Casings or Wieners in Sheep Casings

Materials

50 lbs. lean beef, bull meat or boneless chucks preferred
50 lbs. regular pork trimmings
100 lbs.

Seasoning

2¾ lbs. salt
  8 oz. sugar
  6 oz. white pepper
  2 oz. ginger
  2 oz. onion powder
  6 oz. Prague powder*
3½ to 5 lbs. dry skim milk powder, depending on State
     laws
 10 lbs. ice—increase to 15 lbs. if cereal is used

* Trade-mark product (See Sausage Formula §1).

Directions: Follow same instructions for grinding and mixing as given in Sausage Formula §3.

Instructions previously given for smoking, cooking and chilling apply to these formulas for products manufactured with limited equipment.

Soup Manufacture—Intermediate Quantity Basis

In one respect quantity soup production is suggestive of cooking in the home kitchen. That is the production first of a soup stock by boiling meat, fish or vegetables, or various combinations of them. These stocks are then used, in a second-stage operation, for the production of the concentrated soups, suitable for canning or bottling. However, while this process is essentially a two-stage one, emphasis should be placed upon the rapid spoilage of the soup stock. Therefore, the second step should follow the first as rapidly as possible, because the use of preservatives is subject to severe, and varying, governmental regulations, and the use of refrigeration is costly, if only because of the cost of cooling and reheating.

To illustrate the manufacture of soups for canning, therefore, there are given formulations for the preparation of two types of stock, and from them four types of soup. From this information, the necessary modifications for other products can readily be made.

Soup Formula §1

Bone Stock

Meat Bones	50 lbs.
Lean Beef	50 lbs.
Carrots	12 lbs.
Turnips	12 lbs.
Onions	12 lbs.
Celery	6 lbs.
Salt	6 lbs.
Water	25 gal.

Directions: Remove meat from bones, chop all meat, saw up bones, and add to cold water. Let stand for 3 hours, then heat slowly to boiling point with pressure steam. Add chopped vegetables and salt. Simmer for 5 hours, adding water to keep volume. Filter through cloth, avoiding use of filters in which iron or steel comes into contact with the solution.

Soup Formula §2
Vegetable Stock

Carrots	24 lbs.
Turnips	24 lbs.
Celery	24 lbs.
Onions	24 lbs.
Salt	1 lb.
Pepper	1 lb.
Pimento	4 oz.
Thyme	2 oz.
Marjoram	2 oz.
Celery Seed	2 oz.
Cloves	¼ oz.
Water	25 gal.

Directions: Chop vegetables. Add all ingredients to water, bring to a boil and simmer for 2 hours. Strain.

Soup Formula §3
Oxtail Soup

Bone Stock	25 gal.
Carrots	9 lbs.
Turnips	8 lbs.
Leeks	2 lbs.
Onions (dried)	1 lb.
Salt	1¼ lb.
Sugar	12 oz.
Peppercorns	1½ oz.
Allspice	1 oz.
Celery Seed	½ oz.
Cloves	¼ oz.
Bay leaves	¼ oz.
Sherry Wine	

Directions: Chop the turnips, carrots and leeks. Add them to the bone stock, together with dried onions and spices, bring to a boil and simmer for 2 hours. Turn off heat, and stir in salt and sherry. When cool, fill into containers, adding 1 oz. cooked oxtail.

Soup Formula §4
Mock Turtle Soup

Bone Stock	25 gal.
Beef Extract	9 lbs.
Carrots	9 lbs.
Onions (dried)	1 lb.
Salt	1¼ lb.
Sugar	12 oz.
Peppercorns	1½ oz.
Allspice	¾ oz.
Marjoram	½ oz.
Thyme	1 oz.
Cloves	¼ oz.
Bay leaves	¼ oz.

Directions: Similar to Soup Formula §3, except that when cooking is finished 1 ounce of basil is stirred in and allowed to stand for 15 minutes. Then soup is strained. Add ¼ oz. diced cooked meat per container. This meat is prepared from equal quantities of calves heads, calves hearts and half the quantity of calves liver. The batch is brought to a boil, skimmed and let simmer for 2½ hours. Meat and tongues are removed from the bones, and then all meat is diced for use in containers.

Soup Formula §5
Vegetable Soup

Vegetable Stock	25 gal.
Potatoes	9 lb.
Carrots	5 lbs.
Turnips	5 lbs.
Tomatoes	5 lbs.
Peas	3 lbs.
Rice	3 lbs.
Salt	1 lb.
White Pepper	3 oz.
Water	12 gal.

Directions: Chop vegetables, add carrots and turnips to water, bring to a boil and simmer for 45 minutes. Then add potatoes, and simmer for 15 minutes longer. Then add other ingredients, and bring to a boil.

Soup Powders

Two ingredients, commonly mixed in about equal weights form the basis of these products—dehydrated vegetables and monosodium glutamate, which is available from several manufacturing companies and many jobbers, especially those supplying food product producers. The bulking ingredients, which should amount to 3-4 times the weight of the combined vegetables and monosodium glutamate, are vegetable protein and flour (or starch). The seasonings are salt, sugar (in some soups), and pepper and other spices and ground herbs. For cream-type soups, milk powder is added.

Precise formulations for various kinds of soup powders are not available, partly because this business is characterized by trade secret and patent restrictions, and partly because distinctive formulas require considerable experimentation.

Cake Mixing

While various methods are used in commercial cake mixing, the one that is of most general usefulness is the blending method. In that, the shortening and sugar are blended and then the other ingredients are incorporated into the mixture.

Cake Formula §1

Layer Cake

Shortening	15 pounds
Sugar	40 pounds
Flavor (See Introduction to this chapter)	
Eggs	20 pounds
Flour	30 pounds
Salt	10 ounces
Baking Powder	1½ pounds
Milk	28 pounds

Directions: Cream shortening, sugar, and flavoring. Add eggs gradually, creaming thoroughly. Then add alternately, sifted dry ingredients and milk. Mix until smooth.

Cake Formula §2

Pound Cake Type

Shortening	20 pounds
Sugar	36 pounds
Flavor (See Introduction to this chapter)	
Eggs	22 pounds
Flour	30 pounds
Salt	12 ounces
Baking Powder	5 ounces

Directions: Cream shortening, sugar, and flavoring. Add eggs gradually, creaming thoroughly. Then add alternately, sifted dry ingredients. Mix until smooth.

Cake Formula §3
Sponge Cake

Eggs . . . . 20 pounds
Egg yolks . . . . 15 pounds
Flavor (See Introduction to this chapter)
Sugar . . . . 34 pounds
Flour . . . . 30 pounds
Salt . . . . 14 ounces
Baking Powder . . . . 14 ounces

Directions: Separate eggs. Beat egg yolks and flavoring until very thick. Beat egg whites until stiff but not dry and gradually beat in sugar. Fold in well-beaten egg yolks and gradually fold in the sifted dry ingredients.

Cake Formula §4
Angel Food

Egg Whites . . . . 90 pounds
Salt . . . . 14 ounces
Cream of Tartar . . . . 1 pound 4 ounces
Sugar . . . . 90 pounds
Flavor (See Introduction to this chapter)
Flour . . . . 30 pounds

Directions: Beat egg whites until frothy, then gently add salt and cream of tartar. Continue beating until stiff but not dry. Fold in sugar, then flavoring. Fold in sifted flour slowly.

Cake Formula §5
Chocolate Cake

Shortening . . . . 20 pounds
Sugar . . . . 40 pounds
Eggs . . . . 20 pounds
Flour . . . . 30 pounds
Salt . . . . 15 ounces
Cocoa . . . . 5 pounds
Soda . . . . 10 ounces
Buttermilk . . . . 32 pounds
Vanilla . . . . 5 ounces

Directions: Cream shortening and sugar until light. Add eggs gradually and cream until well mixed. Add sifted dry ingredients alternately with the buttermilk and vanilla. Mix until smooth.

Cake Formula §6
Cheese Cake

Eggs	10 pounds
Pectin	1 pound 4 ounces
Water	4 gallons
Sugar	60 pounds
Cream of tartar	12 ounces
Shortening (preferably butter)	3 pounds
Cottage Cheese	30 pounds
Flour	4 pounds

Directions: Separate eggs. Beat egg whites. Dissolve the pectin in boiling water, then add 48 pounds of the sugar. When dissolved, add the cream of tartar. When cool, add this mixture to the beaten egg whites. Blend shortening, cheese, and flour, then add the egg yolks, sugar, and milk. Fold in pectin-egg white mixture.

Bun Formula §1

(a) Ferment

Flour	1 pound 8 ounces
Yeast	9 ounces
Sugar	6 ounces
Milk Powder	6 ounces
Water	3 quarts

Directions: Dissolve the sugar and milk powder in the water and stir in the yeast, then the flour. Hold at 90°F (32°C) for one hour.

(b) Dough

Flour	12 pounds
Shortening	2 pounds 4 ounces
Sugar	1 pound
Salt	1½ ounces
Fruit (Currants, Raisins, Chopped Citron, etc.)	3 pounds
Flavor (See Introduction to this chapter)	

Mix ingredients in (b) in above order and add them to the ferment (a). Hold at 82°F (28°C) for one and one-half hours. Bake at 460°F (238°C).

Bun Formula §2

Hot Cross Buns

(a) Ferment (Same as (a) Ferment of Bun Formula §1)

(b) Dough

Flour	12 pounds
Shortening	1 pound 8 ounces
Sugar	1 pound 14 ounces
Salt	1½ ounces
Spice	¾ ounces
Fruit (Currants and Chopped Candied Citrus Peel) . . .	3 pounds 8 ounces
Flavor (See Introduction to this chapter)	

Mix ingredients in (b) in above order and add them to the ferment (a) of Bun Formula §1. Hold at 82°F (28°C) for one and one-half hours. Bake at 460°F (238°C).

Cracker Formula §1

Oyster Crackers

Flour	100 pounds
Lard	18 pounds
Salt	2 pounds
Yeast	2½ ounces
Sodium Bicarbonate	1 pound 10 ounces
Water	7 gallons

Directions: Mix 60 pounds of the flour with the yeast and 6 gallons of the water and allow to stand for 18 hours. Break up dough, and mix in all remaining ingredients but the flour, which is sifted into the mass. Mix thoroughly. Let stand 3 hours. Bake for 5-8 minutes at 500°F (260°C).

Cracker Formula §2
Graham Cracker

Graham Flour	50 pounds
White Flour	50 pounds
Powdered Sugar	24 pounds
Butter	5 pounds
Shortening	9 pounds 6 ounces
Sodium Bicarbonate	10 ounces
Ammonium Hydroxide (concentrated)	10 ounces
Water	3 gallons
Salt	12 ounces
Light Molasses	3 quarts
Vanilla Extract	12 ounces

Directions: The ammonium hydroxide is dissolved in the water. Sugar, butter, and shortening are creamed and then salt, molasses, and vanilla added. Then the ammonium hydroxide-water solution is added and flour and soda sifted into the mass. Bake 5-8 minutes at 500°F (260°C).

Almond Macaroons

Almond Paste	12 pounds
Sugar	12 pounds
Flour	1 pound 8 ounces
Egg Whites	72
Salt	3 ounces
Grated Citrus Fruit Peel	6 ounces
Flavor (See Introduction to this chapter)	

Directions: Mix ingredients in order and bake in slow oven for about 25 minutes.

Candied Fruit

The method of candying fruit must be varied to fit the kind of fruit and, to a lesser extent, to the variety. While obviously all these variations cannot be included here, the following method for cherries should enable the user to work out a method for his particular needs:

Candied Cherries

(1) Cover the fruit with a hot solution prepared by dissolving 3 pounds 12 ounces of sugar per gallon of water. The temperature of 120°F (49°C) is held for 1 day, then (2) the syrup is drained off and 14 ounces additional sugar per gallon is dissolved in it. It is heated to boiling, poured over the cherries, and allowed to stand for another day at 120°F. The same process is continued throughout additional steps as follows:

Step	Sugar Added to Syrup	Temperature	Time
#3	6 ounces per gal.	120°F (49°C)	1 day
#4	14 ounces per gal.	120°F (49°C)	1 day
#5	12 ounces per gal.	140°F (60°C)	2 days

Finally, bring fruit to boil in syrup and allow to drain for 2 days.

Note: The foregoing method is for *candied* cherries. *Glacéd* fruits may be prepared by:

(1) Dissolving 3 pounds 12 ounces of sugar per gallon of water, inverting by adding 1 ounce tartaric acid and heating to boiling, and dipping the fruit in this solution at 140°F (60°C).

(2) Dipping the fruit in a 1% pection solution for 1 minute, then drying at 120°F (49°C) for 3 hours.

Beverage Powder

Sucrose (Fine crystals of Cane Sugar) . . .	1000 g.
Citric Acid	2 g.
Color and Flavor	

Directions: This basic formula is suitable for the production of a wide variety of fruit drinks, the only change necessary being some reduction in the above amount of citric acid in non-citrus fruit flavors. As suggested in the introduction to this chapter, obtain your color and flavor from a manufacturer specializing in that field. This will not only insure that your color is made of FD&C permissible colors, but also give you a really good flavor, which is essential under competitive conditions. A most necessary feature of the new flavor powders is the so-called "locked-in flavor," which gives exceptional "shelf-life" to the product.

Dessert Powder

Corn Sugar . . . . 400 g.
Cane Sugar . . . . 400 g.
Corn Starch . . . . 200 g.
Flavor and Color

Directions: Mix powders and package promptly. The corn sugar should be obtained in fine crystal form so it will not separate in the packages on handling. As stated in regard to the beverage powder above, the color and flavor should be obtained from a manufacturer specializing in them.

The above formula is suitable for a number of dessert flavors. For chocolate flavor, part of the cane sugar is replaced by cocoa. For gelatin desserts, the corn starch is replaced by ½ its proportion of edible-grade gelatin, and 10 g. of citric or tartaric acids (fine crystals) are added.

Ice Cream Powder §1

Powdered Arrow Root . . . . 320 g.
Corn Starch . . . . 280 g.
Sucrose (Cane Sugar, Fine Crystals) . . . 400 g.
Color and Flavor

Directions: Mix the powders in the above order and package promptly. Instruct the user to mix 4 ounces of the powder with 1 quart of a milk-cream mixture, and freeze.

Ice Cream Powder §2

Low Calorie

Powdered Arrow Root . . . . 490 g.
Corn Starch . . . . 490 g.
Gelatin . . . . 15 g.
Sodium Alginate . . . . 5 g.
*Calcium Cyclohexyl Sulfamate . . . . . 2 g.
Flavor and Color

* Manufacturers of synthetic sweeteners include Chas. Pfizer & Co., 630 Flushing Ave., Brooklyn 6, N.Y.; and Abbott Laboratories, North Chicago, Ill.

Directions: Mix the powders in the above order and package promptly. Instruct the user to mix 4 ounces of the powder with one quart of milk, adding a minimum of cream.

Catsup Formula

Tomato Pulp	25 pounds
Paprika	3 drams
Cayenne Pepper	1 dram
Mustard	2 drams
White Pepper	3 drams
Cinnamon	2 drams
Celery Seed	2 drams
Onion Powder	2½ drams
Sodium Chloride (Table Salt)	8 drams
Cane Sugar	3 pounds
Vinegar (5% Acetic Acid)	1 quart

Directions: The process of catsup making depends upon discontinuing the boiling when the tomato pulp (tomatoes from which skins and seeds have been removed) has reached proper consistency. The seasonings (all in fine-ground form), should be added to the hot pulp with stirring, after which the salt (sodium chloride), sugar, and vinegar are stirred into the mass.

Tomato Sauce

Tomato Puree	8 gal.
Vinegar	3 gal.
Salt	3 lb.
Sugar	2½ lb.
White Pepper	½ oz.
Cinnamon	¼ oz.
Ginger	⅛ oz.
Cloves	⅛ oz.
Allspice	1 oz.

Directions: Boil the tomato puree and the vinegar together for 1 hour. Then add the other ingredients and simmer for three hours.

Mint Sauce

Mint	2 lbs.
Sugar	4 lbs.
Salt	4 oz.
White Vinegar	4 gal.
Malt Vinegar	4 gal.

Directions: Soak finely-chopped mint in mixed vinegars for about 10 hours. Then stir in sugar and salt and soak for 5 hours longer. Filter.

Tomato Chutney

Tomato Puree	4 gal.
Vinegar	2 gal.
Sugar	16 lb.
Salt	10 oz.
Flour	6 lb.
Onions	9 lbs.
Raisins	2 lb.
Sultana Raisins	2 lb.
Shallots	4 oz.
Mace	1 oz.
Ginger	1 oz.
Cloves	⅓ oz.
Garlic	⅓ oz.
Red Pepper	⅓ oz.

Directions: Chop onions, shallots and raisins. Use all spices in fine-ground form. Add vinegar to tomato puree, and stir in all other ingredients. Boil for 1 hour.

English Chutney

Cored and pared tart apples	4 pounds
Raisins (seeded)	7 ounces
Green Peppers (seeded)	7 ounces
Onion	3 ounces
Lemon Rind	½ ounce
Sodium Chloride (Table Salt)	½ ounce
Sugar	12 ounce
Ginger	¾ ounce
Tartaric Acid	½ ounce
Citric Acid	2 ounces

Directions: The vegetables are cut to size and cooked slowly with the other ingredients for about one hour or until quite thick.

Chili Sauce

Fresh Tomatoes	7 pounds
Red Peppers	12 ounces
Green Peppers	6 pounds
Onions	1½ pounds
Sugar	6 ounces
Sodium Chloride (Table Salt)	1½ ounces
Vinegar 5%	1 quart
Cloves	1 dram
Allspice	1 dram
Cinnamon	1 dram

Directions: The vegetables are cut to size and cooked slowly with the other ingredients until thick.

Vegetable Relish

Tomatoes (green)	3 pounds
Tomatoes (ripe)	1½ pounds
Cabbage	¾ pound
Green Peppers	7 ounces
Red Peppers	10 ounces
Celery	3 ounces
Onions	10 ounces
Cucumber (pared)	3 ounces
Brown Sugar	14 ounces
Sodium Chloride (Table Salt)	3 ounces
Mustard	1 dram
Paprika	1 dram
Vinegar 5%	3 pints

Directions: Clean and chop vegetables. Add salt and let stand 12 hours. Press out and pour off liquid. Add other ingredients and cook for about one hour or until transparent.

Citrus Fruit Coating

Ethyl Abietate	100 g.
Morpholine	30 ml.
Water	900 ml.

Directions: Dissolve the ethyl abietate in the morpholine and stir vigorously into water until the emulsion is formed. Apply to citrus fruit to form a coating.

Cream Horseradish

Horseradish	10 lb.
Vinegar	1½ gal.
Salt	2 lbs.
Mustard	2 lbs.
Condensed Milk	8 oz.
Flour	2 lbs.
Sugar	1½ lbs.
Pepper	⅛ oz.
Allspice	⅛ oz.
Cloves	⅛ oz.
Cinnamon	¼ oz.
Water	1 gal.

Directions: Prepare brine by dissolving salt in 1 gal. water. Scrape horse-radish roots and soak in brine for 12 hours. Remove from water and shred finely. Simmer in vinegar for 1½ hours. Add other ingredients and simmer for 20 minutes longer.

Salad Dressing §1

Corn Starch	50 g.
Vinegar (6% Acetic Acid)	80 ml.
Salt	15 g.
Sugar	25 g.
Mustard	6 g.
Pepper	1.5 g.
Egg Yolk	50 ml.
Water	230 ml.
Cottonseed Oil	420 ml.

Directions: Heat the starch in the water to 180°F (80°C) in high-speed mixer, allow to cool, add sugar, salt and spices, then the egg yolk, and finally the oil (slowly) continuing the mixing throughout.

Salad Dressing §2

Agar-agar (powdered)	10 g.
Starch	30 g.
Gum Tragacanth	5 g.
Sugar	25 g.
Pepper	0.1 g.
Mustard	6.0 g.
Paprika	1.0 g.
Turmeric	0.5 g.
Cottonseed Oil	400 ml.
Water	580 ml.

Directions: Soak the agar-agar in the water, stir with high-speed mixer until uniform; add starch which has been heated to 175°F in 100 ml. of water, add the seasonings, then the gum, and finally the oil, continuing the stirring all the time until a homogenous mixture is obtained.

Salad Dressing §3
French Dressing

Refined Cottonseed Oil	500 ml.
Tarragon Vinegar	75 ml.
Cider Vinegar	75 ml.
Corn Syrup	15 ml.
Lemon Juice, Concentrated	15 ml.
Water	180 ml.
Fruit Pectin	15 g.
Sugar	60 g.
Salt	20 g.
Paprika	20 g.
Onion Salt	1 g.
Garlic Salt	½ g.
Pepper	½ g.
*Color	½ g.

* See first section of this chapter.

Directions: Mix the solids thoroughly by stirring and sifting, and stir them into the oil. Then stir the pectin into the oil. Add 50 ml. of water to the concentrated lemon juice and pour it into the oil while stirring. Then with continued stirring, also pour in the two kinds of vinegar, the corn syrup and the remainder of the water. This is a commercial formula designed to meet the needs of quantity production.

Mayonnaise §1

Egg Yolk	110 ml.
Mustard	9 g.
Paprika	5 g.
Pepper	0.5 g.
Sugar	22 g.
Salt	7 g.
Vinegar	65 ml.
Water	33 ml.
Cottonseed Oil	770 ml.

Directions: Stir eggs for 40-50 seconds in high-speed stirrer. Add spices, sugar, and salt and stir for 5 minutes more. Add half the oil slowly, then the water and vinegar, then the remainder of the oil, continuing stirring throughout.

Mayonnaise §2

Refined Cottonseed Oil	900 ml.
Egg Yolk	100 ml.
Water White Vinegar	50 ml.
Lemon Juice, Concentrated	10 ml.
Water	40 ml.
Sugar	15 g.
Salt	15 g.
Mustard	8 g.
Fruit Pectin	5 g.

Directions: Mix the solids thoroughly i.e., salt, sugar, mustard, and pectin, while mixing continue to pour in about half the water and then the egg yolk. Then with further mixing add the oil slowly and then the balance of the water, except for about 30 ml. of the water which is added to the mixed vinegar and lemon juice. This mixture is added last with continued stirring.

Curry Powder §1

Mustard	125 g.
Ginger	125 g.
Red Pepper	65 g.
Cinnamon	250 g.
Fenugreek	250 g.
Allspice	65 g.
Coriander	30 g.
Turmeric	30 g.

Directions: All spices should be ground through a 60-mesh screen and then well-mixed. When so ground, they oxidize quite rapidly on standing, and should be placed in an air-tight container.

Curry Powder §2

Turmeric	300 g.
Fenugreek	180 g.
Coriander	120 g.
Ginger (dark)	100 g.
Cumin Seed	60 g.
Pepper, Black	60 g.
Pepper, Cayenne	60 g.
Celery Seed	30 g.
Caraway Seed	30 g.
Cardamom	30 g.
Mace	30 g.

Directions: The same as Curry Powder §1.

Jelly Thickener

Pectin	550 g.
Corn Sugar	450 g.

Directions: Mix thoroughly and package promptly.

Precautions: When purchasing materials for food manufacture, be sure to specify edible grades.

Worcestershire Sauce

Salt	60 g.
Onion	60 g.
Mustard	60 g.
Curry	30 g.
Pimento	8 g.
Cloves	4 g.
Cayenne Pepper	4 g.
Black Pepper	4 g.
Jamaica Ginger	4 g.
Sherry	400 ml.
Vinegar 5%	550 ml.

Directions: Mix ingredients and heat gently for about 1½ hours. All solid ingredients should be fine powders (through 60 mesh) or fine crystals.

Marshmallow

Cane Sugar	800 g.
Gelatin	16 g.
Powdered Egg White	15 g.
Citric Acid	1 g.
Vanilla Extract	1 ml.
Water	400 ml.

Directions: Soak the gelatin in 100 ml. of the water. Dissolve the citric acid in 10 ml. of the water, add another 10 ml. to the egg white, and heat the remainder of the water with the sugar to boiling. Then add it to the citric acid solution. Whip the egg white-water mixture, add it to the boiled syrup, and continue whipping while adding the gelatin solution. When cool, whip in vanilla.

Baking Powder

Cream of Tartar (Potassium Bitartrate)	480 g.
Sodium Bicarbonate	325 g.
Starch	200 g.

Directions: Mix powders dry. The production of a free-flowing product depends upon exclusion of moisture from the process and package.

Chapter 10

FARM AND GARDEN PRODUCTS

Animal Feeds

In preparing food for animals it is to be emphasized that suitable adjustments must be made to fit the actual conditions, which include climatic conditions (part of the country), the breed, and the method of using, i.e., whether the animals are caged as in a battery house or are permitted to run loose indoors or outside. Most mashes for laying hens or other adult poultry assume that whole grain is also fed, as scratch feed or otherwise.

Animal Feed §1

Turkey Starting Ration

Standard Wheat Middlings	150 g.
Wheat Bran	150 g.
Feeding Oatmeal	100 g.
Pulverized Oats	100 g.
Yellow Corn Meal	50 g.
Alfalfa Leaf Meal (20% Protein)	100 g.
Soybean Oil Meal	70 g.
Meat Scrap (High Protein)	160 g.
Dried Buttermilk	80 g.
Ground Oyster Shell	10 g.
Salt	10 g.
Cod Liver Oil	20 g.

Directions: Mix the oil, salt, and oyster shell through the meal, then mix in other ingredients. Since all quantities in this formula, and the following feed formulas, are stated in grams, they may be conveniently multiplied by replacing grams by pounds, or any convenient multiple thereof (e.g. divide by ten and use pounds instead of grams, etc.).

Animal Feed §2

Turkey Growing Ration

Standard Wheat Middlings	150 g.
Wheat Bran	150 g.
Pulverized Oats	200 g.

Yellow Corn Meal	100 g.
Alfalfa Leaf Meal (20% Protein)	100 g.
Soybean Oil Meal	100 g.
Meat Scrap (High Protein)	120 g.
Dried Buttermilk	50 g.
Ground Oyster Shell	20 g.
Salt	10 g.

Directions: The same as Animal Feed §1.

Animal Feed §3

Turkey Breeder Ration

Standard Wheat Middlings	175 g.
Wheat Bran	175 g.
Pulverized Oats	175 g.
Yellow Corn Meal	90 g.
Alfalfa Leaf Meal (20% Protein)	135 g.
Meat Scrap (High Protein)	175 g.
Dried Buttermilk	45 g.
Ground Oyster Shell	20 g.
Salt	10 g.

Directions: The same as Animal Feed §1.

Animal Feed §4

Turkey All-Mash Breeder Ration

Pulverized Oats	240 g.
Ground Wheat	200 g.
Corn Meal	180 g.
Wheat Bran	100 g.
Standard Wheat Middlings	100 g.
Alfalfa Leaf Meal (20% Protein)	50 g.
Meat Scrap (High Protein)	40 g.
Dried Buttermilk	40 g.
Fish Meal	30 g.
Ground Oyster Shell	10 g.
Salt	5 g.
Poultry Feeding Oil (400 Units Vitamin D; 2000 Units Vitamin A per g.)	5 g.

Directions: The same as Animal Feed §1.

Animal Feed §5
Chick Starting Ration

Yellow Corn Meal . . . . 260 g.
Wheat Bran (or Ground Wheat) . . . . 150 g.
Wheat Middlings . . . . 150 g.
Soybean Oil Meal . . . . 150 g.
Pulverized Oats . . . . 100 g.
Alfalfa Leaf Meal (20% Protein) . . . . 50 g.
Meat Scrap . . . . 50 g.
Dried Skim Milk . . . . 25 g.
Liver Meal (or Dried Yeast) . . . . . 20 g.
Limestone (Added Manganese) . . . . . 18 g.
Steamed Bone Meal . . . . 15 g.
Salt (Iodized) . . . . 10 g.
Poultry Feeding Oil (2000 Units Vitamin A; 400
    Units Vitamin D per g.) . . . . . . 2 g.

Directions: The same as Animal Feed §1.

Animal Feed §6
All-Mash Chick and Broiler Ration

Yellow Corn Meal . . . . 630 g.
Soybean Oil Meal . . . . 200 g.
Meat Scrap . . . . 50 g.
Alfalfa Leaf Meal, (20% Protein) . . . . 10 g.
Dried Skim Milk . . . . 50 g.
Liver Meal (or Dried Yeast) . . . . . 25 g.
Limestone (Added Manganese) . . . . . 19 g.
Steamed Bone Meal . . . . 10 g.
Iodized Salt . . . . 5 g.
Poultry Feeding Oil (400 Units Vitamin D;
    2000 Units Vitamin A) . . . . . . 1 g.

Directions: The same as Animal Feed §1.

Animal Feed §7

Lower Cost Chicken Mash—Requires Good Pasture

Yellow Corn Meal	380 g.
Wheat Bran	100 g.
Wheat Middlings	100 g.
Pulverized Oats	100 g.
Soybean Oil Meal	150 g.
Alfalfa Leaf Meal, (20% Protein)	50 g.
Meat Scrap	75 g.
Limestone (Manganese Added)	20 g.
Steamed Bone Meal	15 g.
Iodized Salt	10 g.

Directions: The same as Animal Feed §1.

Animal Feed §8

Chicken Breeder and Laying Ration

Yellow Corn Meal	300 g.
Wheat Bran	100 g.
Wheat Middlings	100 g.
Pulverized Oats	100 g.
Soybean Oil Meal	150 g.
Meat Scrap	75 g.
Alfalfa Leaf Meal, (20% Protein)	65 g.
Dried Skim Milk	25 g.
Liver Meal (or Dried Yeast)	35 g.
Limestone (Manganese added)	20 g.
Steamed Bone Meal	15 g.
Iodized Salt	10 g.
Poultry Feeding Oil (400 units Vitamin D; 2000 units A per g.)	5 g.

Directions: The same as Animal Feed §1.

Animal Feed §9

Poultry Summer Grain Mixture

Wheat	600 g.
Corn (Yellow)	200 g.
Oats	200 g.

Directions: Mix thoroughly.

Animal Feed §10

Poultry Winter Grain Mixture

Wheat	400 g.
Corn (Yellow)	400 g.
Oats	200 g.

Directions: Mix thoroughly.

Animal Feed §11

Dairy Cattle Mineral Supplement
(Per 1000 g. of feed)

Steamed Bone Meal	10 g.
Salt	10 g.
Pulverized Limestone	10 g.

Directions: Mix thoroughly and use in following formulas. When feeding chiefly grass hay and corn silage, the salt should be increased to 15 g. per 1000 of feed, and the limestone to 25 g. per 1000.

Animal Feed §12

Dairy Cattle Grain Mixture for Low Protein
Roughages (Timothy Hay or Corn Stover
and Corn Silage)

Corn Meal	300 g.
Wheat Bran	150 g.
Standard Wheat Middlings	120 g.
Soybean Oil Meal	100 g.
Cottonseed Meal (41%)	100 g.
Corn Distillers' Grains	150 g.
Molasses	50 g.
Minerals (See Animal Feed §11)	30 g.

Directions: Mix thoroughly.

Animal Feed §13

Dairy Cattle Grain Mixture for Medium Protein
Roughages (Mixed Hay and Corn Silage)

Corn and Cob Meal	250 g.
Ground Barley	150 g.
Ground Oats	100 g.
Ground Wheat	170 g.
Ground Soybeans	300 g.
Minerals (See Animal Feed §11)	30 g.

Directions: Mix thoroughly.

Animal Feed §14

Dairy Cattle Grain Mixture for High Protein Roughages (Legume Hay and Corn Silage)

Corn and Cob Meal	330 g.
Ground Oats	150 g.
Wheat Bran	150 g.
Molasses	90 g.
Ground Soybeans	250 g.
Minerals (See Animal Feed §11)	30 g.

Directions: Mix thoroughly.

Animal Feed §15

Dairy Cattle Grain Mixture for Legume Silage and Hay Roughage, Early Pasture and Dry Cows

Corn and Cob Meal	450 g.
Ground Oats	250 g.
Wheat Bran	220 g.
Linseed Oil Meal	50 g.
Minerals (See Animal Feed §11)	30 g.

Directions: Mix thoroughly.

Animal Feed §16

Daily Feeding Schedules for Horses

Idle horses.—Principally roughages, cornstalks, fodder, straw, or some other cheap roughage, with 8 to 12 pounds of alfalfa, clover, or soybean hay daily, or if leguminous roughages are not available enough concentrates may be fed to meet the horse's requirements.

Light work.—One-third to three-quarters of a pound of grain and 1¼ to 1½ pounds of hay for each 100 pounds of live weight.

Medium work.—Three-quarters to 1 pound of grain and 1 to 1½ pounds of hay for each 100 pounds of live weight.

Heavy work.—1 to 1¼ pounds of grain and I pound of hay for each 100 pounds of live weight.

No hard and fast rule can be applied to feeding all horses, as their requirements differ with the individual. The foregoing suggestions are given as general guides which can be used for average horses at various kinds of work. A good rule to follow is to divide the three feeds as follows:

Morning feed.—Three-eighths of the grain and one-quarter of the daily allowance of hay.

Noon feed.—Three-eighths of the grain and one-quarter of the hay.

Night feed.—One-quarter of the grain and one-half of the hay.

From the foregoing rules it will be seen that most of the hay is fed at night, thereby allowing the horse ample time to digest the roughage. Most of the grain is fed during the day.

When horses are turned on pasture at night, very little, if any, hay should be fed in the morning. This will depend on the growth of the pasture.

Animal Feed §17

Fox Feed

Muscle Meat	480 g.
Liver	120 g.
Viscera (Other than Liver)	100 g.
Ground Green Bone	50 g.
Vegetables (Rich in Vitamin A Precursors)	50 g.
Commercial Fox Meal	200 g.

Directions: The vitamin A vegetables are chiefly carrots and tomatoes. The above is a cold weather formula. In hot weather decrease muscle meat considerably and increase meal proportionately.

Animal Feed §18

Dog Feed—Dry Meal

Corn Meal	300 g.
Wheat Middlings	200 g.
Meat Scraps	150 g.
Fish Meal	100 g.
Wheat Bran	100 g.
Skim Milk Powder	100 g.
Bone Meal	20 g.
Alfalfa Meal	20 g.
Salt	10 g.

Directions: Mix the meat scraps and fish meal, and stir in other ingredients in above order.

Horse Liniment §1
Blister Salve

Red Mercuric Oxide	200 g.
Petrolatum	800 g.

Directions: Warm petrolatum until nearly liquid, and stir in the red mercuric oxide until thoroughly mixed. Cut away hair and rub into area to be blistered. Bandage well and remove in 3-4 days.

Precaution: Very poisonous.

Horse Liniment §2

Red Mercuric Oxide	120 g.
Cantharides (powder)	120 g.
Lard	900 g.

Directions: Warm lard until nearly liquid and stir in mercuric oxide and cantharides, until thoroughly mixed. Rub into area to be blistered and bandage well.

Precaution: Very poisonous.

Horse Liniment §3

Tincture of Iodine	180 ml.
Spirits of Camphor	180 ml.
Glycerin	180 ml.
Isopropyl Alcohol	475 ml.

Directions: Mix in above order. Apply to area to be treated with thorough rubbing and bandage well.

Hoof Treatment §1

Paraffin	240 g.
Beeswax	240 g.
Pine Tar	480 g.

Directions: Melt paraffin, stir in beeswax, and continue heating until melting is complete. Stir in pine tar.

Hoof Treatment §2

Cupric Sulfate	300 g.
Ferrous Sulfate	300 g.
Zinc Sulfate	300 g.

Directions: All materials must be in fine crystal or powder form. Mix thoroughly, apply to affected area, and bandage. Used especially for thrush and canker.

Animal Antiseptic §1
Salve

Benzoic Acid . . . . 120 g.
Salicylic Acid . . . . 60 g.
Lanolin . . . . 500 g.
Petrolatum . . . . 500 g.

Directions: Warm lanolin and petrolatum together until melted, and stir in the acids, being sure to continue stirring until solidified so no separation can occur.

Animal Antiseptic §2
Lotion, Especially for Hoofs

Copper Sulfate . . . . 330 g.
Water . . . . 1000 ml.

Directions: Dissolve copper sulfate in water.

Animal Antiseptic §3
Lotion

Phenol . . . . 120 ml.
Formalin 40% . . . . 100 ml.
Water . . . . 900 ml.

Directions: Warm phenol (carbolic acid) until melted, warm water to same temperature, and add the phenol to the water with stirring. When cool, stir in the formalin.

Precaution: Phenol is injurious to skin.

Animal Antiseptic §4
Healing Salve

Salicylic Acid . . . . 40 g.
Ichthammol . . . . 40 g.
Zinc Oxide Ointment . . . . 1000 g.

Directions: Mix thoroughly. Apply daily.

Animal Antiseptic §5
Astringent Lotion

Salicylic Acid . . . . 30 g.
Tannic Acid . . . . 30 g.
Alcohol . . . . 1000 ml.

Directions: Dissolve acids in alcohol. Apply daily.

Animal Antiseptic §6
Healing Oil

Salicylic Acid . . . . 100 g.
Balsam of Peru . . . . 60 g.
Olive Oil . . . . 1000 ml.

Directions: Mix the balsam and oil and stir in the salicylic acid until thoroughly dispersed. Apply daily.

Sheep Dip

Rotenone Powder (5% R) . . . . 1 g.
Colloidal Sulfur . . . . 10 g.
Water . . . . 1000 ml.

Directions: Mix the rotenone preparation with the sulfur and stir vigorously into the water. This suspension should be stable enough so that it settles very slowly and requires only occasional stirring. It is very effective against ticks.

Dusting Powder for Cattle

Sodium Fluosilicate . . . . 500 g.
Phenothiazine . . . . 250 g.
Flour . . . . 250 g.

Directions: Mix powders thoroughly by stirring or sifting. Dust thoroughly into coat of animal, taking care, of course, to guard against contamination of food or water. This preparation is effective against many cattle insects.

Fly Spray for Animals

Nicotine Sulfate (40% Solution) (Black Leaf 40) 10 g.
Lactic Acid . . . . 10 g.
Water . . . . 980 ml.

Directions: Dissolve the nicotine sulfate and the lactic acid in the water. Apply as a spray to horns and other parts of body where flies are troublesome.

Precautions: Toxic to man and all other warm-blooded animals.

Disinfectant and Insecticide for Poultry Houses

O-Phenylphenol	10 g.
Pine Oil	10 ml.
Sulfonated Mineral Oil	80 ml.
Water	1000 ml.

Directions: Mix the *o*-phenylphenol with the oils and stir the mixture vigorously into the water. This spray is an effective disinfectant and insecticide for poultry-house use. It should not be used when poultry are present, but if the houses are sprayed when empty, the residual spray that adheres to walls is not sufficiently toxic to the poultry to present a serious hazard.

Whitewash for Poultry Houses

Calcium Hydroxide	60 g.
Sodium Hydroxide	20 g.
Concentrated, Ammonium Hydroxide	10 ml.
Water	1000 ml.

Directions: Dissolve the sodium hydroxide in 100 ml of the water, and mix the calcium with the remainder of the water. Mix the solutions, and add the ammonium hydroxide.

Precaution: Sodium hydroxide is destructive to all animal tissue, so avoid spattering this solution in whitewashing. Also avoid inhaling ammonia fumes.

Poultry Roost Paint

Nicotine Sulfate (40% Solution) (Black Leaf 40)	400 g.
Inert powder	600 g.

Directions: Mix thoroughly. Usually the 40% nicotine can be purchased already mixed. Use 225 g. (½ pound) per 100 feet of perch. Apply just before roosting time, and arrange for ventilation.

Precautions: Avoid poisoning animals or human beings with excess or loose material.

Poultry Litter Spray

Lindane	10 g.
Light Mineral Oil	1000 ml.

Directions: Dissolve the Lindane in the mineral oil and spray just enough to wet litter. As a perch paint, use 225 g. (½ pound) of this solution per 100 feet of perch.

Poultry Ointment

Nicotine Sulfate (40% Solution) (Black Leaf 40) (See Poultry Roost Paint)	20 g.
White Petrolatum	1000 g.

Directions: Melt petrolatum and stir in nicotine sulfate (40%), continuing stirring to assure that no separation occurs during solidification. Apply under wings and around vent.

Precaution: Be careful to avoid poisoning animals or human beings with excess or loose material.

Poultry Dust

Rotenone	2.5 g.
Talc	1000 g.

Directions: Because of difficulty of mixing this small quantity of rotenone completely, it is better to purchase rotenone in a 5% or 10% form, and use proportionately more than above. Dust thoroughly into feathers. Only one application is recommended.

Poultry Dip §1

Lindane	3 g.
Water	1000 ml.

Directions: It is usually more convenient to purchase dilute solution of Lindane, and use proportionately more than given above. Dip birds into solution. Two or three applications are recommended at fortnightly intervals.

Poultry Dip §2

Soap	8 g.
Flowers of Sulfur	15 g.
Water	1000 ml.

Directions: Dissolve soap in water and stir in sulfur. This solution must be stirred before and during use.

Poultry Dip §3

DDT . . . . 2.5 g.
Water . . . . 1000 ml.

Directions: If possible, buy the DDT as a dilute solution and use proportionately more than above. Dip the birds momentarily.

Plant Food §1

For Hydroponic Solution

Magnesium Sulfate . . . . 2½ g.
Sodium Nitrate . . . . 1½ g.
Sodium Monohydrogen Phosphate . . . 1½ g.
Potassium Chloride . . . . 1 g.
Ferrous Sulfate . . . . .07 g.
Zinc Sulfate . . . . .01 g.
Manganese Sulfate . . . . .01 g.
Sodium Borate . . . . .01 g.
Water . . . . 5000 liter

Directions: To add correctly the four small quantities at end of formula, dissolve 5 g. each of zinc sulfate, manganese sulfate, and sodium borate and 35 g. of ferrous sulfate, in 500 ml. of water and add 5 ml. of this solution to 5000 ml. of water, in which the other salts have been dissolved.

Plant Food §2

Fertilizer for Flowers

Ammonium Nitrate . . . . 2 g.
Potassium Nitrate . . . . 1 g.
Ammonium Phosphate . . . . ¾ g.
Calcium Sulfate . . . . ¼ g.
Ferrous Sulfate . . . . ¼ g.
Ammonium Chloride . . . . ¼ g.
Water . . . . 5000 ml.

Directions: Dissolve salts in water.

Growth Activator

*Indoleacetic Acid . . . . .02 g.
Alcohol . . . . .5 ml.
Water . . . . 1000 ml.

* Instead of indoleacetic acid, a more up-to-date growth substance is gibberellin, which is being produced by S. B. Penick & Co., 50 Church St., New York 7, N.Y. Their trade-mark product Brellin is so formulated that 2½ g. of it, when dissolved in 1 pint (473 ml.) of water, gives a solution containing 10 parts per million of gibberellic acid.

Directions: Dissolve 1 g. of the indoleacetic acid in 50 ml. of alcohol. Then add 1 ml. of this solution to 1000 ml. water. This preparation is used to soak cut ends of cuttings for 2-4 days before planting in rich soil, to accelerate rooting.

Deer Repellent

Coal Tar	2 ml.
*Tegin	20 g.
Water	1000 ml.

* Trade-mark product of Goldschmidt Chemical Co., 153 Waverly Pl., New York 14, N.Y.

Directions: Dissolve the Tegin in the water, warm to 104°F (40°C) and stir in coal tar until emulsified. Apply to tree trunks.

Cat and Dog Repellent §1

Liquid

Oil of Mustard	5 ml.
Nitrobenzene	5 ml.
Alcohol	990 ml.

Directions: Mix liquids in above order.

Precaution: Oil of mustard blisters skin and nitrobenzene is poisonous, both as liquid and vapor.

Cat and Dog Repellent §2

Powder

Pulverized Mustard Seed	300 g.
Pulverized Capsicum	200 g.
Flour	500 g.

Directions: Mix mustard and capsicum with the flour.

Precaution: Avoid contact of these powders with skin or eyes, or by inhalation.

Pesticide Formulas

All the preparations used for the destruction and control of objectionable insects, plants, and animals are commonly grouped under the heading of Pesticides. This section includes preparations used indoors and out-of-doors, and in the latter group comprises both preparations used to destroy weeds, and preparations used to protect vegetation. The last class includes products used to control plant diseases as well as those employed to control insects and other organisms which are injurious to plants.

The objective of this book is to give up-to-date and useful formulas, relatively easy to prepare and apply, for as many as possible of these preparations. One major class has been intentionally curtailed, namely, the insecticides, fungicides, and parasiticides which are used on plants to be used as food for man or fodder for livestock. The successful use of these preparations must meet four exacting conditions: (1) they must be applied in such concentration and under such conditions that the concentration of toxic agent which remains in the final product—fruit or vegetable—complies with sound safety practices, including government standards; (2) they must be effective against the particular type of infestation present; (3) they must be used at the particular time in the life cycle of the organism or disease when the application is most effective, and (4) the pesticide must remain on the plant long enough to accomplish its purpose.

From the foregoing conditions it is readily apparent that one of the primary requirements of effective utilization of any plant pesticide is the realization of the particular type of disease, or of animal or vegetable organism which causes infestation. This information obviously does not fall within the province of this book. However, there still remains the range of simple formulations, often comprising just one active ingredient, for the common ornamental plants and shrubs, that can be given in this book. In using them there is one control condition that should always be remembered. *Never overlook the possibility of a toxic effect by any of these materials upon human beings or domestic animals.* For while it is true that many of them are quite specific in their action, and have been chosen because of their relatively lower toxicity to warm-blooded animals, the fact remains that sensitization is a highly individual matter. Some individuals are allergic to virtually all of these substances. Therefore, in using any pesticide, even those not known to be poisonous, take every precaution to avoid exposure of people and domestic animals. This applies particularly to DDT, which is often used in the form of spray so that a relatively large amount may be unintentionally inhaled. Remember that no preparation in this section may be called nontoxic to warm-blooded animals. All that can be said in this connection is that some are instantly or promptly poisonous, even in relatively small concentrations, and that others may not be poisonous until higher concentrations are reached.

Garden Insecticide Spray §1

General Purpose Spray

Rotenone Powder (4% rotenone)	2 g.
Pyrethrum Extract (2% pyrethrum) . . .	8 ml.
Sulfonated Castor Oil	4 ml.
Water	1000 ml.

Directions: Mix the oil and water and stir well. Add this mixture to the rotenone powder, stirring until a uniform paste has been obtained. Then add the pyrethrum extract slowly, with constant stirring. This product is effective against many varieties of beetles, leaf rollers, aphids, thrips, spiders, mites and other pests.

Garden Insecticide Spray §2
Thrip Spray

Sugar	1200 g.
Paris Green	15 g.
Water	900 ml.

Directions: Dissolve the sugar in the water (moderate heating will speed this process). Allow to cool. Mix the Paris Green with 50 ml. of water and stir into the sugar solution, continuing the stirring until uniform. To use this formula add one part to thirty parts of water and apply as a spray. It is effective against many varieties of thrips, including those that infest roses, orchids, gladiolas, etc. It may be applied to flowers as well as foliage.

Precaution: Remember that Paris Green is toxic to all life.

Garden Insecticide Spray §3
Tree Spray

Nicotine Sulfate (40% Solution) (Black Leaf 40)	400 g.
Flour	50 g.
Lubricating Oil	1000 ml.

Directions: Mix the nicotine sulfate and flour thoroughly with the oil by stirring. This mixture will separate and should be stirred or shaken before use. To use, add one part of it to 200 parts of water and spray onto the trees. It may be used for all trees and ornamental shrubs and will not injure foliage..

Precautions: Toxic to man and other warm-blooded animals.

Insecticide Spray §4

Pyrethrum (20% solution) . . . . . . 20 ml.
DDT . . . . 3 g.
Petroleum Oil . . . . 120 ml.
Dispersing Medium (see Chapter I) . . . . 830 ml.

Directions: Dissolve the pyrethrum and DDT in the petroleum oil and add the dispersing medium. This product is formulated for an aerosol type package and dispersing medium.

Precautions: Regard this spray as potentially toxic to man and animals.

Insecticide Spray §5

Japanese Beetle Insecticide

Fish Oil Soap . . . . 75 ml.
Water . . . . 225 ml.
Carbon Disulfide . . . . 700 ml.

Directions: Stir the soap and water until fully mixed, then add the carbon disulfide with vigorous stirring until a uniform emulsion has been obtained. To apply this preparation dilute it 100 times with water and apply it to the ground under the infected bush or treat at the rate of three pints per square foot. It must be applied early in the year, because it is designed to kill the larvae of the beetle.

Garden Insecticide Spray §6

Weevil and Maggot Pesticide

*BHC (36% Gamma) . . . . 20 g.
**Attaclay . . . . 40 g.
***Marasperse N . . . . 1 g.
****Igepon T-77 . . . . 1 g.
Water . . . . 1000 ml.

    * 1,2,3,4,5,6 Hexachlorocyclohexane.
    ** Trade-mark product of Attapulgus Co., 210 W. Washington Sq., Philadelphia, Pa.
    *** Trade-mark product of Marathon Corp., Rothschild, Wis.
    ****Trade-mark product of General Dyestuff Corp., 435 Hudson St., New York 14, N.Y.

Directions: Mix powders. Disperse in water. This is an insecticide spray with an objectionable odor, which somewhat limits its use.

Precaution: Regard as toxic to man and animals.

Garden Insecticide Spray §7

Ants, Grasshoppers, Beetle Grubs in Lawns

Chlordane	20 g.
*Attaclay	28 g.
**Marasperse N	1 g.
***Igepon T-77	1 g.
Water	1000 ml.

* Trade-mark product of Attapulgus Co., 210 W. Washington Sq., Philadelphia, Pa.
** Trade-mark product of Marathon Corp., Rothschild, Wis.
*** Trade-mark product of General Dyestuff Corp., 435 Hudson St., New York 14, N.Y.

Directions: Mix powders. Disperse in water.

Precautions: Toxic to man and animals.

Garden Insecticide Spray §8

Grasshopper and Thrip Insecticide

Toxaphene	20 g.
*Attaclay	28 g.
**Marasperse N	2 g.
**Ignepon AP-78	1 g.
Water	1000 ml.

* Trade-mark product of Attapulgus Co., 210 W. Washington Sq., Philadelphia, Pa.
** Trade-mark product of Marathon Corp., Rothschild, Wis.
*** Trade-mark product of General Dyestuff Corp., 435 Hudson St., New York 14, N.Y.

Directions: Mix powders. Disperse in water.

Precaution: Toxic to man and animals.

Garden Insecticide Spray §9

Mite Insecticide

*Aramite	4 g.
Water	1000 ml.

* Trade-mark product of U.S. Rubber Co., 1230 Avenue of the Americas, New York 30, N.Y.

Directions: Dissolve Aramite in water.

Garden Insecticide Spray §10

Grasshoppers, Wireworms, Springtails

Heptachlor	20 g.
*Attaclay	28 g.
**Marasperse N	1 g.
***Igepon T-77	1 g.
Water	1000 ml.

* Trade-mark product of Attapulgus Co., 210 W. Washington Sq., Philadelphia, Pa.
** Trade-mark product of Marathon Corp., Rothschild, Wis.
*** Trade-mark product of General Dyestuff Corp., 435 Hudson St., New York 14, N.Y.

Directions: Mix powders. Disperse in water.
Precautions: Toxic to man and animals.

Insecticide Spray §11

DDT Spray

Exterior Spray for Flies

Ethylene Dichloride	900 ml.
DDT	125 g.

Directions: Dissolve the DDT in solvent by stirring. Use the product as an interior spray for flies. It is effective against certain other flying insects. It may be directed against wall and trees.
Precaution: Regard this spray as potentially toxic to man and animals.

Insecticide Spray §12

Cotton Insect Control

Aldrin	400 g.
*Attaclay	510 g.
Urea	29 g.
**Marasperse CB	50 g.
***Duponol M. E. Dry	10 g.

* Trade-mark product of Attapulgus Co., 210 W. Washington Sq., Philadelphia, Pa.
** Trade-mark product of Marathon Corp., Rothschild, Wis.
*** Trade-mark product of E. I. du Pont de Nemours Co., Wilmington 98, Del.

Directions: Mix powders. Use with 40 parts water at rate of 1 gallon (of above) per acre for thrip control and 2 gallons per acre for bollweevil control. When bollworms are present, add 0.5 pounds per acre DDT to spray mix.

Precaution: Regard as toxic to man and animals.

Garden Insecticide Powder §1

Tree Dust

Sulfur	750 g.
Calcium Hydroxide	150 g.
Lead Arsenate	100 g.

Directions: Mix the lead arsenate and calcium hydroxide thoroughly by stirring or sifting, and then incorporate this mixture in the same way in the sulfur. All three ingredients should be finely powdered to insure thorough mixing. In use, this product should be applied to the tree when wet with dew or rain, to insure sticking. It is effective against many types of infestation.

Precaution: This formulation is strongly toxic to man and animals, so take full precautions, especially against inhalation when it is being prepared or applied.

Garden Insecticide Powder §2

Root Insect Powder

Aldrin Dust Concentrate (25%)	20 g.
Fertilizer	1000 g.

Directions: Mix the aldrin concentrate with the fertilizer by stirring solids together, first adding the aldrin to a smaller portion of the fertilizer. This preparation is particularly effective against rootworms and other soil insects.

Precaution: Users of Aldrin-fertilizer mixtures should obtain Shell Agricultural Bulletin SC 53-16 "Aldrin for Soil Insect Control" from the Shell Chemical Corp., P.O. Box 1617, Denver 1, Col.

Garden Fungicide §1

Fungus Dust

Copper Sulfide, Anhydrous	25 g.
Copper Hydroxide	975 g.

Directions: Mix the copper sulfide thoroughly with the calcium hydroxide. Apply as a dusting powder to fungus on plants. Where the fungus grows on bark, so that there is no danger of the powder reaching the foliage, a higher proportion of the copper sulfide may be used, so that the preparation will be more rapid in its action.

Garden Fungicide §2

Lawn Spray

*Cadminate	1 g.
Water	2500 ml.

* Trade-mark product of Mallinckrodt Chemical Co., 2nd & Mallinckrodt Sts., St. Louis 7, Mo.

Directions: Dissolve powder in water and spray turf. Apply every three or four weeks. This small quantity is enough for 60 square feet of lawn.

Garden Fungicide §3

Snow Mold Lawn Spray

*Tersan	1 g.
Water	2500 ml.

* Trade-mark product of E. I. du Pont de Nemours Co., Wilmington 98, Del.

Directions: Same as Garden Fungicide §2.

Plant Disease Spray

Blight Control

*Dithane D-14	2 g.
Calcium Hydroxide	1 g.
Zinc Sulfate	1 g.
**Ultrawet D S	1 g.
Water	1000 ml.

* Trade-mark product of Rohm and Haas Co., 222 W. Washington Sq., Philadelphia 5, Pa.
** Trade-mark product of Atlantic Refining Co., 260 S. Broad St., Philadelphia 1, Pa.

Directions: Dissolve the four active ingredients in water. Spray infected plants.

Garden Plant Dusting Powder

Blights and Some Mildews

*Fermate	80 g.
Flowers of Sulfur	920 g.

* Trade-mark product of E. I. du Pont de Nemours Co., Wilmington 98, Del.

Directions: Mix thoroughly.

Seed Fumigant

Ethylene Dichloride	600 ml.
Carbon Tetrachloride	400 ml.

Directions: Mix liquids. Apply to seed and keep in closed container. When used at rate of 2 ml. per pound of seed (or 3 ounces per 100 pounds), this product is effective against most insects, but not disease micro-organisms.

Precaution: This product and its ingredients are poisonous to skin and tissues, and the vapor is poisonous on inhalation.

Grasshopper Mash

Calcium Arsenate	12 g.
Alcohol	15 ml.
Water	600 ml.
Bran	400 g.
Sawdust	200 g.

Directions: Mix the alcohol with 30 ml. of the water, and dissolve the calcium arsenate in this solution. Mix the bran and sawdust, and sprinkle the solution throughout it. Add remainder of water to bran with stirring until saturated. Note: Sawdust is used for economy; if not available, use all bran.

Precaution: Poisonous to man and animals.

Cutworm Mash

Calcium Arsenate	12 g.
Cane Sugar	120 g.
Alcohol	15 ml.
Water	600 ml.
Bran	600 g.

Directions: Mix the alcohol with 30 ml. of the water, and dissolve the calcium arsenate in this solution. Then sprinkle it throughout the bran. Dissolve the sugar in the remainder of the water, and add this solution to the bran with stirring until saturated.

Precaution: Poisonous to man and animals.

Grafting Wax

Rosin	900 g.
Lanolin	100 g.
Turpentine	100 ml.
Alcohol	400 ml.

Directions: Heat rosin and lanolin together until melted. Cool to 176°F (60°C), and add turpentine. Stir until uniform and then mix in alcohol.

Tree Banding Composition
For Caterpillars

Calcium Carbonate	200 g.
Calcium Hydroxide	100 g.
Rosin	100 g.
Wood Tar	30 g.
Crude Oil	600 ml.

Directions: Heat rosin, sprinkling on it the calcium hydroxide until all is incorporated. Then add oil, tar, and calcium carbonate, stirring until uniformly mixed.

Herbicide §1

Isopropyl phenyl carbonate	500 g.
*Hi-Sil	460 g.
**Marasperse N	20 g.
***Igepon AP-78	20 g.

* Trade-mark product of Columbia Chemical Div., Pittsburgh Plate Glass Co., Grant Bldg., Pittsburgh, Pa.
** Trade-mark product of Marathon Corp., Rothschild, Wis.
*** Trade-mark product of General Dyestuff Corp., 435 Hudson St., New York 14, N.Y.

Directions: Mix powders. Dissolve in 100 parts of water as herbicide for quack grass, Bermuda grass, and other grasses. Preparation is *relatively* nontoxic to broad-leaved plants.

Precaution: Regard as toxic to man and animals.

Herbicide §2

Ammonium Sulfamate	150 g.
Water	850 ml.

Directions: Dissolve the ammonium sulfamate in water and spray on foliage and weeds. This strong spray will kill all vegetation and therefore, it is used only where no cultivated plants are nearby. It will kill poison ivy and other toxic plants.

Precaution: Regard as toxic to man and animals.

Herbicide §3

Furfurol	125 ml.
Kerosene	425 ml.
Toluene	425 ml.

Directions: Mix, adding the furfurol last. This strong spray will kill all vegetation.

Precaution: Regard as toxic to man and animals.

Herbicide §4

Broad-Leaved Weed Killer in Turf

2,4-D	14 g.
Water	8000 ml.

Directions: Obtain an herbicide containing a compound of 2,4-D (2,4-dichlorophenoxyacetic acid). There are many such compounds available; the important consideration is to use such a quantity of the one you have so that 14 g. of 2,4-D content will be contained in 8000 ml. (about 2 gallons) of water. This is to be sprayed on 1000 square feet of turf to injure selectively most broad-leaved weeds and leave the turf uninjured. For the more resistant weeds, somewhat more equivalent 2,4-D per 1000 square feet, and repeated applications, are required. This necessarily reduces the margin between injury to weeds and that to turf. Avoid spray reaching garden plants.

Herbicide §5

Crab Grass Killer in Turf

Sodium Arsenite	17 g.
Water	4000 ml.

Directions: Dissolve the sodium arsenite in the 4000 ml. (about 1 gallon) of the water and apply to 1000 square feet of turf. Spray in late May or early June.

Precautions: Poisonous to man and animals. With sodium arsenite and most crab grass killers, the margin between killing the crab grass and the turf is not too great.

Appendix A

Chemical Manufacturers

This list has been prepared to help the users of this book. It is relatively short, and necessarily omits many manufacturers, both large and small. The reader is urged to use this list only in emergencies and to depend upon his Classified Telephone Directory, or the more complete lists available from such organizations as the Reinhold Publishing Co., 430 Park Ave., New York, N.Y. and Chemical Week, 330 West 42 St., New York, N.Y.

Note also that many of these companies have, in addition to the address listed, many offices in other cities.

Acheson Dispersed Pigments Co., 2250 E. Ontario St., Philadelphia 34, Pa.
Acme Resin Corp., 1401 S. Circle Ave., Forest Park, Ill.
Acme Shellac Products Co., 108 Blanchard St., Newark 5, N.J.
Adelphi Paint & Color Works, Inc., 86 Dumont Ave., Ozone Park 17, N.Y.
Advance Solvents & Chemical Corp., 245 Fifth Ave., New York 16, N.Y.
Aetna Color & Chemical Co., Inc., 60 Linden Ave., E. Paterson, N.J.
Afta Solvents Corp., 470-484 W. 128 St., New York 27, N.Y.
Air Reduction Co., Inc., Chemical Div., 150 E. 42 St., New York 17, N.Y.
Alco Products Inc., Schenectady 5, N.Y.
Aldrich Chemical Co., Inc., 3747 N. Booth St., Milwaukee 12, Wis.
Alliance Color & Chemical Co., 33 Avenue P, Newark 5, N.J.
Allied Asphalt & Mineral Corp., 217 Broadway, New York 7, N.Y.
Amalgamated Chemical Corp., Rorer & Ontario Sts., Philadelphia 34, Pa.
American Agricultural Chemical Co., 50 Church St., New York 7, N.Y.
American Bitumuls & Asphalt Co., 200 Bush St., San Francisco 20, Cal.
American Chlorophyll Div., Strong, Cobb & Co., Inc., P.O. Box 231, Lake Worth, Fla.
American Cholesterol Products Inc., Milltown, N.J.
American Cyanamid Co., 30 Rockefeller Plaza, New York 21, N.Y.
American Lanolin Corp., 13 Railroad St., Lawrence, Mass.
American Lecithin Co., Inc., 57-01 32 Ave., Woodside 77, N.Y.
American Maize Products Co., 250 Park Ave., New York 17, N.Y.
American Mineral Spirits Co., Mountain Ave., Murray Hill, N.J.
American Monomer Corp., 511 Lancaster St., Leominster, Mass.
American Oil & Supply Co., 238 Wilson Ave., Newark 5, N.J.
American Potash & Chemical Corp., 3030 W. 6 St., Los Angeles 54, Cal.
American Tar Co., Ft. of Wallingford Ave., Seattle, Wash.
Amsco Solvents & Chemical Co., 4619 Reading Rd., Cincinnati 29, Ohio
Angler Adhesives Div., Interchemical Corp., 120 Potter St., Cambridge 42, Mass.
Ansul Chemical Co., 1 Stanton St., Marinette, Wis.
Antara Sales Div., General Aniline & Film Corp., 435 Hudson St., New York 14, N.Y.
Arapahoe Chemical Inc., 2800 Pearl St., Boulder, Col.

Archer-Daniels-Midland Co., Chemical Products Div., 2191 W. 110 St., Cleveland 2, Ohio
Armour Chemical Div., Armour & Co., 1355 W. 31 St., Chicago 9, Ill.
Asbury Graphite Mills, Inc., Asbury, N.J.
Atlantic Refining Co., 260 S. Broad St., Philadelphia 1, Pa.
Atlas Powder Co., Wilmington 99, Del.

B

B B Chemical Co., 784 Memorial Dr., Cambridge 39, Mass.
Baird Chemical Corp., 10 W. 33 St., New York 1, N.Y.
Bakelite Co., Div. Union Carbide & Carbon Corp., 30 E. 42 St., New York 17, N.Y.
Baker & Adamson Products Div., Allied Chemical & Dye Corp., 40 Rector St., New York 6, N.Y.
Baker Castor Oil Co., 120 Broadway, New York 5, N.Y.
Baker Perkins, Inc., 1000 Hess St., Saginaw, Mich.
Baltimore Paint & Color Works, 2325 Annapolis Ave., Baltimore 30, Md.
Barber-Colman Co., 1300 Rock St., Rockford, Ill.
Barclay Chemical Co., Inc., 75 Varick St., New York 13, N.Y.
Bareco Wax Co., Div. Petrolite Corp., P.O. Box 2009, Tulsa 1, Okla.
Barrett Div., Allied Chemical & Dye Corp., 40 Rector St., New York 6, N.Y.
Bay Chemical Co., Div. Morton Salt Co., 120 E. LaSalle St., Chicago 3, Ill.
Beaumont Birch Co., 1505 Race St., Philadelphia 2, Pa.
Becco Chemical Div., Food Machinery & Chemical Corp., Station B, Buffalo 7, N.Y.
Benzol Distributors Inc., Georges Rd. at P.R.R., Dayton, N.J.
Berkshire Chemical Inc., 420 Lexington Ave., New York 17, N.Y.
Berry Asphalt Co., P.O. Box 800, 805 N. Clay St., Magnolia, Ark.
Bonewitz Chemical, Inc., 1735 N. Roosevelt Ave., P.O. Box 560, Burlington, Iowa
Borden Co., Chemical Div., 350 Madison Ave., New York 17, N.Y.
Bowser, Inc., 1302 E. Creighton Ave., Ft. Wayne 2, Ind.
Brown Co., 150 Causeway St., Boston 14, Mass.

C

Godfrey L. Cabot, Inc., 77 Franklin St., Boston 10, Mass.
Carbide & Carbon Chemical Co., Div. Union Carbide Corp., 30 E. 42 St., New York 17, N.Y.
Carboline Co., 331 Thornton Ave., St. Louis 19, Mo.
Carborundum Co., Niagara Falls, N.Y.
Carlisle Chemical Works, Inc., West St., Reading 15, Ohio
Carnegie Chemical Mfg. Co., 6363 Wilshire Blvd., Los Angeles 48, Cal.
Catalin Corp. of America, 1 Park Ave., New York 16, N.Y.
Celanese Corp. of America, Chemical Div., Dept. 56, 180 Madison Ave., New York 16, N.Y.
Central Solvents & Chemical Co., 2540 W. Flournoy St., Chicago 12, Ill.
Chapman Chemical Co., P.O. Box 138, 60 N. 3 St., Memphis 1, Tenn.
Chesebrough Mfg. Co., Cons., 17 State St., New York 4, N.Y.
John A. Chew, Inc., 60 E. 42 St., New York 17, N.Y.
Chipman Chemical Co., Inc., P.O. Box 309, Bound Brook, N.J.
Chloral Chemical Corp., 171 Lombardy St., Brooklyn 22, N.Y.
Ciba Co., Inc., 627 Greenwich St., New York 14, N.Y.
Claremont Pigment Dispersion Corp., 39 Powerhouse Rd., Roslyn Heights, L.I., N.Y.

Colgate-Palmolive Co., 300 Park Ave., New York 22, N.Y.

Colonial Chemical Co., Inc., 4014 28 Ave., S.W. Seattle 6, Wash.

Columbia-Southern Chemical Corp., Sub. Pittsburgh Plate Glass Co., 1 Gateway Center, Pittsburgh 22, Pa.

Columbia Wax Co., 530 Riverdale Dr., Glendale 4, Cal.

Columbian Carbon Co., 380 Madison Ave., New York 17, N.Y.

Colyer Pectin Co., 10 W. 47 St., New York 36, N.Y.

Commercial Solvents Corp., 260 Madison Ave., New York 16, N.Y.

Cornwell Chemical Corp., 24 E. 38 St., New York, N.Y.

Cowles Chemical Co., 7016 Euclid Ave., Cleveland 3, Ohio

Crescent Chemical Co., 15 Park Row, New York 38, N.Y.

Crowley Tar Products Co., Inc., 271 Madison Ave., New York 16, N.Y.

Crown Chemical Corp., 240 India St., Providence 3, R.I.

D

Damon Chemical Co., Inc., Box 774, Alliance, Ohio

Darlington Chemical Co., 1420 Walnut St., Philadelphia 2, Pa.

Davison Chemical Co. Div., W. R. Grace & Co., 101 N. Charles St., Baltimore 3, Md.

Detrex Chemical Industries, 14331 Woodrow Wilson Ave., Box 501, Detroit 32, Mich.

Dewey & Almy Chemical Co., Div., W. R. Grace & Co., 62 Whittemore Ave., Cambridge 40, Mass.

Diamond Alkali Co., 300 Union Commerce Bldg., Cleveland 14, Ohio

Dodge & Olcott, Inc., 180 Varick St., New York 14, N.Y.

Dow Chemical Co., Midland, Mich.

E. I. du Pont de Nemours & Co., Inc., Wilmington 98, Del.

Duval Sulphur & Potash Co., 17 Floor Mellie Esperson Bldg., Houston 2, Tex.

E

Eastman Chemical Products, Inc., Kingsport, Tenn.

Ecclestone Chemical Co., Inc., 2679 Guoin St., Detroit 7, Mich.

Enjay Co., Inc., 15 W. 51 St., New York 19, N.Y.

Enthone Inc., 442 Elm St., New Haven, Conn.

Esso Standard Oil Co., 15 W. 51 St., New York 19, N.Y.

Euclid Chemical Co., 1534P Hayden Ave., Cleveland 12, Ohio

Eureka Chemical Co., 41 Sheridan St., San Francisco 3, Cal.

Evans Chemetics, Inc., 250 E. 43 St., New York 17, N.Y.

F

Felton Chemical Co., 599 Johnson Ave., Brooklyn 37, N.Y.

Fine Organics Inc., 211 E. 19 St., New York 3, N.Y.

Fisher Chemical Co., 220 E. 42 St., New York 17, N.Y.

Florasynth Laboratories, Inc., 900 Van Nest Ave., P.O. Box 12, New York 62, N.Y.

Fluor Products Co., Div., Fluor Corp., 12000 E. Washington Blvd., Whittier, Cal.

Foote Mineral Co., 18 W. Chelton Ave., Philadelphia 44, Pa.

Franklin Glue Co., 119 W. Chestnut St., Columbus 15, Ohio

Fritzsche Bros., Inc., 76 9th Ave., New York 11, N.Y.

G

Gane's Chemical Works, Inc., 677 5th Ave., New York 22, N.Y.

Geigy Chemical Corp., 89 Barclay St., New York 8, N.Y.

General Chemical Div., Allied Chemical & Dye Corp., 40 Rector St., New York 6, N.Y.
General Color Co., 24 Ave. B, Newark 5, N.J.
General Dyestuff Corp. Div., General Aniline & Film Corp., 435 Hudson St., New York, N.Y.
General Electric Co., 1 River Rd., Schenectady 5, N.Y.
General Mills, Inc., 400 2nd Ave., S., Minneapolis, Minn.
Georgia Kaolin Co., 433 N. Broad St., Elizabeth, N.J.
Givaudan Flavors, Inc., 330 W. 42 St., New York 36, N.Y.
Glidden Co., 900 Union Commerce Bldg., Cleveland 14, Ohio
Glycerine Corp. of America, 36 W. 44 St., New York 36, N.Y.
Glyco Products Co., Inc., Empire State Bldg., New York 1, N.Y.
Goldschmidt Chemical Corp., 153 Waverly Pl., New York 14, N.Y.
B. F. Goodrich Co., 500 S. Main St., Akron, Ohio

H

Halocarbon Products Corp., 82 Burlews Ct., Hackensack, N.J.
Hampden Color & Chemical Co., 5 Albany St., Springfield, Mass.
Harshaw Chemical Co., 1945 E. 97 St., Cleveland 6, Ohio
Hercules Powder Co., Inc., 978 Market St., Wilmington 99, Del.
Hewitt-Robins Inc., 666 Glenbrook Rd., Stamford, Conn.
Heyden Chemical Corp., 342 Madison Ave., New York 17, N.Y.
Hoffmann La Roche, Inc., Vitamin Div., Roche Park, Nutley 10, N.J.
Hooker Electrochemical Co., 4715 Buffalo Ave., Niagara Falls, N.Y.
Hughes Gelatine Co., 3500 St. Aubin Ave., Detroit 7, Mich.

I

Imperial Paper & Color Corp., Pigment Color Div., Glen Falls, N.Y.
Industrial Chemical Co., 610 Hearst Ave., Berkeley 2, Cal.
Industrial Chemical Specialties Co., 2411 Cedar Bayou Rd., P.O. Box 456, Baytown, Tex.
Industrial Oil Products Corp., Margaret & Pearce Sts., Philadelphia 37, Pa.
Industrial Raw Materials Corp., 575 Madison Ave., New York 22, N.Y.
International Minerals & Chemical Corp., 20 N. Wacker Dr., Chicago 6, Ill.

J

Jefferson Chemical Co., Inc., P.O. Box 303, Houston 1, Tex.
Johns-Manville, 22 E. 40 St., New York 16, N.Y.
Joy Chemical, Inc., 133 Webster St., Pawtucket, R.I.

K

Kaiser Chemical Div., Kaiser Aluminum & Chemical Sales, Inc., 1924 Broadway, Oakland 12, Cal.
Kelco Co., 120 Broadway, New York 5, N.Y.
M. W. Kellogg Co., 711 3rd Ave., New York 17, N.Y.
Spencer Kellogg & Sons Inc., 98 Delaware Ave., Buffalo 5, N.Y.
Kem Products Co., Inc., 227-229 High St., Newark 2, N.J.
Kentucky Color & Chemical Co., 600 N. 34 St., Louisville 12, Ky.
H. Kohnstamm & Co., Inc., 83-93 Park Pl., New York 7, N.Y.
Koppers Co., Inc., Koppers Bldg., Pittsburgh 19, Pa.

L

LaMotte Chemical Products Co., Towson, Baltimore 4, Md.
Landers-Segal Color Co., 78 Delevan St., Brooklyn 31, N.Y.
Luminous Resins Inc., 166 W. Washington St., Chicago 2, Ill.
Luzerne Rubber Co., Muirhead Ave., Trenton 7, N.J.

M

M C Supply Co., Box 321 Muskegon, Mich.
Magnus, Mabee & Reynard, Inc., 16 Desbrosses St., New York 13, N.Y.
Magruder Color Co., Inc., 2385 Richmond Terrace, Staten Island 2, N.Y.
Maher Color & Chemical Co., 1700 N. Elston Ave., Chicago 22, Ill.
Mallinckrodt Chemical Works, 2 & Mallinckrodt Sts., St. Louis 7, Mo.
Manganese Chemical Corp., 1540 Rand Tower, Minneapolis 2, Minn.
Marbon Chemical Div., Borg-Warner Corp., 1926 W. 10th Ave., Gary, Ind.
Marley Co., Inc., 222 W. Gregory Blvd., Kansas City 14, Mo.
Marlyn Chemical Co., Inc., 156 & Forsythe, Calumet City, Ill.
Mason Color & Chemical Works, Inc., 206 Broadway, E. Liverpool, Ohio
Maumee Chemical Co., 2 Oak St., Toledo 5, Ohio
McGean Chemical Co., 1040 Midland Bldg., 101 Prospect Ave., N.W., Cleveland 15, Ohio
Merck & Co., Inc., Chemical Div., Rahway, N.J.
Metasap Chemical Co., Sub. Nopco Chemical Co., Logan & Davis Sts., Harrison, N.J.
M. Michel & Co., Inc., 90 Broad St., New York 4, N.Y.
Midland Adhesive & Chemical Corp., 2600 Goodrich, Ferndale, Detroit 20, Mich.
Midland Tar Distillers Inc., 1143 E. Jersey St., Elizabeth, N.J.
Mineral Oil Refining Co., P.O. Box 625, Dickinson, Tex.
Mineral Pigments Corp., Washington Blvd., Muirkirk, Md.
Minerals & Chemical Corp. of America, 21 Essex Turnpike, Menlo Park, N.J.
Monarch Chemical Works, Inc., 22 & Ave. H, E. Omaha, Neb.
Monsanto Chemical Co., Inorganic Chemical Div., 710 N. 12 Blvd., St. Louis 1, Mo.
Monsanto Chemical Co., Organic Chemical Div., 800 N. 12 Blvd., St. Louis 1, Mo.
Monsanto Chemical Co., Plastic Div., 100 Monsanto Ave., Springfield 2, Mass.
Montrose Chemical Co., 104-12 Lister Ave., Newark 5, N.J.

N

National Aniline Div., Allied Chemical & Dye Corp., 40 Rector St., New York 6, N.Y.
National Chemical & Plastics Co., 1424 Philpot St., Baltimore 31, Md.
National Gypsum Co., 325 Delaware Ave., Buffalo 2, N.Y.
National Lead Co., 111 Broadway, New York 6, N.Y.
National Oil & Supply Co., 172-180 Frelinghuysen Ave., Newark 5, N.J.
National Petro-Chem Corp., 99 Park Ave., New York 16, N.Y.
National Rosin Oil Products, Inc., Rockefeller Center, New York 20, N.Y.
National Starch Products, Inc., 270 Madison Ave., New York 16, N.Y.
Naugatuck Chemical Div., United States Rubber Co., 203 Elm St., Naugatuck, Conn.
New Jersey Zinc Co., 160 Front St., New York 38, N.Y.
Newport Industries, Inc., 230 Park Ave., New York 17, N.Y.
New York Quinine & Chemical Works, 50 Church St., New York 8, N.Y.
Ninol Laboratories, Prudential Plaza, Chicago 1, Ill.

Nopco Chemical Co., Logan & Davis Sts., Harrison, N.J.
Norda Essential Oil & Chemical Co., 601 W. 26 St., New York 1, N.Y.
Nuodex Products Co., Inc., 830 Magnolia Ave., Elizabeth, N.J.

O

Ohio Lime Co., Woodsville, Ohio
Ohio Solvents & Chemical Co., 3470 W. 140 St., Cleveland 11, Ohio
Oil & Chemical Products Inc., 295 Madison Ave., New York 17, N.Y.
Okonite Co., 1940 Canal St., Passaic, N.J.
Olin Mathieson Chemical Corp., Baltimore 3, Md.
Onyx Oil & Chemical Co., Warren & Morris Sts., Jersey City 2, N.J.

P

Pacific Coast Borax Co., Div. Borax Consolidated, Ltd., 100 Park Ave., New York 17, N.Y.
Pacific Vegetable Oil Corp., 62 Townsend St., San Francisco, Cal.
Peerless Chemical Co., 3850 Oakman Blvd., Detroit 4, Mich.
Peerless Oil & Chemical Corp., 51 Ave. & 27 St., Long Island City 1, N.Y.
Penick & Ford, Ltd., Inc., 420 Lexington Ave., New York 17, N.Y.
Pennsylvania Color & Chemical Co., Pine Run Rd., Doylestown, Pa.
Pennsylvania Detergents Co., 274 E. Ashmead St., Philadelphia 44, Pa.
Pennsylvania Industrial Chemical Corp., 120 State St., Clairton, Pa.
Pennsylvania Salt Mfg. Co., 3 Penn Center Plaza, Philadelphia 2, Pa.
Petroleum By-Products & Chemical Corp., 15 Whitehall St., New York 4, N.Y.
Charles Pfizer & Co., Inc., 630 Flushing Ave., Brooklyn 6, N.Y.
Philadelphia Quartz Co., 1146 Public Ledger Bldg., Philadelphia 6, Pa.
Phillips Chemical Co., 757 Adams Bldg., Bartlesville, Okla.
Pittsburgh Coke & Chemical Co., 2000 Grant Bldg., Pittsburgh 19, Pa.
Polar Chemicals Inc., 141 Howe St., Lewiston, Me.
Procter & Gamble Dist. Co., P.O. Box 599, Cincinnati 1, Ohio

Q

Quaker Oats Co., Chemical Dept., Merchandize Mart Plaza, Chicago 54, Ill.
Quaker Rubber Corp., Tacony & Comly Sts., Philadelphia 24, Pa.

R

Reichhold Chemicals Inc., RCI Bldg., White Plains, N.Y.
Reilly Tar & Chemical Corp., 1615 Merchant Bank Bldg., 11 S. Meridan St., Indianapolis 4, Ind.
Republic Chemical Corp., 94 Beekman St., New York 38, N.Y.
Ringwood Chemical Corp., 120 S. LaSalle St., Chicago 3, Ill.
Robinson, Wagner Co., Inc., 110 E. 42 St., New York 17, N.Y.
Rohm & Haas Co., Washington Sq., 712 Locust St., Philadelphia 5, Pa.
Rola Extract Co., 341 E. 3 St., Erie, Pa.
Rubber Corp. of America, 274 Ten Eyck St., Brooklyn 6, N.Y.
Ruberoid Co., 500 5th Ave., New York 36, N.Y.

S

Sandoz Chemical Works, Inc., 61-63 Van Dam St., New York 13, N.Y.
Seaboard Chemical, Inc., 30 Foster St., Salem, Mass.

Seaplant Chemical Corp., 63 David St., New Bedford, Mass.
Shawinigan Resins Corp., 644 Monsanto Ave., Springfield 1, Mass.
Sheffield Chemical Div., Sheffield Farms Co., Inc., P.O. Box 630, Norwich, N.Y.
Shell Chemical Corp., 50 W. 50 St., New York 20, N.Y.
Shepherd Chemical Co., 2803 Highland Ave., Cincinnati 12, Ohio
Solvay Process Div., Allied Chemical & Dye Corp., 61 Broadway, New York 6, N.Y.
Solvents & Chemical Group, 2540 W. Fluornoy St., Chicago 12, Ill.
L. Sonneborn Sons, Inc., 300 4th Ave., New York 10, N.Y.
Southern Dyestuff Corp., P.O. Box 1045, Charlotte 1, N.C.
Specialty Resins, Inc., 32 & Spring Garden St., Philadelphia 4, Pa.
Spencer Chemical Co., Dwight Bldg., Kansas City 5, Mo.
Standard Agricultural Chemical, Inc., 1301 Jefferson St., Hoboken, N.J.
Standard Chlorine Chemical Co., Inc., 115 Jacobus Ave., S. Kearny, N.J.
Stauffer Chemical Co., 380 Madison Ave., New York 17, N.Y.
Sterwin Chemical, Inc., 1450 Broadway, New York 18, N.Y.
Swift & Co., Union Stock Yards, Chicago 9, Ill.

T

Tar Residuals, Inc., 420 Lexington Ave., New York 17, N.Y.
Tennessee Corp., 617-29 Grant Bldg., Atlanta, Ga.
Texas Solvents & Chemical Co., 8501 Market St., Houston, Tex.
Thiokol Chemical Corp., 780 N. Clinton Ave., Trenton 7, N.J.
Thomasset Colors, Inc., 338 Wilson Ave., Newark 5, N.J.
Turco Products, Inc., 6135 S. Central Ave., Los Angeles 1, Cal.

U

Ultra Chemical Works, Inc., 2 Wood St., Paterson, N.J.
Union Carbide Corp., 30 E. 42 St., New York 17, N.Y.
U.S. Industrial Chemical Co., Div. National Distillers Products Corp., 99 Park
Ave., New York 16, N.Y.
United States Gelatin, Div. Peter Cooper Corp., Gowanda, N.Y.
United States Gypsum Co., 300 W. Adams St., Chicago 6, Ill.
United States Mica Co., Inc., Jordan & Van Dyke Sts., E. Rutherford, N.J.
United States Potash Co., 30 Rockefeller Plaza, New York 20, N.Y.
United States Rubber Co., 1230 Ave. of the Americas, New York 20, N.Y.
United States Sanitary Specialties Corp., 1001 S. California Ave., Chicago 12, Ill.
United States Varnish Co., 625 Franklin Ave., P.O. Box 2, Hasbrouck Heights, N.J.
Universal Atlas Cement Co., 100 Park Ave., New York 17, N.Y.

V

van Ameringen-Haebler Inc., 521 W. 57 St., New York 19, N.Y.
Velsicol Chemical Corp., 330 E. Grand Ave., Chicago 11, Ill.
Victor Chemical Works, 155 N. Wacker Dr., Chicago 6, Ill.
Virginia-Carolina Chemical Corp., 401 E. Main St., Richmond 8, Va.

W

Charles A. Wagner Co., Inc., 4453 N. 6 St., Philadelphia 40, Pa.
Warwick Wax Co., Sub. of Sun Chemical Corp., 1010 44 Ave., Long Island City,
N.Y.
West Virginia Pulp & Paper Co., 230 Park Ave., New York 17, N.Y.

Western Dry Color Co., 600 W. 52 St., Chicago 9, Ill.

Western Solvents & Chemical Co., 6472 Selkirk Ave., Detroit 11, Mich.

Westvaco Chlor-Alkali Div. Food Machinery & Chemical Corp., 161 E. 42 St., New York 17, N.Y.

Whitfield Chemical Co., 14225 Schaefer Highway, P.O. Box 3956, Detroit 27, Mich.

Will & Baumer Candle Co., Inc., P.O. Box 711, Syracuse 1, N.Y.

Wisconsin Solvents & Chemical Corp., 1719 S. 83 St., Milwaukee 14, Wis.

Witco Chemical Co., 122 E. 42 St., New York 17, N.Y.

Wollen Chemical & Supply Co., 126 6th Ave., Paterson 4, N.J.

Wolverine Solvents & Chemical Co., 1500 Century Ave. S.W., Grand Rapids 9, Mich.

Wyandotte Chemical Corp., Wyandotte, Mich.

Appendix B

Laboratory Equipment and Chemical Supply Houses

American Instrument Co., Silver Spring, Md.
Burrell Corp., 2223 5th Ave., Pittsburgh 19, Pa.
Clay Adams Co., 141 E. 25 St., New York 10, N.Y.
Eberbach Corp., 200 E. Liberty St., Ann Arbor, Mich.
Fisher Scientific Co., 717 Forbes St., Pittsburgh 18, Pa.
S. G. Frantz Co., Brunswick Pike & Kline Ave., Box 1138, Trenton 6, N.J.
H-B Instrument Co., American & Bristol Sts., Philadelphia 40, Pa.
Jarrell-Ash Co., 26 Farwell St., Newtonville 60, Mass.
Arthur S. La Pine & Co., 6001 S. Knox Ave., Chicago 29, Ill.
Metalab Equipment Corp., 244 Duffy Ave., Hicksville, N.Y.
Palo Lab Supplies, 81 Reade St., New York 7, N.Y.
Precision Scientific Co., 3737 W. Cortland St., Chicago 47, Ill.
E. H. Sargent & Co., 4647 W. Foster Ave., Chicago 30, Ill.
Scientific Glass Apparatus Co., 100 Lakewood Terrace, Bloomfield, N.J.
Standard Scientific Supply Corp., 34 W. 4 St., New York 12, N.Y.
Arthur H. Thomas Co., 230 S. 7 St., Philadelphia 5, Pa.
W. S. Tyler Co., 3615 Superior Ave., Cleveland 14, Ohio
W. M. Welch Mfg. Co., 1515 Sedgwick St., Chicago 10, Ill.
Wilkens-Anderson Co., 4525 W. Division St., Chicago 51, Ill.

Appendix C

Weights and Measures

Metric System—Weight

10 milligrams = 1 centigram
10 centigrams = 1 decigram
10 decigrams = 1 gram (= 0.002204 pounds (avoirdupois))

10 grams = 1 dekogram
10 dekograms = 1 hektogram
10 hektograms = 1 kilogram (= 2.204 pounds (avoirdupois))

Metric System—Volume

10 milliliters = 1 centiliter
10 centiliters = 1 deciliter
10 deciliters = 1 liter (= 1.057 U.S. liquid quarts)

1 milliliter of water at 40° C weighs close to 1 gram, and 1 liter of water weighs close to 1 kilogram

U.S. Avoirdupois System—Weight

27 11/32 grains = 1 dram   (= 1.772 grams)
327.5 grains = 16 drams = 1 ounce (= 28.35 grams)
16 ounces = 1 pound (= 453.6 grams)

U.S. Liquid Measure

4 gills = 1 pint (= 473.2 milliliters)
2 pints = 1 quart (= 946.3 milliliters)
4 quarts = 1 gallon (=3,785 milliliters—3.785 liters)

U.S. Dry Measure

2 pints = 1 quart (=1,101 milliliters—1.101 liters)
8 quarts = 1 peck (= 8.10 liters)
4 pecks = 1 bushel (= 35.24 liters)

U.S. Apothecaries System—Weight

20 grains = 1 scruple (= 1.296 grams)
3 scruples = 1 dram (= 3.888 grams)
8 drams = 1 ounce (= 31.10 grams)
12 ounces = 1 pound (= 373.24 grams)

Apothecaries Fluid Measure

60 minims = 1 fluid dram (=3.697 milliliters)
8 fluid drams = 1 fluid ounce (= 29.57 milliliters)

322

U.S. Troy System—Weight

24 grains = 1 pennyweight (=1.555 grams)
20 pennyweights = 1 ounce (=31.10 grams)
12 ounces = 1 pound (=373.24 grams)

British Units

The metric system is, of course, the same in British usage as in the U.S. The basis of the British system of weights is also the same as the U.S. pound. However, the British Imperial gallon is equal to 1.201 U.S. gallons (or = 4.546 liters) and the other British liquid measure units are proportionately larger than those in the U.S. liquid measure. The British Imperial bushel is equal to 1.032 U.S. bushels (or = 36.37 liters) and the other British dry measure units are proportionately larger than those in the U.S. dry measure.

Appendix D

The following is a list of the names of a number of industrial trade publications and directories, together with the names of their publishers:

Chemical, Chemical Processing, Ceramic, Concrete Product and Plastic Industries

Aerosol Age
  Aerosol Publications, Caldwell, N.J.
Agricultural Chemicals
  Industry Publications, Inc., Caldwell, N.J.
Ceramic Industry
  Industrial Publications, Inc., 5 S. Wabash Ave., Chicago 13, Ill.
Chemical Processing
  Putman Publishing Co., 111 E. Delaware Pl., Chicago 11, Ill.
Chemical Week
  McGraw-Hill Publishing Co., 330 W. 42 St., New York 36, N.Y.
Concrete Products
  Maclean-Hunter Publishing Corp., 79 Monroe St., Chicago 3, Ill.
Farm Chemicals
  Ware Bros. Co., 317 N. Broad St., Philadelphia 7, Pa.
Journal of Agricultural & Food Chemistry
  Reinhold Publishing Corp., 430 Park Ave., New York 22, N.Y.
Naval Stores Review & Terpene Chemicals
  Naval Stores Review, 624 Gravier St., New Orleans 12, La.
Plastics World
  Cleworth Publishing Co., 1 River Rd., Cos Cob, Conn.
Soap & Chemical Specialties
  MacNair-Dorland Co., Inc., 254 W. 31 St., New York 1, N.Y.

Cleaning & Dyeing Industries

American Dry Cleaner
  American Trade Magazines, Inc., 21 W. Huron St., Chicago 10, Ill.
National Cleaner & Dyer
  The Reuben H. Donnelley Corp., 305 E. 45 St., New York 17, N.Y.

Cosmetic Industry, Beauty Culture, etc.

American Hairdresser & Beauty Culture
  American Hairdresser Publishing Co., 20 W. 45 St., New York 36, N.Y.
American Perfumer & Aromatics
  Moore Publishing Co., Inc., 48 W. 38 St., New York 18, N.Y.
Drug & Cosmetic Industry
  Drug Markets, Inc., 101 W. 31 St., New York 1, N.Y.

Food and Feed Industries

American Soft Drink Journal
  McFadden Business Publications, 316 Peachtree St., N.E., Atlanta 8, Ga.

Bakers Review
   Wm. R. Gregory Co., 33 W. 42 St., New York 36, N.Y.
Bakers Weekly
Biscuit & Cracker Baker
   American Trade Publishing Co., 71 Vanderbilt Ave., New York 17, N.Y.
Feedstuffs
   The Miller Publishing Co., 2501 Wayzata Blvd., Minneapolis 5, Minn.
Food Business & Food Marketing
   Putman Publishing Co., 111 E. Delaware Pl., Chicago 11, Ill.
Meat
   Meat, 50 E. Van Buren St., Chicago, 5, Ill.
National Provisioner
   The National Provisioner Inc., 15 W. Huron St., Chicago 10, Ill.

Metals and Metalworking Industries

American Machinist
   McGraw-Hill Publishing Co., Inc., 330 W. 42 St., New York 36, N.Y.
Metal Finishing
   Finishing Publications, Inc., 381 Broadway, Westwood, N.J.

Packaging Industry

Glass Packer
   Ogden Publishing Co., 55 W. 42 St., New York 36, N.Y.
Modern Packaging
   Modern Packaging, 575 Madison Ave., New York 22, N.Y.

Paint Industry

American Paint Journal
   American Paint Journal Co., 2911 Washington Ave., St. Louis 3, Mo.
Paint Industry Magazine
   Heckel Publishing Co., Inc., 1321 Arch St., Philadelphia 7, Pa.
Paint & Varnish Production
   Powell Magazines, Inc., 855 Avenue of the Americas, New York 1, N.Y

Purchasing Directories and Annuals

Buyers Purchasing Digest
   Buyers Purchasing Directory Co., 13233 Euclid Ave., Cleveland 12, Ohio
Chemical Materials Catalog
   Reinhold Publishing Corp., 430 Park Ave., New York 22, N.Y.
Chemical Week Buyer's Guide
   McGraw-Hill Publishing Co., 330 W. 42 St., New York 36, N.Y.
Conover-Mast Purchasing Directory
   Industrial Directories, Inc., 205 E. 42 St., New York 17, N.Y.
Paint Industry Materials Manual & Technical Year Book
   Heckel Publishing Co., Inc., 1321 Arch St., Philadelphia 7, Pa.

Appendix E

CERTIFIED DYES

(U.S. Food, Drug and Cosmetic Act of 1938)

FD&C Color (For Foods)	*Trade Name*	*Color Index No.*
Blue No. 1	Brilliant Blue FCF	....
Blue No. 2	Indigotine (Indigo Carmine)	1180
Violet No. 1	Acid Violet 6B	697
Green No. 1	Guinea Green B	666
Green No. 2	Light Green SF Yellowish	670
Green No. 3	Fast Green FCF	....
Red No. 1	Ponceau 3R	80
Red No. 2	Amaranth	184
Red No. 3	Erythrosine	773
Red No. 4	Ponceau SX	....
*Yellow No. 1	Naphthol Yellow S, Sodium Salt	10
*Yellow No. 2	Naphthol Yellow S, Potassium Salt	10
*Yellow No. 3	Yellow AB	22
*Yellow No. 4	Yellow OB	61
Yellow No. 5	Tartrazine	640
Yellow No. 6	Sunset Yellow FCF	....

D&C Color (For Cosmetics)	*Trade Name*	*Color Index No.*
Blue No. 3	Alizarine Irisol Base	1073
Blue No. 4	Alphazurine FG	671
Blue No. 5	Alizarine Astrol B	1075
Blue No. 6	Synthetic Indigo	1177
Blue No. 7	Patent Blue A, Sodium Salt	714
Blue No. 8	Patent Blue A, Calcium Salt	714
Blue No. 9	Indanthrene Blue GCD	1113
Violet No. 1	Benzyl Violet 4B	697
Violet No. 2	Alizarine Irisol Base	1073
Green No. 4	Light Green SF Yellowish	670
Green No. 5	Alizarine Cyanine Green CG	1078
Green No. 6	Alizarine Cyanine Green Base	1078
Green No. 7	Fast Acid Green B	667
Red No. 5	Calcocid Scarlet 2R	79
Red No. 6	Lithol Rubine B, Sodium Salt	163
Red No. 7	Lithol Rubine B, Calcium Toner	....
Red No. 8	Lake Red C, Sodium Salt	165
Red No. 9	Lake Red C, Barium Toner	....

* Steps have been taken to decertify for use in foods the colors so marked. When this is done, these colors may be assigned new D&C or Ext. D&C numbers.

D&C Color (For Cosmetics)	*Trade Name*	*Color Index No.*
Red No. 10	Lithol Red R	189
Red No. 11	Lithol Red, Calcium Toner	....
Red No. 12	Lithol Red, Barium Toner	....
Red No. 13	Lithol Red, Strontium Toner	....
Red No. 14	Lake Red D	214
Red No. 15	Lake Red D, Barium Toner	....
Red No. 16	Lake Red D, Calcium Toner	....
Red No. 17	Sudan 3	248
Red No. 18	Oil Red OS	....
Red No. 19	Rhodamine B, Hydrochloride	749
Red No. 20	Rhodamine B, Acetate	749
Red No. 21	Tetrabromofluorescein FL	....
Red No. 21	Tetrabromofluorescein XX	....
Red No. 22	Eosine YS, Sodium Salt	768
Red No. 23	Eosine YSK, Potassium Salt	768
Red No. 24	Tetrachlorofluorescein	....
Red No. 25	Tetrachlorofluorescein NA	....
Red No. 26	Tetrachlorofluorescein K	....
Red No. 27	Tetrachloro-tetrabromofluorescein	....
Red No. 28	Phloxine B	778
Red No. 29	Bluish Orange TR	....
Red No. 30	Helindon Pink CN	....
Red No. 31	Brilliant Lake Red R	35
Red No. 32	Gil Red XO	....
Red No. 33	Fast Acid Magenta B	30
Red No. 34	Lake Bordeaux, Calcium Salt	190
Red No. 35	Toluidine Red	69
Red No. 36	Permaton Red	....
Red No. 37	Rhodamine B, Stearate	....
Orange No. 3	Orange G	27
Orange No. 4	Orange II	151
Orange No. 5	Dibromofluorescein	....
Orange No. 6	Dibromofluorescein, Sodium Salt	....
Orange No. 7	Dibromofluorescein, Potassium Salt	....
Orange No. 8	Dichlorofluorescein	....
Orange No. 9	Dichlorofluorescein, Sodium Salt	....
Orange No. 10	Diiodofluorescein	....
Orange No. 11	Erythrosine, Yellowish Na	772
Orange No. 12	Erythrosine, Yellowish K	772
Orange No. 13	Erythrosine, Yellowish NH	772
Orange No. 14	Orange TR	....
Orange No. 15	Alizarine	1027
Orange No. 16	Dibromodiiodofluorescein	....
Orange No. 17	Permaton Orange	....
Yellow No. 7	Fluorescein	766
Yellow No. 8	Uranine, Sodium Salt	766
Yellow No. 9	Fluorescein, Potassium Salt	766
Yellow No. 10	Quinoline Yellow, Water Soluble	801
Yellow No. 11	Quinoline Yellow, Spirit Soluble	800

D&C Color (For Cosmetics)	*Trade Name*	*Color Index No.*
Brown No. 1	Resorcine Brown Y	234
Black No. 1	Naphthol Blue Black	246

D&C Color (For External Use)	*Trade Name*	*Color Index No.*
Blue No. 1	Methylene Blue, Zinc Free	922
Blue No. 2	Methylene Blue, Zinc Double Chloride	922
Blue No. 3	Patent Blue AS	673
Blue No. 4	Alizarine Sapphire B	1054
Blue No. 5	Calcogas Blue NA	. . . .
Violet No. 1	Anthraquinone Violet B	1080
Violet No. 2	Alizarine Irisol R	1073
Green No. 1	Naphthol Green B	5
Red No. 1	Amido Naphthol Red 60	57
Red No. 2	Pigment Scarlet NA	216
Red No. 3	Violamine R	758
Red No. 4	Dichlorotetraiodofluorescein	. . . .
Red No. 5	Rose Bengal TD, Sodium Salt	777
Red No. 6	Rose Bengal TDK, Potassium Salt	777
Red No. 7	Alizarine Carmine	1034
Red No. 8	Fast Red A	176
Red No. 9	DBL Ponceau Bordeaux BL	84
Red No. 10	Azo Rubine A	179
Red No. 11	Fast Crimson GR	31
Red No. 12	Orange R Royal Scarlet	141
Red No. 13	Crocein Scarlet MOO	252
Orange No. 1	Fanchon or Hansa Orange	. . . .
Orange No. 2	Dinitrofluorescein	. . . .
Yellow No. 1	Metanil Yellow, Sodium Salt	138
Yellow No. 2	Metanil Yellow, Calcium Salt	. . . .
Yellow No. 3	Fast Light Yellow 3G	636
Yellow No. 4	Polar Yellow 5G	642
Yellow No. 5	Hansa Yellow	. . . .
Black No. 1	Coomassie Fast Black B	307

INDEX

Acid washing of masonry, 134
Additives for food products, 251-252
Air freshening spray, 167
All-purpose cream, 225-226
Aluminum paint, 87-88
Angel food cake, 276
Animal, antiseptic, 297
Animal astringent lotion, 297
Animal dandruff treatment, 171
Animal feed, 289-295
Animal fly spray, 298
Animal healing oil, 298
Animal healing salve, 297
Anodic coating on metal, 120
Anticorrosive paint for metal, 78
Anti-perspirant, 233
Antiseptic, animal, 297
Asbestos shingle paint, 84
Astringent lotion, animal, 298
Automobile cleaner-polish, 124-126
Automobile lacquer, 57
Automobile polish, 124-126

Baby powder, 237
Baking powder, 288
Bath, bubble, 227
Bath salts, 238
Beverage powder, 280
Bleach, hair, 211
Bleach, laundry, 144
Bleach, Wood, 8-10
Blight control, 309
Blister salve, 296
Bluing detergent, 144
Bluing laundry compound, 144
Body powder, 236
Bottle washing compound, 137
Bologna, 256-258
Braunschweiger, 261-263
Brick paint, 83-84
Bright-dip solution for metal, 98-100
Brush cleaner, paint, 93
Brushing lacquer for wood, 50-51, 53-54
Bubble bath, 227
Bun, 277-278

Cake, 275-277
  angel food, 276
  cheese, 277
  chocolate, 276
  layer, 275
  pound, 275
  sponge, 276
Calking compound, 138
Candied cherries, 280
Cat and dog repellent, 302
Caterpillar composition, 311
Catsup, 282
Cattle feed supplement, dairy, 293
Cattle grain mixture, dairy, 293
Cement, Portland, 127
Cement, rubber, 171
Certified colors, 326-328
Certified dyes, 326-328
Cheese cake, 277
Chemical companies, 313-321
Chemical stains for wood, 29-31
Chemical suppliers, 313-321
Cherries, candied, 280
Chicken feed, 291-292
Chili Con Carne, 270-271
Chili sauce, 283
Chlorinated rubber paint, 89
Chocolate cake, 276
Chutney, English, 283
Chutney, tomato, 283
Citrus fruit coating, 284
Cleaners, glove, 156
Cleaner, hand, 200-203
Cleaner, metal, 123-125
Cleaner, paint, 165
Cleaner, paint-brush, 166
Cleaner, rug, 166
Cleaner, shoe, 151-152
Cleaner, straw-hat, 166
Cleaner, wall paper, 165
Cleaner-polish, 46-47
  lotion, 46-47
  silicone, 47
Cleaning fluid, dry, 155-156
Cleaning powder, household, 145

Cleaning solution, electrolytic, 112-113
    glass, 136-137
Cleansing cream, 222
Cleansing lotion, 223
Clear lacquer for metal, 56-57
Clear lacquer for wood, 50-52
Cold cream, 221-222
Cold water paint, 85-86
Color, certified, 326-328
Color, cosmetic, 199-326
Color rinse, hair, 211
Coloring concrete, 131
Coloring food products, 251-252
Coloring solutions for metal, 101-108
Compact, face powder, 235
Companies, chemical, 313-321
Concrete, 128-131
    coloring, 131
    floor paint, 82-83
    integral waterproofing, 129-130
    Mixing, 128
    surfacing, 130
Corn beef loaf, 269-270
Cosmetic(s), 199-250
    color, 199, 326
    perfume, 199
    preservative, 200
Cotton insect spray, 307
Crab grass killer, 312
Crackers, 278-279
Crack filler, wood, 60
Crackle lacquer for wood, 55
Cream.
    all-purpose, 225-226
    cleansing, 222
    cold, 221-222
    deodorant, 232-233
    emollient, 224-225
    foundation, 224
    hand, 205-206
    Horseradish, 284
    mascara, 228
    rouge, 236
    shaving, 217-219
    vanishing, 220-221
Cream-type polish, 47
Curry powder, 287
Cuticle softener, 238
Cutworm mash, 310

Dairy cattle feed, 293-294

Dairy cattle grain mixture, 293
Dandruff treatment, animal, 171
Deer repellent, 302
Defroster, windshield, 137
Denture powder, 231
Deodorant cream, 232-233
Deodorant, space, 168
Deodorant stick, 233
Dessert powder, 281
Detergent, bluing, 144
Detergent, dishwashing, 140-142
Detergent, washing machine, 142-143
Developer, photographic, 179-185
Dipping lacquer for metal, 57
Directions, 2
Dishwashing liquid, 141-142
Dishwashing powder, 140-141
Disinfectant, household, 169
Disinfectant, poultry house, 299
Dog feed, 295
Dog repellent, 302
Dog shampoo, 171
Dressing, French, 286
Dressing, hair, 212
Dressing, salad, 285-286
Dry-bright floor polish, 148-149
Dry cleaning fluid, 155-156
Dry cleaning powder for pets, 172
Dust repellent polish, 47
Dusting powder for cattle, 298
Dye, certified, 326-328
Eau de cologne, 249
Elastic varnish, 39

Electrolytic cleaning solution, 112-113
Electrolytic protective solution, 120
Electroplating methods, 111-112
Electroplating solution, 112-119
Emollient cream, 224-225
Enamel, nail, 237
Enamel remover, nail, 237-238
English chutney, 283
Equipment, 3
Equipment supply houses, 321.
Exterior wood paint, 60-62, 66-69
Eye shadow, 228
Eyebrow pencil, 229

Face powder, 234-235
    compact, 235
    liquid, 235

Feed
  animal, 289-295
  chick, 291-292
  dog, 295
  fox, 295
  horse, schedule for, 294
  supplement, 293
  turkey, 289-290
Fertilizer for flowers, 301
Filler, wood, 31-33
  liquid, 32-33
  paste, 31-32
Fire extinguishing powder, 176
Fireproofing solutions, 177
Fire-resistant paint, 89
Fire-resistant whitewash, 86
Fixing bath, 188-190
Flat lacquer for wood, 52, 54
Flavor, fruit, 253-254
Flavor, synthetic, 253-254
Flea treatment for pets, 172
Floor cleaner, tile, 145
Floor
  lacquer for wood, 51
  paint for concrete, 82-83
  polish, 146-149
    dry-bright, 148-149
    water-resistant, 146-147
  varnish, 36, 38, 40, 41
Flower fertilizer, 301
Fluid-spray packaging, 6
Fluorescent paint, 88
Fluorescent plaster, 133
Fly spray, exterior, 307
Fly spray for animals, 298
Food products, 251-288
  additives for, 251-252
  coloring, 251-252
Formulas, Selection of, 1
Foundation cream, 224
Fox feed, 295
Frankfurters, 255-256
French dressing, 286
Fruit coating, citrus, 284
Fruit flavor, 253-254
Fumigant, seed, 310
Fungus dust, 308
Furniture lacquer, 50, 52
Furniture polish, 44-48
Furniture varnish, 37, 38, 41

Garden insecticide sprays, 303-308
Glass cleaning solution, 136-137
Glass, fluorescent lacquer for, 136
Glass, metallizing, 135-136
Glaziers' putty, 138
Glossy lacquer, 50, 52, 54, 56, 57
  for metal, 56-57
  for wood, 50, 52, 54
Glove cleaner, 156
Glue, 169-170
Government requirements for labeling, 6
Grafting wax, 310
Grasshopper mash, 310
Grasshopper spray, 306-307
Grease remover, 95
Growth activator, 301

Hair
  bleach, 211
  dressing, 212
  lacquer, 216
  lotion, 212
  rinse solution, 210
    color, 211
    henna, 210
  "tonic," 212-213
  wave-set, 217
Hand cleaner, 200-203
  soap type, 203
  "waterless," 202
Hand cream, 205-206
Hand lotion, 204-205
Hand soap, liquid, 203
Hardener, photographic, 187
Healing oil (animal), 298
Healing salve (animal), 297
Henna rinse, 210
Herbicide (weed killer), 311
Hoof lotion, 297
Horse feeding, 294
Horse liniment, 296
Horseradish, cream, 284
Household cleaning powder, 145
Household paste, 170
Household insecticide, 172-174
Hydrogen peroxide bleach for wood, 10
Hydroponic solution, 301
Hypo eliminator, 190

Ice cream powder, 281
Industrial publications, 324-325

Ingredients, procurement of, 1
Ink eradicator, 164-165
Insect powder, household, 173-174
Insect powder, root, 308
Insect repellent, 174
Insecticide, poultry house, 299
Insecticide sprays, garden, 303-308
Insecticide spray, household, 172-173
Intensifier, photographic, 191-192
Interior wood paint, 70-75

Japanese beetle spray, 305
Jelly thickener, 288
Joint ceiling compound, 138

Kalsomine, 86

Labeling, 6
  Government requirements for, 6
Laboratory equipment supply houses,
    321
Lacquer
  automobile, 57
  fluorescent, for glass, 136
  furniture, 50, 52
  hair, 216
  metal, 55-59
    clear, 56-57
    dipping, 57
    glossy, 56-57
    metal powder, 58
    pigment for, 58
    spraying, 57
  spraying, for wood, 52, 54
  thinner, 59
  wood, 49-55
    brushing, 50, 51, 53, 54
    clear, 50-52
    crackle, 55
    flat finish, 52, 54
    floor, 51
    glossy, 50, 51, 54
    opaque, 53-54
    semi-gloss, 50, 53
    water resistant, 51, 54
Latex paint for wood, 73-75
Laundry bleach, 144
Laundry compound, 142-144
  bluing, 144
Laundry detergent, 142-144
Lavender water, 249

Lawn spray, 309
  snow mold, 309
Layer cake, 275
Leather polish, 150
Liniment, horse, 296
Lipstick, 229
Liquid face powder, 235
Liquid filler for wood, 32-33
Liquid furniture polish, 44-45
Liquid hand soap, 203
Liquid soap, 145
Litter spray, poultry, 299
Liver sausage, 266-267
Lotion
  anti-perspirant, 233
  cleaner-polish, 46-47
  cleansing, 223
  hair, 212
  hand, 204-205
  shaving, 219-220
  skin freshening, 227
  sun tan, 240-242

Macaroons, 279
Marine spar varnish, 35
Marshmallow, 288
Mascara, cream, 228
Mash, chicken, 291
Mash, turkey, 290
Masonry, acid washing of, 134
Masonry paint, 78-81
Mayonnaise, 286-287
Measures, weights and, 2
Measures, weights and (tables), 322-323
Metal
  anodic coating on, 120
  "bright-dip" solution, 98-100
  cleaner, 123-125
    protective, 124
  coloring solution, 101-108
  foil packaging, 5
  lacquer, 55-59
  painting, 76
  pickling solution, 96-98
  polish, 121-122
  powder lacquer, 58
  primer, 77
  protective solution, 109, 120
    electrolytic, 120
  satin finish solution, 100-101

soak cleaner, 96
  grease remover from, 95
Metalizing formulas, 109-111
Metalizing, glass, 135-136
Mildew dusting powder, 309
Minced lunch meat, 259-260
Mint sauce, 282
Mite spray, 306
Mixed oil polish, 42-44
Mixing varnish for paint, 37
Mock turtle soup, 274
Mortar, 134
Mothproofing spray, 175
Moth spray, 175
Mouth wash, 232

Nail enamel, 237
  remover, 237-238
Nail white, 238
Neutralizing powders for permanent
    wave solutions, 217
Neutralizing solutions for permanent
    wave solutions, 217

Opaque lacquer for wood, 53-54
Oxtail soup, 273

Package design, 5
Packaging, 5-6
  fluid-spray, 6
  in bottles, 5
  metal foil, 5
  "squeeze bottle," 6
  transparent plastic, 5
Paint, 60-90
  aluminum, 87-88
  asbestos shingle, 84
  chlorinated rubber, 89
  cleaner, 165
  cold water, 85-86
  fire-resistant, 89
  concrete floor, 82-83
  fluorescent, 88
  brick, 83-84
  masonry, 78-81
  metal, 76-79, 87
    aluminum type, 87
    anticorrosive, 78
  plaster, 84-85
  remover, 90-92
  wood, 60-76

aluminum type, 87-88
  chalking, 67
  chalk-resistant, 67
  exterior, 60-62, 66-69
  priming, 60, 61, 66, 70, 71
  synthetic resin oil-type, 68, 72
  synthetic resin—varnish type, 68
  synthetic resin, water-emulsion type,
    69
  interior, 70-75
  latex base, 73-75
  oil-pigment-drier type, 60-67, 70-71
  oil-pigment-drier type, toning pig-
    ments for, 63-65
Painting metal, 76
Painting wood, 59-60
Paperhangers' paste, 93
Paste filler for wood, 31-33
Paste furniture polish, 46
Paste, household, 170
Paste, paperhangers', 93
Patching plaster, 133
Penetrating stain for wood, 20-24
Pet product, sanitary, 171-172
Perfume bases, 244-248
Perfume, cosmetic, 199
Perfume stick, 250
Permanent wave solution, 216
  neutralizing powders for, 217
  neutralizing solutions for, 217
Pesticide, garden, 303-308
Pet repellent, 302
Photographic
  developer, 179-185
  fixing bath, 188-190
  formula, 179-198
  hardener, 187
  hypo eliminator, 190
  intensifier, 191-182
  reducer, 192-195
  stop bath, 186-187
Pickling solution, metal, 96-98
Pigment for metal lacquer, 58
Pigment oil stain for wood, 14-20
Pigment, tinting, for aluminum paint, 88
Pipe-joint putty, 138
Plant foods, 301
Plant growth activator, 301
Plaster, 132-134
  brown coat, 131
  corrective, 133

finishing coat, 132
fluorescent, 133
paint, 84-85
patching, 133
quick-setting, 133
scratch-coat, 132
Plastic packaging, transparent, 5
Polish, 44-48, 121-122, 146-150, 151-155
cream-type, 47
dust repellant, 47
furniture, 44-48
floor, 146-149
general purpose, 149
leather, 150
lotion-cleaner, 46-47
metal, 121-122
mixed oil, 44
self-cleaning, 48
shoe, 151-152
silicone, 47
stove, 153-155
wax, 44-48
wood, 42-48
Polishing varnish, 38
Pork Sausage, 264-266
Portland cement, 127
Poultry
dip, 300
dust, 300
grain mixture, 292-293
litter spray, 299
ointment, 300
roost paint, 299
Poultry-house disinfectant and insecticides, 299
whitewash, 299
Pound cake, 275
Powder
baby, 237
baking, 288
beverage, 280
body, 236
curry, 287
denture, 231
dessert, 281
face, 234-235
liquid, 235
ice cream, 281
tooth, 230-231
Preservative, cosmetic, 200
Preservative stain for wood, 11-14

Primer, metal, 77
Priming coat, wood paint, 60, 61, 66, 70,
71
Protective solution for metal, 109
Putty, 138
softener, 139
softener and remover, 139

Ration, chicken, 291-292
Ration, turkey, 289-290
Reducer, photographic, 192-195
Relish, vegetable, 284
Remover, nail enamel, 237-238
Remover, paint, 90-92
Repellent, deer, 302
Roach powder, 174
Rodenticide, 176
Root insect powder, 308
Rouge, cake, 236
Rouge, cream, 236
Rubber cement, 171
Rubbing varnish, 37, 41
Rug cleaner, 166

Saddle soap, 151
Salad dressing, 285-286
Salami, 263-264
Sanitizing product, 168
Satin-finish solution for metal, 100-101
Sauce, chili, 283
Sauce, mint, 282
Sauce, tomato, 282
Sauce, Worcestershire, 288
Sausages, 255-272
Seed fumigant, 310
Selection of formulas, 1
Self-cleaning polish, 48
Semi-gloss lacquer for wood, 50, 53
Shampoo, 206-209
dog, 171
liquid cream lotion, 208
non-foaming, 208
soapless type, 207-209
soap type, 206
Shaving cream, 217-219
brushless, 219
lather forming, 218
Shaving lotion, 219-220
Shaving soap, liquid, 219
Sheep dip, 298
Shellac solution, 33

Shellac varnish, 39
Shoe cleaner, 152
Shoe polish, 151-152
Shoe whitener, 152
Silicone cleaner-polish, 47
Silicone hand cream, 206
Silicone polish, automobile, 124-126
Skin freshening lotion, 227
Skinless frankfurters, 255-256
Smoked links, 267-268
Snow mold lawn spray, 309
Soak cleaner, metal, 96
Soap
  hand, liquid, 203
  liquid, 145
  saddle, 151
  shampoo, 206
  shaving, 219
Soup, 272-275
  bone stock, 272
  Mock turtle, 273
  oxtail, 273
  vegetable, 273
Space deodorant, 168
Spirit stain for wood, 25-29
Sponge cake, 276
Spotting soap, 156
Spray
  cotton insect, 307
  fly, exterior, 307
  garden, 303-308
  grasshopper, 306-307
  insecticide, 303-308
  lawn, 309
  mite, 306
  thrip, 304, 306
  tree, 304
  weevil, 305
Spraying lacquer for metal, 57
Spraying lacquer for wood, 52, 54
"Squeeze bottle" packaging, 6
Stop Bath, 186-187
Stain remover, 157-165
Stain, wood, 11-29
  chemical, 29-31
  penetrating, 20-24
  pigment oil, 14-20
  preservative, 11-14
  spirit, 25-29
  water, 29
Stove polish, 153-155

Straw hat cleaner, 166
Stucco, 133-134
Sun protection formula, 239-242
Sun tan cream, 240
Sun tan oil, 239
Surfacing, concrete, 130
Synthetic flavor, 253-254
Synthetic syrup, 253-254
Syrup, synthetic, 253-254

Termite treatment, 175
Thickener, jelly, 288
Thinner for lacquer, 59
Thrip spray, 304, 306
Tile floor cleaner, 145
Toilet water, 249-250
Tomato chutney, 283
Tomato sauce, 282
"Tonic," hair, 212-213
Toning for wood paint, 63-65
Tool varnish, 36
Tooth powder, 230-231
Toothpaste, 230
Trade directories, 324-325
Trade publications, 324-325
Tree banding composition, 311
Tree dust, 308
Tree spray, 304
Turkey feed, 289-290
Turkey ration, 289-290

Vanishing cream, 220-221
Varnish, 34-42
  elastic, 39
  floor, 36, 38, 40, 41
  furniture, 37, 38, 41
  marine spar, 35
  mixing (paint), 37
  polishing, 38
  rubbing, 37, 41
  shellac, 39
  tool, 36
  water resistant, 40, 41
Veal loaf, 268-269
Vegetable relish, 284
Vegetable soup, 273-274

Wall paper cleaner, 165
Wall paper remover, 166
Washing machine compound, 142-143
"Waterless" hand cleaner, 202

Waterproofing concrete, 129-130
Waterproofing solution, 177-178
Water-resistant floor polish, 146-147
Water-resistant lacquer for wood, 51, 54
Water-resistant varnish, 40, 41
Water stain for wood, 29
Wave-set, hair, 217
Wave solution, permanent, 216
Wax polish, 44-48
Weevil spray, 305
Weights and measures, 2
Weights and measures, tables, 322-323
Whitener, shoe, 152
Whitewash, 85-86, 299
  fire-resistant, 86
  poultry house, 299
Windshield defroster, 137
Wood
  bleach, 8-10
  crack filler, 60
  filler, 31-33
    liquid, 32-33
    paste, 31-32

lacquer, 49-55
  spraying, 52, 54
paint, 60-76
  chalking, 67
  chalk-resistant, 67
  exterior, 60-62, 66-69
  latex base, 73-75
  oil-pigment-drier type, 60-67, 70-71
  priming, 60, 61, 66, 70, 71
  synthetic resin oil type, 68, 72
  synthetic resin—varnish type, 68
  synthetic resin, water-emulsion type,
    69
painting, 59-60
polish, 42-48
stain, 11-29
  chemical, 29-31
  penetrating, 20-24
  pigment oil, 14-20
  preservative, 11-14
  spirit, 25-29
  water, 29
Worcestershire sauce, 288